AN INTRODUCTION TO

The Philosophy of Science

Arthur Pap

AN INTRODUCTION TO

THE PHILOSOPHY

OF SCIENCE

WITH AN EPILOGUE BY
Brand Blanshard

The Free Press of Glencoe

For information, address:

The Free Press of Glencoe

A DIVISION OF THE MACMILLAN COMPANY, THE CROWELL-COLLIER PUBLISHING COMPANY

60 Fifth Avenue, New York 11

Second Printing, 1962

Designed by Katherine Purcell

Library of Congress Catalog Card Number: 61–10901

Preface
for General
Readers

This book is addressed to scientists and philosophers interested in the conceptual foundations and the methodology of modern science. The philosophical problems discussed in it are not the exclusive concern of professional philosophers but must impress themselves on any reflective scientist who is not so absorbed in specialized research as to lose sight of fundamentals. The present intellectual climate, in the United States at any rate, is decidedly favorable to such contact between science and philosophy as occurs in the philosophy of science. On the one hand, scientists have become more "philosophical" owing to conceptual or methodological difficulties: *conceptual* difficulties mainly in recent quantum physics, *methodological* difficulties mainly in psychology and the social sciences. On the other hand, the rise of analytic philosophy in the English-speaking countries, which is indissolubly linked to progress in logic and semantics, has brought scientific precision into philosophy, making philosophy more reputable in the eyes of scientists who used to be repelled by its impressionistic vagueness and metaphysical speculations. Indeed, analytic philosophy *is* analysis of concepts and hence is an integral part of thorough science. The philosophy of science is here conceived as indistinguishable from analytic philosophy except that the analysis is restricted to concepts and problems that are especially relevant to science. It should be distinguished from a different conception of the philosophy of science as a speculative synthesis of the fruits of scientific research.

Analytic philosophy of science may be divided into (1) general logic or methodology of science and (2) philosophies of specific sciences, addressing themselves to conceptual difficulties peculiar to particular sciences. The conditions of scientific meaningfulness of statements, the theory of probability, and the logic of explanation are problems falling into the former subdivision; the analysis of time and force as physical concepts, the problem of indeterminacy and objective reality in quantum physics, the problem of intervening variables in psychology, and the problem of teleological explanation and mechanistic "reduction" of biology are problems pertaining to particular sciences. The main emphasis of this book is on problems of the former type, where a lot of specialized scientific knowledge is, fortunately for the author, dispensable and a thorough grasp of logic in the broadest sense is more important. But there are also special sections devoted to physics (Chapter 4, A, B, C, Chapter 7, C, Chapter 17, B, C, D, E), psychology (Chapter 4, D, Chapter 20), biology (Chapter 19), mathematics (Chapter 5, Chapter 7, A, B), and social science (Chapter 21).

I have conscientiously aimed at elementary though reasonably thorough discussion and exposition of the problems of widest interest, without refraining from the expression of controversial views of my own. If, in spite of this aim, the reader should occasionally feel handicapped by his ignorance of logic, he need not give up. He can easily remedy this deficiency in his intellectual background by studying one of the numerous excellent textbooks of logic that college teaching has brought upon the American book market. In this connection the glossary of technical terms of logic, semantics, and methodology should also prove helpful.

ARTHUR PAP

New Haven
June, 1959

Preface
for Instructors

In attempting to delimit the content of the philosophy of science course, we face the problem of explaining how, if at all, it differs from the content of courses in logic and epistemology. Some confusion in defining closely related philosophical disciplines arises from a failure to distinguish between what may be called "philosophy of science-in-general" and philosophies of specific sciences, such as the philosophy of physics or the philosophy of psychology. The former deals with concepts and methods present in all the sciences—"explanation," "inductive generalization," "truth," and the like. Undoubtedly, logic courses overlap a good deal with philosophy of science-in-general, especially if they include scientific methodology and theory of probability. To avoid too much overlap, much that goes under the label "scientific methodology" may well be left to the philosophy of science course, while the logic course focuses on the formal theory of inference, deductive and inductive. If the philosophy of science course has its place primarily in a graduate program for philosophy majors, formal logic should, for obvious reasons, be a prerequisite. Where the course is a so-called "service course," this requirement can hardly be enforced, and the instructor will simply have to bring in as much formal logic as needed for reasonably rigorous analysis.

Epistemology can hardly be distinguished from philosophy of science-in-general, provided its problems are problems of logical justification of beliefs and not (psychological) problems of genetic explanation of beliefs. One might feel that epistemology is a more inclusive discipline in that it covers the logical analysis of common-sense knowledge as well as of scientific knowledge. Actually this is a difference not in problem areas but merely in illustrative materials used: problems such as the distinction between genuine and pseudo explanation, or the justification of induction, can be discussed with reference to everyday reasoning as well as with reference to scientific reasoning, and in fact the philosophy of science instructor will have to give more attention to everyday illustrations if many of the students lack a scientific background. To the question of what the philosophy of science course can offer the "liberal arts" student not majoring in a science, the answer here suggested is that it can offer everything it can offer to the science student except technical scientific illustrations. (This is not true, of course, of a more specialized course in the philosophy of some specific science. But such courses can be offered only in graduate schools anyway, in the form of seminars, and then a select professional audience can be secured more easily.) If the absence of such illustrative material should lead one to call the course "epistemology" instead of "philosophy of science," it is of little consequence.

It has already been mentioned that in an ideally constructed course curriculum (the "ideal" implies an ignoring of such undignified practical matters as the size of the enrollment) formal logic should be a prerequisite for admission to the philosophy of science course. *Mutatis mutandis*, the same may be said with regard to a minimum background in science— say, a year of physics, a year of mathematics, or both. The reason for this latter requirement, however, is that it saves the instructor the labor of explaining elementary science along with the philosophical points he is making. It is *not* that only the science student could be *interested* in philosophy of science. The course is by no means destined to failure if it is addressed to laymen in science, especially if the instructor is qualified (as he should be) to explain as much elementary science as is needed for an appreciation of the philosophical problems. It is just as easy to motivate an interest in science through the study of philosophy of science as the other way around.

In terms of reading materials, three approaches may be distinguished: (1) readings relevant to philosophy of science from the history of philosophy, (2) methodologically reflective papers from the history of science, (3) contemporary analytical papers in philosophy of science (such as are collected in Feigl and Sellars' *Readings in Philosophical Analysis* and in Feigl and Brodbeck's *Readings in the Philosophy of Science*). Approach 1 is undesirable, since the philosophy of science course presents a singular opportunity to clear the philosophy classroom of the atmosphere of venerable antiquity and historical erudition and to think about philosophical problems "from scratch." (This criticism of the historical approach does not imply that reference to classical epistemologists, such as Hume and Kant, is to be altogether avoided.) Approach 2 has the virtue of establishing direct contact with science and of eliminating reliance on the middlemen, the writing philosophers of science. It should appeal especially to the science major, who in this way can be made to reflect upon scientific methods and concepts without moving too far from his professional field of study. On the other hand, it will scare off philosophy majors with little or no background in science. Approach 3, then, offers itself for the philosophy major. But the problem remains of finding an approach that serves the science and the nonscience student at the same time, since in most cases the audiences cannot be sufficiently segregated on the basis of background. The solution of this problem must be left to the judgment of the individual instructor.

The lists of "Selected Readings" at the end of each chapter were compiled by Bernard Berofsky of Columbia University.

ARTHUR PAP

New Haven
June, 1959

Contents

PART TWO   *Mathematics, Logic, and Experience*

PART THREE   *Induction and Probability*

PART FOUR *Causality and Laws of Nature*

PART FIVE *Explanation and Justification*

Part One

MEANING
AND
VERIFIABILITY

INTRODUCTION

Science
& Philosophical
Criticism

The scientific mentality may be roughly characterized as the tendency to suspend belief until evidence of the appropriate kind is produced, and then to believe the proposition in question only to the degree that the available evidence warrants it, without excluding the possibility of a future disconfirmation. What kind of evidence is appropriate depends, of course, on the nature of the proposition. A theory about the origin of the solar system cannot be verified by experiment; it would, however, be perverse rather than "scientific" to refuse to believe it on the ground that it has not been verified the way, say, the proposition that water has the molecular structure H_2O has been verified. This latter proposition, in turn, cannot be verified by direct observation as can the proposition "Butter melts when heated to 90°F," but it would be unintelligent to be skeptical about it because one cannot "see" a water molecule and the hydrogen and oxygen atoms that allegedly compose it. Again, the law of universal gravitation cannot be demonstrated as the laws of algebra can, but it would be perverse to refuse to act on it in spite of millions of confirming observations just because it is not, after all, logically necessary, i.e., such that it would be self-contradictory to suppose it false. (One of the major tasks of the philosophy of science, incidentally, is to distinguish different kinds of "proofs," corresponding to different kinds of propositions, and thereby to prevent a confusion of different standards of justification of beliefs; and further, to make explicit, and possibly correct, the criteria which scientists instinctively apply in evaluating the degree to which the known evidence warrants a given proposition.)

Now, the above definition of "scientific mentality" is often used to characterize a *philosophical* mind. A philosopher is supposed to be a critical man, not necessarily in the sense of one who "criticizes" accepted beliefs and habits more than the average man does, but in the sense of one who demands proof, justification, reasons—and in this sense stands above the crowd. But since obviously not all scientific minds are also philosophical minds, it won't do to define "philosophical" in this broad way. What exactly it is that differentiates philosophical criticism from the sort of criticism that scientists hurl at religious dogmas—e.g., the dogma that the earth stands still at the center of the universe, or that man is not a natural descendant of the ape or less manlike animal species—is not easy to define. But whereas philosophy and science were barely distinct when men started to ask theoretical questions, the increasing specialization of theoretical inquiry has led to a sharp professional separation of philosophy from science, so sharp that most philosophers nowadays are almost as ignorant of science as most scientists are of philosophy. Whether or not this state of affairs is desirable, and if undesirable, avoidable, it at least constitutes a challenge to specify a differentia of *philosophical* criticism. We venture the following suggestion: a philosopher not only asks for evidence or reasons; he realizes more than does the average scientist, let alone the "man in the street," that the question of *meaning* is prior to the question of *truth*. That is, we cannot assess the degree to which the known facts warrant belief in a proposition unless we are fairly clear about the meaning of that proposition. Thus it is surely otiose to argue whether the existence of God can be reconciled with well-confirmed scientific theories, unless one is clear about the meaning of the word "God"—a condition which is rarely fulfilled in emotional arguments between atheists and devout believers. How can we possibly hope to discover whether the proposition "God created the world" is true, or at least whether it is compatible with the teachings of modern science, unless we know what it means? Now, if we define philosophy as an indefatigable, unprejudiced search for truth, we fail to differentiate it from science. If we define it as an obstinate search for clear meaning, we come much closer to a differentiating definition. And the fact that so much of professional philosophy in this age of scientific specialization is indeed dominated by analysis of the meanings of such fundamental terms as "cause," "probability," "reality," "truth," "good," "thing," "certainty," "measurement," "mental" indicates that such a definition, vague as it is (so is the defined word), is not entirely arbitrary.

Be this as it may, the next question, which arises immediately once we define philosophical criticism as a search for clear meanings of statements and questions, is what method one is to use in order to find what one looks for. To this question a philosophical school that, more than any other, has been and is continuing to be in close contact with scientific developments, variously called *logical empiricism* or *logical positivism*, gives an answer that, at first sight at any rate, is very simple: to find the meaning of a statement, find out how one would go about verifying it, or what sort of evidence one would accept as establishing its truth. Let us call this principle the *verifiability principle of meaning.* If we are critical in the distinctively philosophical way, we shall soon find that this guide to the discovery of meaning is itself none too clear, but we in the philosophy of science must imitate the scientists in beginning with crude formulations that may serve as steppingstones, as it were, to their own refinement.

1, Examine nature of evidence
2. The method of proof depends on the nature of the thing in question.

CHAPTER I

Semantical Concepts

A. SEMANTIC MEANING AND VERIFIABILITY

To begin with, the verifiability principle as stated is ambiguous, and so it is apt to give rise to purely verbal disputes, i.e., disputes that arise only because the same word is interpreted in different ways. For what is the meaning of "meaning"? In their famous pioneer work *The Meaning of Meaning*, Ogden and Richards distinguished something like seventeen meanings of the word "meaning." For our purposes discrimination of three senses will suffice; we shall label them *semantic, syntactic,* and *pragmatic* meaning. Semantic meaning, as we propose to use the term, is exclusively a property of statements: the semantic meaning of a statement is that state of affairs whose existence would make the statement true. The word "fact" is more current in ordinary language than the clumsy "state of affairs," but we avoid it here for a good reason: if a statement is false, then it has just as definite a semantic meaning as it would have if it were true—indeed, it has the same semantic meaning whether it be true or false. But to a false statement no fact corresponds at all; to speak here of a fact that does not exist though it might have existed would be far more clumsy than to speak of a state of affairs in the sense of a *possibility* that may or may not be actualized. To illustrate: What is the semantic meaning of the statement, "The train really (not just apparently) moves now"? This is to ask which state of affairs must exist at the time denoted by "now" if the statement is to be true. As an alternative terminology, which has the advantage of reminding us of the close connection between the concept of semantic meaning and the concept of truth, let us call this state of affairs the *truth-condition* of the

[6]

statement. Now, our principle is best interpreted as a guide to the discovery of the truth-condition (not to be confused with the truth!) of a statement. How, indeed, do we go about verifying whether the train really moves? If we notice that it changes its position relative to a train on the parallel track, we are still in doubt, for it may be the latter train that really moves. But if we observe a change of position relative to the station platform, or relative to any object that is fixed on the earth, then we are convinced. Conclusion: The statement means semantically that the train changes its position relative to the earth.

Let us keep in mind that the verifiability principle addresses itself only to semantic meaning, not to meaning in any other sense of this highly ambiguous word. It is a proposed analysis of the concept of semantic meaning, or "truth-condition," in terms of the concept of verification. As we shall see in due course, even after this initial clarification it still faces great difficulties, but first let us appreciate its usefulness a little. Suppose somebody were to jump to conclusions and say, "I guess 'X really moves' generally means 'X changes its position relative to the earth, or relative to an object fixed on the earth,' since this is the way we verify the occurrence of a real motion." He could easily be refuted if we pointed out that a man might walk in a moving train in the direction opposite to its motion and with exactly the train's speed, so that relative to the earth he would remain stationary. Suppose he then modified his analysis as follows: " 'X *really moves*' means 'X changes position relative to *some* visible body in the environment of X.' " But this analysis is even more absurd, since it would then be just as true to say that the station platform really moves as that the train really moves— whereas the station platform just does *not* move in the sense in which the word is ordinarily used. Let us take one more step: how would one verify that, contrary to appearances, the earth really moves, as asserted by scientists and educated laymen since Copernicus? Surely not by observing that the earth changes position relative to itself! But then "real motion" does not mean in this context what it means in the context "the train really moves." If the evidence that, practically unattainable though it may be, would establish it as certain that the earth really moves is that an observer stationed on a fixed star and equipped with a powerful telescope would observe the earth to change position, then "the earth really moves" means that the earth changes position relative to the fixed stars.[1] One result, therefore, of the application of the verifiability prin-

1. ". . . The question whether the earth moves or not amounts in reality to no more than this, to wit, whether we have reason to conclude, from what has been observed by astronomers, that if we were placed in such and such circumstances, and such or such a position and distance both from the earth and sun, we should perceive the former to move among the choir of the planets, and appearing in all respects like one of them." (Berkeley, *The Principles of Human Knowledge*, sec. 58.)

ciple to this case is that the expression "real motion" does not stand for one concept, but for a family of similar concepts. A more interesting consequence, however, is the following: Suppose we asked a classical physicist whose semantic self-consciousness was not above average whether the earth would still move if all other bodies in the universe were destroyed. He would probably reply, "Yes, according to the law of inertia it would move on forever along that straight line which was the direction of the tangential velocity component at the moment when its gravitational attraction by the sun discontinued." But how could one even in principle verify that it moved if there was no other body relative to which it changed position? If one could not, then the verifiability principle seems to force the conclusion that the statement, "The earth would still move," has no semantic meaning at all. As we shall see later, an implicit adherence to this principle has indeed led physicists to abandon the Newtonian concepts of absolute space, time, and motion, though we shall also see that the story is far more complicated than this over-simplified preliminary version.

One more illustration may be useful to convey a preliminary understanding of the verifiability principle, though it may at the same time foreshadow a serious criticism of it. Suppose that in your rare moments of speculation you entertained the possibility that absolutely every body in the universe is constantly expanding, though it is impossible to detect this because all bodies expand at the same rate. What, now, is the semantic meaning of this hypothesis? The positivist, who may be said to be a refiner of the pragmatist principle, "A difference that makes no difference is no difference," will argue that it has no semantic meaning at all: for the only way of verifying that a body expands is by comparison with other bodies (e.g., yardsticks) that themselves do not expand or at least do not expand at the same rate; and if all bodies expand at the same rate, then one cannot verify whether any of them expands. If the statement *seems* to be true or false, seems to describe a genuine possibility, the positivist will say the reason is its grammatical similarity to statements which are verifiable, e.g., "All heated pieces of iron expand at the same rate." A critic of the positivist principle might reply: "How could you find out that the statement was in principle unverifiable unless you understood it? Unless you understood it, you would not be able to conclude that the very supposition of its being either confirmed or disconfirmed by observations contradicts what it asserts. And since, as the positivists themselves have emphasized, understanding a statement and knowing its truth-condition are one and the same thing, you should admit that a statement may be unverifiable and still have a semantic meaning."

We shall see later that this criticism cannot be lightly dismissed. Undoubtedly there is in science a usage of the word "meaningless" according to which a statement like the above hypothesis would be condemned as meaningless just because it is in principle unverifiable, i.e., just because it cannot be specified in what way observations made in a world in which it was true would differ from observations made in a world in which it was false. More accurately, what the word "meaningless" *means* in this usage is just "in principle unverifiable"—though we have not yet made the meaning of the latter expression precise. But though nobody could hope to know whether a statement that was meaningless in this sense was true or false, and though it would make no practical difference whatever whether it was true or false, it does not follow that it could not *be* true or false, i.e., describe a conceivable state of affairs.

B. SEMANTIC AND PRAGMATIC MEANING

Semantic meaning, we have said, is a property of statements. Imperatives, for example, have no semantic meaning; we do not call them true or false, but obeyed or disobeyed. Now, in a derived sense we can also speak of the semantic meaning of a *predicate*, because it is of the nature of predicates to be used in statements characterizing a certain subject-matter. The semantic meaning of a predicate is that aspect of it which determines whether an ascription of it to something or other is true or false. For example, whether or not a statement of the form "X is a father" is true depends upon the semantic meaning of the predicate "father." If "X is a father" is true if and only if X is a male parent, then the property of *being a male parent* is the semantic meaning of "father."[2] Following John Stuart Mill, many logicians call this the *connotation* of the predicate: the criterion by which it is determined whether the predicate is applicable to this or that object. But the word "connotation" itself has certain connotations in its everyday use that make it desirable to avoid it in an exact discussion. For example, we might say that for so-and-so the word "father" connotes financial worries, and for so-and-so self-confidence, and for so-and-so an age of at least thirty. But the properties that we psychologically associate with a predicate are no part of its semantic meaning unless the truth or falsehood of an ascription of the predicate depends on their presence. To be sure, statements are true or false not just by virtue of the "facts" but also by virtue of the conventional meanings of the words. If everybody in a given society observed the rule to apply the word "father" to X if and only if X was a

---

2. The distinction between properties and classes is a controversial subject that may be ignored in this context.

male parent older than thirty, then the property of being older than thirty would be part of the semantic meaning of "father" *in that society,* and statements of the form "X is a father" as interpreted in that society would be true only if X was older than thirty.

Nevertheless, even with regard to predicates for which no explicit definitions are codified we can distinguish properties that, within a given language community, are *criteria of true applications* from properties that are not so regarded though most or all of the objects of which the predicate is true may have them and though some people may mentally associate them with the predicate. Suppose, for example, that all Republican congressmen were corruptible and that this was so widely known that every voter immediately thought of corruptibility when he heard the expression "Republican congressman." (That on the supposition made there soon would be no Republican congressmen is probable, but irrelevant in this context.) Still, corruptibility would not be *semantically* meant by "Republican congressman" as long as the voters granted the logical possibility of there being incorruptible Republican congressmen, for if it were so meant then "incorruptible Republican congressman" would be as self-contradictory an expression as "square with unequal sides."

Now, thoughts and other kinds of mental states that are causally connected with a linguistic expression without being directly relevant to the question of truth constitute the *pragmatic* meaning of the expression. Normally, a man who utters the sentence, "It will rain," with a tone of conviction believes that it will rain. But whether or not he believes what he said is irrelevant to the question of whether what he said is true. Therefore the belief is no part of the truth-condition of the sentence. Banker X who hates all communists without exception may feel a surge of hatred whenever he hears someone referred to as a communist; nevertheless this hatred has nothing to do with the semantic meaning of "communist" in X's usage as long as X admits that a person could *be* a communist even if he did not hate him. Or imagine a man in whose experience there never have been any blonde girls except slim and blue-eyed ones, and who therefore inevitably imagines a slim and blue-eyed girl whenever he hears the expression "a blonde girl." Such images constitute part of the pragmatic meaning of the expression for that man, but as long as he answers the question, "Could you conceive of a blonde who is fat, or who is not blue-eyed?" affirmatively, slimness and blue-eyedness are not *semantically* meant by "blonde girl" even for him.

What is frequently called "emotive" meaning is a species of pragmatic meaning as here conceived. Some philosophers, notably logical positivists, have maintained that value statements, such as "It is wrong to steal from the poor," "Beethoven was a great composer," "It is your duty to fight for your fatherland," have *only* emotive meaning. But whether or not they have semantic meaning also, we can see that their semantic meaning, whatever it may be, must be distinct from their emotive meaning relative to the speaker. For otherwise they would be descriptions of the speaker's emotions, hence true or false according to whether or not the described emotions were present, and hence not *value* statements at all. If in an autobiographical mood I reported, "I dislike seeing the poor robbed, I greatly admire Beethoven as a composer," and so on, I would be engaged in introspective description, not in evaluation. But here we touch upon a subtle problem of the analysis of evaluation discourse only in passing,[3] our sole purpose being to clarify the concept of semantic meaning by differentiation from other senses of "meaning." It should be noted that in spite of the differences between the various kinds of meaning, they all have in common their involving, in addition to the sign that is said to have meaning and that which is said to be the meaning of the sign, people who produce or interpret the sign. If people in linguistic com-munication are not mentioned, the reason is simply that a more or less constant class of sign interpreters and sign users is presupposed. Thus the statement, " 'Father' semantically means a male parent," is really short for " 'Father' semantically means a male parent for English-speaking people using the word in a biological sense." Even where the sign is a *natural* sign as in "Black clouds signify rain," there is a tacit reference to people whose perception of black clouds causes them to expect rain.

C. SYNTACTIC MEANING

Semantic meaning and pragmatic meaning moreover share the following feature: that which is meant by the linguistic expression is usually not itself a linguistic expression; it is a state of affairs, or a property, or a mental state, or the like. In this respect *syntactic* meaning is a peculiar sort of meaning. One expression syntactically means other expressions. Thus the word "uncle" means the word "man" as well as the word "brother," in the sense that if "X is an uncle" is true, it follows that "X is a man" and "X is a brother" are also true. In natural language syntactic meaning derives from semantic meaning: if "X is a man" is deducible from "X is an uncle," the reason lies not in any intrinsic properties of the words "man" and "uncle," but in the fact that "man" semantically means a property that is part of the semantic meaning of the word "uncle."

One might allege as an exception to this principle of the priority of semantic meaning to syntactic meaning the case in which one sentence is derivable from (as a consequence of) other sentences not by virtue of

3. A more detailed analysis may be found in Chapter 21.

any reference of descriptive terms to something outside of language, but by sole virtue of the rules for manipulating so-called *logical* words, i.e., words such as "or," "and," "not," and "all" that are determinants of the total meaning of a statement but do not mean anything by themselves. Thus "Either *X* is not introverted or *X* is not a mathematician" follows from "*X* is not an introverted mathematician," and this logical relation is independent of the meanings of the descriptive words "introverted" and "mathematician." The second sentence is *formally* derivable from the first; i.e., one needs no understanding of the descriptive words to see that this logical relation holds. But even here the semantic dimension of meaning is prior to the syntactic dimension. No statement can be true *solely* by virtue of its form: even the tautology "He is a scientist or he is not a scientist" is a tautology only if the word "scientist" has the same meaning in both occurrences. Note that we sometimes say, without being guilty of contradiction, "*X* is, and is not, an *A*," intending of course, the word represented by *A* in different senses. Again, if relations of logical consequence depended only on syntactic form, then "All good musicians are good people" should follow from "All musicians are people" just as "All brown horses are brown animals" follow from "All horses are animals."

For the above reasons, it is really confusing to speak of meaning in the syntactic sense at all, and of a kind of truth, "formal truth," that allegedly derives exclusively from syntactical rules, i.e., rules governing manipulation of symbols without regard to any semantic meanings.[4] In any ordinary use of the word "meaning," to say that one word means other words is to say that it is used in order to refer to other words, as when the grammarian uses the word "adjective" in order to refer to such words as "red" and "hard." And again this is meaning in the semantic sense (note that semantic meaning is sometimes called "reference"). But since some prominent writers do speak of a syntactical dimension of meaning, we do well to distinguish this sense of "meaning" from the others.

D. A PRIORI AND EMPIRICAL
STATEMENTS

We turn now to a preliminary differentiation of kinds of *statements* in order to single out the kind of statement to which alone the verifiability principle addresses itself. We have seen that the latter is intended as a

---

4. For a detailed discussion of formal or logical truth, see Chapter 6.

guide to the discovery of the truth-condition of a statement. As synonym for "truth-condition," we have also used the expression "state of affairs described," where a state of affairs was informally defined as a possibility which may or may not be actual. (If it is actual, then the statement describes a fact, or is true.) But in this sense no state of affairs is described by such statements as "All bachelors are unmarried," "Anything that is red is colored," "If *A* is father of *B* and *B* is father of *C*, then *A* is grandfather of *C*," "If this is a metal and all metals expand when heated, then this will expand when heated." Whether or not it makes sense to speak of empirical verification of such statements, it will be agreed that they do not *require* empirical verification. We can see that they are true by just thinking about the meanings of the terms, without recourse to experience. In this sense they are *a priori* statements, not empirical statements. Now, most advocates of the verifiability principle in one form or another would restrict it to statements that are claimed to be empirical. For if one were to hold that with regard to any statement whatever, to understand its semantical meaning is to be able to specify the kind of experience or observations that would lead one to assert it as true, then it is doubtful whether a priori statements could be said to be semantically meaningful; and then the very concept of "a priori truth" would be thrown out, whereas logical positivists would in general accept the distinction between a priori and empirical truth, though they reject traditional interpretations of the concept "a priori truth" (cf. Chapters 5 and 6).

The logical positivist, then, says: If you claim to be making an empirical statement, you must substantiate this claim by describing the kind of experience that would establish your statement as true—in other words, you must specify what difference the truth of the statement would make to human experience. If no such difference can be specified, then either your statement is a priori and so says nothing specifically about the actual world (a priori statements following a phrase of Leibnitz, are often said to be true in all possible worlds), or it lacks semantical meaning altogether, however rich it may be in pragmatic meaning.

E. MEANING AND MEANINGFULNESS

But it is time to become somewhat more precise. In the first place, the logical positivist as portrayed so far seems to do two jobs at once: to offer a guide to the discovery of the semantical meaning of an empirical statement, and also to set up a criterion for deciding whether a statement claimed to be empirical has a semantical meaning at all, or more

verifiable principle of meaning
verifiable principle of meaningfulness

simply, *is* empirical. But these are different jobs. If to specify the meaning of an empirical statement is to describe the method of its verification, then of course it follows that the statement is meaningless if it is not verifiable. But one could consistently agree that a statement that is not a priori must be empirically verifiable if it is semantically meaningful at all, and reject the claim that describing the method of verification of a statement, or the sort of *evidence* that would lead one to accept it, is *the same as* saying what it means. For example, if I asked a physicist how he would verify that there was an electrical field in a certain spatial region, he would describe experiments such as placing an electroscope at the appropriate place and seeing whether its leaves diverged. But he might well deny that what he meant by his theoretical statement was just that such and such experiments would, were they performed, have such and such outcomes. Let us, therefore, split the positivist principle into the verifiability principle of *meaning* and the verifiability principle of *meaningfulness*. The former says that the meaning of a statement is identical with the empirical evidence that would establish its truth; the latter that a statement is meaningful if and only if it is empirically verifiable. The former entails the latter, but it is not obvious that the latter entails the former.

Secondly, the term "verifiable" has so far been used rather loosely. For example, is the empirical statement "All bodies near the surface of the earth fall with approximately constant acceleration" verifiable in the sense that one can describe the sort of experience that would establish it as true? Certainly not; experience can only render it more and more probable; to suppose it false would be logically consistent with any conceivable, and any conceivable amount of, experience of which the human race is capable. The example calls attention to the distinction between verification and confirmation, to be explored in the next chapter.

Selected Readings

Bar-Hillel, Y., "Logical Syntax and Semantics," *Language*, 1954.

Black, M., "The Semiotic of Charles Morris," in M. Black, *Language and Philosophy* (Ithaca, N.Y., 1949).

Carnap, R., *Foundations of Logic and Mathematics* (International Encyclopedia of Unified Science, I, no. 3, Chicago, 1939).

———, *Introduction to Semantics* (Cambridge, Mass., 1942).

———, *Meaning and Necessity* (Chicago, 1956).

Frege, G., "On Sense and Nominatum," in H. Feigl and W. Sellars (eds.), *Readings in Philosophical Analysis* (New York, 1949).

Hospers, J., *Introduction to Philosophical Analysis* (New York, 1953), chap. 1.

Morris, C. W., *Foundations of the Theory of Signs* (International Encyclopedia of Unified Science, I, no. 2, Chicago, 1938).

——, *Signs, Language, and Behavior* (New York, 1946).

Quine, W. V., *Word and Object* (Cambridge, Mass., 1960), chap. 3, 4.

——, "Notes on the Theory of Reference," in W. V. Quine, *From a Logical Point of View* (Cambridge, Mass., 1953).

a semantically meaningful statement can be either true or false

CHAPTER 2

Verifiability, Confirmability, & the Empiricist Language

A. VERIFICATION AND CONFIRMATION

We cannot intelligently evaluate the contention that a statement that is not of the a priori kind is meaningful (in the relevant sense) only if it is in principle verifiable, unless we are clear about the intended sense of the words "verification" and "possible *in principle*." Ordinarily when we speak of verification of a statement, we mean the process of finding out, coming to know, that it is true. Obviously, only true statements can be verified in this sense; and since false statements are just as meaningful as true statements (a semantically meaningful statement, remember, is *either* true or false), it stands to reason that the logical positivists do not mean "verification" in this sense. They rather mean it in the more inclusive sense of "coming to know *whether* the statement is true." But with regard to most, if not all, scientific statements that we accept as true on the authority of scientists, it is evident that they cannot be known to be true with absolute certainty, the sort of certainty that proverbially attaches to the proposition that "two and two make four." We can easily conceive of observations that would disconfirm them; the scientists accept them as highly confirmed hypotheses, not as propositions that have been demonstrated from self-evident axioms. This is true especially of statements describing what we believe to be *laws of nature:* the law of gravitation, the laws of thermodynamics, the laws of chemistry, the laws of heredity —these are all *universal* propositions, stating that under specified condi-

Note

tions such and such happens *always and everywhere*,[1] which have been empirically confirmed. But though they may be practically certain, they are theoretically uncertain in the sense that a future disconfirmation is logically conceivable. To be sure, in saying that their disconfirmation by new experimental or observational findings remains logically conceivable, we are saying little more than that they are not a priori truths. But even if it were just definitional, analytic of the meaning of "empirical," to say that an empirical universal statement is only confirmable, not conclusively verifiable, this would force the positivist to formulate his criterion of meaningfulness in terms of the notion of confirmability, not in terms of the notion of conclusive verifiability. For since it is not just philosophers who, for good or bad reasons, depart from the ordinary use of words, but philosophically neutral scientists who say that such universal statements are never absolutely certain but are only hypotheses that are confirmable while remaining subject to revision at any moment, the thesis that no universal statement of science is ever absolutely certain cannot be dismissed as just a prescription of a novel use of the expression "absolutely certain."

To say that a statement is empirically *confirmable* is to say that possible observations can be described that would, if they were made, bestow some degree of probability on the statement. It is not only grammatically universal statements that are not conclusively verifiable by observations, in the sense that no finite amount of observations could rule out the possibility that they are false, but also grammatically *singular* statements that are inferred from premises some of which are universal. If I say, "This is iron," and someone doubts my assertion, I may not be able to convince him by just getting him to make the relevant observations. For he may not accept the *laws* involved in my interpretation of the observations. If we try to determine the density of the material by weighing, we presuppose the law of the lever that is embodied, as it were, in the beam balance; if we try to determine its melting point, we presuppose the law of thermal expansion embodied in the mercury thermometer. Even if it is just a question of coming to agree about the objective color of a thing, the generalization is taken for granted that the thing will exhibit the same apparent color *whenever and wherever* the same optical and perceptual conditions are realized. Or consider a simple statement about a *past event*, such as "It rained in this locality a short while ago," based on the observation that the ground is wet. If the latter confirms the statement about what happened, the reason is an assumed causal connection between rainfall and wetness of the ground, and to assert

---

1. We neglect here the distinction between deterministic and statistical laws, which will be discussed later (cf. Chapters 11, 12, 13, 17). We shall then see that in the sense here in question statistical laws are just as universal as deterministic laws.

a causal connection between two events is to assert that one kind of event is *regularly* associated with another kind of event (cf. Chapter 14). But the proposition "Whenever it rains the ground gets wet," to which no exception has ever been found, does not entail its converse, "Whenever the ground is wet, it rained shortly before": the effect may in a given instance be produced by a different cause; the inference of "*p*" from "If *p*, then *q*" and "*q*" is at best probable.

B. LOGICAL AND EMPIRICAL POSSIBILITY OF CONFIRMATION

The advocates of the verifiability theory of meaningfulness, then, admit that vast numbers of meaningful empirical statements are not conclusively verifiable—some have even gone to the extreme of denying that *any* empirical statements about the physical world are conclusively verifiable (C. I. Lewis, A. J. Ayer, R. Carnap). What they require is only that any competent observer should be in principle capable of making observations that would *confirm* the statement. (Of course, the very same observations may result in *dis*confirmation of the statement, since if the occurrence of an event *E* increases the initial probability of a statement *p*, then the nonoccurrence of *E* decreases the initial probability of *p*.) That one should be able to conceive of an experience or finite set of experiences that would establish with certainty the truth of the statement, they do not require. But now let us ask what it means to say that it is *possible in principle* to confirm a statement.

Instead of "possibility in principle" some positivists (especially Moritz Schlick) have used the expression "logical possibility." This is meant as possibility of the weakest kind, and we rarely mean that kind in everyday language. If I said, "It is possible that I shall never die," or "It is possible to get from New York to San Francisco in five minutes," all but my philosophical friends would be perplexed, but my assertions would be true if "possible" meant "logical possibility," simply because the propositions said to be possible are *not self-contradictory*. That there should be human beings who have no head is logically impossible if possession of a head is part of the definition of "human being," and logically possible otherwise. That one should be able to see without eyes is logically possible, because it is just as much an empirical discovery that visual impressions depend on what one does with one's eyes (and, a fortiori, on the possession of eyes) as that they do not depend on what one does with one's tongue. We may note in passing that although assertions of logical possibility are trivial in the context of everyday

Confirmed does not necessarily mean true.

life, they are useful in the context of *clarification of meaning*—according to our introductory remarks, the distinctively philosophical business. For example, the statement "It is logically possible that a true proposition should never be believed" would be useful in the context of an inquiry into the meaning of "truth." It might be made in refutation of a proposed definition of "truth" as "that which is fated to be believed in the long run" (C. S. Peirce). If that definition really expressed what we mean by "true," then the statement that there are true propositions that will never be believed as long as mankind exists should sound as self-contradictory to us as the statement "There are bachelors who are happily married" or "There are unmarried husbands."

There are meaningful empirical statements that are just *practically* impossible to confirm, such as "There are mountains on the other side of the moon"—and as this example illustrates, what is practically impossible today may be practically possible tomorrow. Most logical positivists would even grant that the meaningfulness of an empirical statement is compatible with *empirical* impossibility of confirming the statement. A proposition is said to be empirically impossible if it is incompatible with a law of nature—say a law of physics or a law of psychology. Thus the proposition expressed by "Some bodies move with a velocity exceeding the velocity of light as measured from the earth" is empirically impossible, though logically possible, according to the special theory of relativity.

It should be noted that if a proposition p is empirically impossible, it does not follow that the proposition expressed by "p is confirmed" is likewise empirically impossible, for "p is confirmed" does not entail "p is true." Thus a confirmation of the above proposition, which contradicts the special theory of relativity, would not require its truth, i.e. actual occurrence of motions exceeding the velocity of light. It would suffice to make observations that contradict the empirical facts on which that proposition of the special theory is inductively based. The logical point is that if p contradicts a law of nature L, and e is evidence that confirms p, it does not follow that e contradicts L; for e may confirm p without p's being a *necessary* consequence of e. (A simple, though highly hypothetical, illustration: Let $L =$ all men are mortal; $p = x$, who is a man, never dies; $e = x$ has just celebrated his three-hundredth birthday and still is as young-looking and vigorous as on his fiftieth birthday.) Therefore even logical positivists who require empirical possibility of confirmation as a necessary condition of semantical meaningfulness are not driven to the absurd consequence that the negations of statements expressing laws of nature are meaningless. Nevertheless they do well in mitigating the requirement by the substitution of logical possibility for empirical

note

possibility of confirmation. This may be shown in terms of two kinds of statements upon which critics of logical positivism have especially focused attention: statements about the past and statements about other minds.

No doubt statements about past events that have or might have directly entered into the speaker's experience are confirmable by the speaker. Either he remembers the event in question or it is possible that he should remember it; and remembering is a perfectly good method of confirmation. The fact that I seem to remember E is compatible with E's not having occurred—memory is fallible—but it constitutes prima-facie evidence that E really occurred; just as my seeming to see a snake is prima-facie evidence for there being a snake, though it is compatible with there not being a snake—sense perception may deceive. But take a historical statement, such as "Brutus stabbed Caesar," that does not describe an event within the lifetime of a contemporary historian and accordingly could not be confirmed by remembering. If nevertheless it is empirically possible to confirm it, the reason is that there are contingent laws connecting successive events by virtue of which presently observable facts permit us to make inferences to presently unobservable facts. The inference from such and such documentary evidence to the hypothesis that Brutus stabbed Caesar at such and such a time, for example, is more complex but logically of the same character as the inference from wet streets to past rain. Yet, as was emphasized by Hume, it is logically possible that there should be no such uniformity in the succession of events as makes inferences from the present to the past—or, for that matter, from the present to the future—possible in this universe. Thus, if at one time rainfall were followed by wet ground, at another time by bone-dry ground, at still another time by hotter ground; and if conversely wet ground were at one time preceded by rainfall, at another time by scorching sunshine, at still another time by sudden withering of plants and leaves, none of these sequences occurring more frequently than any other—then no inference from rain to wet ground, or conversely, would be possible. But wouldn't it, then, be meaningful, i.e. true or false, to say that Brutus stabbed Caesar, even if the world were so chaotic that historical inference was impossible in it? Nevertheless, if "It is empirically possible that p be confirmed by posterity" entails "There are laws of succession of events," then it is surely empirically impossible that a statement asserting that such and such an event happened several centuries ago be confirmed by posterity in a world devoid of laws of succession.

But once logical possibility of confirmation is substituted for empirical possibility of confirmation, this sort of objection can be answered quite easily by the positivist. He points out that though it may conflict with the laws of biology that a human being live for more than, say, two hundred years, it is not logically impossible; or that at any rate it is not logically impossible that I should have been alive at the time when Brutus stabbed Caesar so as to be able to witness the murder. Therefore it is logically possible that I, the speaker of the historical statement, should have conclusively verified it by direct observation; a fortiori, it is logically possible that I should *confirm* it by inference from present to past, for whether or not laws of succession exist, it is *logically possible* that they should exist. A similar point has been made with respect to statements about other minds, such as "He feels toothache now," "He is thinking of his mother," "He sees the same color that I see when exposed to the same optical stimulation." We can confirm such statements by means of analogical inference from overt behavior to sensations, thoughts, feelings—in short *mental* states of another body that physically and behaviorally closely resembles our own body.[2] But suppose a world in which there are no regular connections at all between mental and physical events: sometimes an optical stimulus is followed by seeing green, at other times the same stimulus is followed by hearing a noise; sometimes pain is accompanied by the sort of facial expression that in this world goes together with pleasure, sometimes by what we call (presuming a regular, causal connection) a "pained" expression; and as before, let us assume there is not even a significant difference in the *degree* to which the various kinds of events are correlated. Indeed, in such a universe psychological words such as "pained," "seeing red," "thinking hard" would not even have a communicable meaning, since we cannot teach someone else what we mean by these words without assuming that such and such forms of behavior or facial expressions or physiological states of another organism are connected with the same sort of mental state we know them to be connected with in our own experience. Yet, that a toothache that is not felt by me, or a thought that is not my thought, occurs in such a universe in which there are no psychophysical laws seems to be a perfectly intelligible proposition. Now, it is a contingent law of psychology, a law of "learning" if you wish, that a mind can acquire beliefs about another mind only indirectly, by inductive inference from observable behavior or physiological processes. Therefore confirmation of a proposition of the above kind seems to be *empirically* impossible. Yet here again, the logical positivist is anxious to show that statements that are meaningful by ordinary standards of meaningfulness are meaningful according to his criterion too: it is, after all, logically possible to acquire true beliefs about another mind directly, i.e., without

2. For more detailed discussion of such analogical inference, see Chapter 4, D.

first perceiving a physical expression of the other mind. Some will say that this is not only logically possible but actually happens in cases of telepathy.

C. KNOWING THE TRUTH-CONDITION
AND KNOWING A METHOD
OF VERIFICATION

But here the following question arises: Suppose that, for whatever reason, I believe that you now feel toothache, though I have not acquired this belief by inference from any physical expression of your toothache—in other words, I have been "screened" from your body as in telepathic card-guessing experiments (of course, verbal communication is excluded too). And suppose that this belief happens to be true, as you unfortunately know. Would it not be strange to say that I had "verified" or "confirmed" that you suffer toothache? I would have a true belief about your mental condition, but my belief would not be based on evidence; it would not be the outcome of any process of verification. This situation suggests that the identification of knowledge of the semantic meaning, the truth-condition, of a statement with knowledge of a method of verification or confirmation of the statement can be maintained only at the cost of violating the ordinary uses of the words "verification," "confirmation," "evidence."

note The point will become clearer in connection with the verifiability principle of _meaning_, which we distinguished from the verifiability principle of _meaningfulness_ under discussion so far. If "John suffers toothache now" means that state of affairs which, if it existed, would be conclusive evidence for its truth, what then is its meaning? Surely not anything that would normally be called a physical expression or symptom of his toothache, such as cavities, groans, statements synonymous with "I have a toothache" uttered by John with apparent sincerity, or the like. For it can be supposed without self-contradiction that John does not suffer toothache in spite of exhibiting the usual symptoms of such a pain, or that he suffers toothache without exhibiting any of the usual symptoms of toothache. This reflection forces the positivist to concede that it is only John's experience of pain that constitutes conclusive evidence for the statement. But evidence for whom? Not for anybody besides John, for John alone can possess this piece of "evidence"; the evidence that is accessible to other people is never "conclusive" in that sense. Evidence for John himself, then? But it surely would be a misuse of the word "evidence" if John said that he has absolutely conclusive evidence, has conclusively verified, that he suffers toothache; his evidence being—that he suffers toothache. So: what is "conclusive" evidence in the relevant sense, cannot properly be called "evidence," and whatever can properly be called "evidence" is not "conclusive" in the relevant sense.

We shall see later (Chapter 4) in more detail how the verifiability principle of meaning led to the behaviorist or *physicalist* trend in psychology and to the *operationist* trend in physics. Critics of these trends are prone to accuse the positivists of confusing the *meaning* of a statement with the *evidence* for it, the reasons for accepting it. The foregoing analysis already enables us to decide to what extent this criticism is just and to what extent it is unjust. It is unjust because no positivist would identify the meaning of a statement with states of affairs whose existence would constitute but *indirect* evidence for the statement. For example, positivists would deny that the facts that constitute a historian's evidence for his hypothesis are any part of the latter's meaning, or that the facts that provide a detective with clues to the identity of the criminal have anything to do with the meaning of the hypothesis that so-and-so is the criminal. To put the matter formally: suppose that an hypothesis h is tested in terms of its consequences $p, q, r, \ldots$. If p is a proposition that can be inferred with high probability from h but that is not a *logical* consequence of h, then it is, if true, evidence for h yet no part of the meaning of h. In other words, it is only if the conjoint assertion of h and denial of its consequence p is self-contradictory (in which case p is said to be a *logical* consequence of h) that p can be said to be part of the meaning of h.

But having revealed the injustice of the criticism, we have at the same time revealed its justice. For the logical consequences of a statement—in contrast to what are usually called *factual* consequences—are simply those statements which we can see to follow from it by just analyzing its meaning, without presupposing any auxiliary premises. And it is obvious that one may know the logical consequences, in this manner, without knowing how he might obtain evidence for the statement in any ordinary sense of "evidence." "That tree is a thousand years old": anybody who understands English knows what this statement means; but people who do not know any *laws* correlating observable features of a tree with its age will not come any nearer to knowing how the statement might be verified by deducing such "consequences" as "That tree is more than 999 years old," "At least one tree is a thousand years old," or the like. Similarly, consider the statement that a given person who cannot speak is now thinking about the properties of the square root of two. Since, by assumption, verbal evidence is precluded and physiologists have not yet discovered precisely what kind of brain-event occurs when a man thinks about the square root of two, we just do not know how such a statement might be confirmed. Even if the requisite physiological knowledge were at hand, we could hardly say that the physiological evidence is what the statement *means*. For if it constituted its meaning, we could not both *understand* the statement sufficiently to be able to ask what physiological evidence for it there is *and* be unable to say what kind of brain-event would afford evidence for it!

D. MEANINGFULNESS AND OBSERVATION STATEMENTS

Perhaps, however, these difficulties are merely the result of insufficient formal precision in the formulation of the verifiability principles of meaning and meaningfulness. Let us try a new, more formal approach, patterned after Carnap's classic paper *Testability and Meaning*. The idea behind the verifiability principle of meaningfulness is that a statement that claims to say something about the actual world—in contrast to a priori statements, which are equally true of any possible world—is meaningful if and only if there are possible observations whose outcome is relevant to the truth or falsehood of the statement. The formalization of this idea requires the notion of an *observation statement*. An observation statement is directly verifiable by observation: "This is red," "The top of the mercury column coincides with the mark 92 at time *t*," "The metal has expanded." Negations, conjunctions, and disjunctions of observation statements in the foregoing sense are also observation statements. Now, obviously all observation statements are meaningful, but not all meaningful statements are observation statements. The problem is to specify logical relations that must obtain between a statement and observation statements if the statement is to be meaningful in spite of its not being itself an observation statement. Let us examine some proposals:

1. The statement must be deducible from a finite class of observation statements (criterion of complete verifiability). But no unrestricted generalization, such as "All bodies near the surface of the earth that fall in a vacuum fall with constant acceleration" or "All bodies exert on each other a force that is directly proportional to the product of their masses and inversely proportional to their distance," satisfies this condition. Some have consistently concluded that such sentences do not express propositions, do not describe states of affairs, at all, but are to be interpreted as *rules* for inferring one observation statement from others. But

it would surely be wiser to follow Carnap in granting semantical meaning to such sentences and accordingly dropping the criterion of complete verifiability.

2. Observation statements must be deducible from the statement, such that it is falsifiable by direct falsification of at least one observation statement (criterion of complete falsifiability). This criterion accords with the notion that what distinguishes an empirical statement from other kinds of statements, both a priori statements and metaphysical statements (such as "Everything is a compound of an unobservable 'substratum' and a set of qualities that inhere in the substratum"), is that it is falsifiable by observations; one cannot maintain it regardless of what experience may disclose. According to the view—which we shall have to examine critically later (cf. Chapter 9, p. 142; Chapter 16, p. 290; Chapter 17, p. 309)—that any unrestricted generalization, although not completely verifiable, is falsifiable by a single instance (a so-called "contrary instance"), this criterion rescues the meaningfulness of unrestricted generalizations. But this is like jumping from the fire into the frying pan: if we contradict an unrestricted generalization, we obtain an unrestricted existential statement from which no observation statement is deducible and which accordingly is not falsifiable by observations. For example: "There is at least one body and at least one time t such that the body falls in a vacuum near the earth at t but falls with an acceleration different from 32 ft/sec². " Surely, no observation could logically compel one to abandon this statement as false—though one may have no good reason for affirming its truth either. Nevertheless, it describes a conceivable state of affairs, a possibility.

Furthermore, each of these criteria has the absurd consequence that the negation of a meaningful statement may be meaningless. Unrestricted generalizations are not completely verifiable; but their negations are existential statements, i.e., statements of the form "Something has property P," and such statements are completely verifiable, since they follow from any observation statement of the form "X has P." And as we have seen, although there are observation statements that contradict an unrestricted generalization, no observation statement contradicts an unrestricted[3] existential statement.

3. The statement either satisfies criterion 1 or it satisfies criterion 2 or else an observation statement is deducible from it in conjunction with other statements without being deducible from the latter alone. The third alternative surely is an important improvement on the earlier formulations. Take, for example, the third Newtonian law of motion, the

---

3. Unrestricted general statements are contrasted with general statements that are shorthand for finite conjunctions or disjunctions of observation statements, e.g., "All the men now in this room are tall," "Some inhabitant of this house is over eighty."

law of the equality of action and reaction. Since it is formulated in terms of unobservables, so-called "theoretical constructs" (see Chapter 3), viz. forces and reaction forces, which cannot be mentioned in observation statements, no observation statements are deducible from it in isolation. But if it is combined with Newton's second law of motion, according to which the force acting on a body is equal to the product of the body's mass times the acceleration imparted to the body, we can deduce the law of the conservation of momentum. The latter does not mention postulated forces, only masses and velocities, and—at first sight at any rate—the terms "mass" and "velocity" seem to be definable by means of observational vocabulary, comprising such terms as "length" and "time lapse." Or consider the law of universal gravitation. Of course it entails *singular* statements, such as "This stone is attracted by the earth with a force that...," but they belong just as much to the theoretical language as the law from which they are derivable. In order to derive testable observation statements from them we have to supplement them with the laws of motion. Here again the second law of motion is useful: if we substitute for the gravitational force acting on the stone the product of the stone's mass times the acceleration of gravity, an elementary mathematical deduction yields the result that the latter does not depend on the stone's mass.[4] This is Galileo's famous discovery: that bodies fall with the same acceleration regardless of differences of mass, provided they fall under the sole influence of gravity. Even though we have not yet reached an "observation statement" in the strict sense, it is rather obvious how the residual deductions are to be made. We eventually reach something like "If this Ping-pong ball and that ball of lead are dropped simultaneously from the top of this evacuated tube, they will reach the bottom of the tube simultaneously."

But although this criterion is much better, it is likewise open to a serious objection. Take a completely nonsensical sentence such as "Being is nothingness in disguise." We need only conjoin it with the sentence "If being is nothingness in disguise, then Eisenhower will be re-elected," and we obtain the (fairly) directly verifiable consequence "Eisenhower will be re-elected." Since this consequence is not deducible from the auxiliary premise alone, criterion 3 is satisfied by our obviously nonsensical sentence. Two amendments to criterion 3 may be suggested:

(a) The statement to which the test of significance is applied should be a really essential premise for the deduction of some observation statements, i.e. the events described by the latter should not be predictable without the help of that premise. Clearly, we could even replace "Being

4. Since $F = mg$, and $F = G \cdot mM/r^2$ (where $m = mass$ of the $stone$, $M = $ mass of the earth, $r = $ radius of the earth, $G = $ gravitational constant), it follows that $mg = G \cdot mM/r^2$, hence $g = G \cdot M/r^2$.

is nothingness in disguise" by its formal denial "Being is not nothingness in disguise," making a corresponding change in the auxiliary premise, and still get the conclusion that Eisenhower will be re-elected. But this way out overlooks that even a theory that is genuinely instrumental to predictions may be logically dispensable in the sense that the same verifiable predictions might be made without it. Thus the theory of Lavoisier that heat is a highly elastic fluid ("caloric") made up of weightless particles from which repulsive forces emanate and which insert themselves between the atoms of solids and liquids when these are heated, led logically to the true prediction that a heated gas would, other things being equal, expand; yet the same predictions are nowadays made by means of the kinetic theory of heat, which is incompatible with the caloric theory.

(b) The auxiliary premises must themselves be meaningful. Our auxiliary premise is obviously meaningless since it contains a meaningless statement as component. But now we have saved our criterion at the expense of making it circular and thus ineffective. To avoid circularity, we would have to characterize the class of statements that may serve as auxiliary premises without using the motion of meaningfulness, because this is the notion that is to be explicated. Could we characterize it simply as the class of observation statements, thus: a statement is meaningful if it either satisfies criterion 1 or 2 or permits the deduction of observation statements from observation statements? Undoubtedly the chief utility of laws and theories consists in their permitting us to predict future observations from present observations; and according to a radically positivistic conception of science, they are nothing but instruments for such prediction. But this is an oversimplified picture of the nature of scientific prediction. It is clear that if a law of the form "All *A* are *B*" is formulated in terms of theoretical concepts, such as "All chemically homogeneous bodies with atomic weight *x* are magnetizable," it cannot serve as a simple bridge from observation statements to observation statements the way "All metals expand when heated" serves as a simple bridge from "This metallic object is being heated now" to "It will expand." It will have to be supplemented with observation statements *and* other, equally theoretical laws before any predictions are derivable from it.[5]

5. In his introduction to the second edition of *Language, Truth, and Logic* (New York: Dover Publications, Inc., 1946), Ayer reformulates the criterion of verifiability as follows: "I propose to say that a statement is directly verifiable if it is either itself an observation-statement, or is such that in conjunction with one or more observation-statements it entails at least one observation-statement which is not deducible from these other premises alone; and I propose to say that a statement is indirectly verifiable if it satisfies the following conditions: first, that in conjunction with certain other premises it entails one or more directly verifiable statements which are not deducible from these other premises alone; and secondly, that these other premises do not include any statement that is not either analytic, or directly verifiable, or

E. REDUCIBILITY OF MEANINGFUL TERMS TO OBSERVABLE PREDICATES

Attempts have been made to improve upon criterion 3 by heaping one subtle qualification on another, in much the same way as the ancient astronomers tried to save the geocentric conception of the universe by heaping epicycles upon epicycles. But it is now widely conceded that this approach to an empiricist criterion of significance is not promising. The approach of Carnap's *Testability and Meaning* is different: it consists in defining an empiricist language by characterizing the undefined ("primitive," as logicians say) descriptive vocabulary of the language as well as the permissible modes of definitional introduction of new descriptive terms, and by describing the structure of the language by specifying which combinations of words yield sentences and which modes of deduction of sentences from others are valid. Thereupon an empirical proposition is defined as a proposition that is not a priori and can be expressed in an empiricist language. The novelty of this approach consists in the replacement of the requirement of (direct or indirect) deducibility of observation statements by the requirement of reducibility—in a sense to be explained presently—of the constituent descriptive terms of a sentence to so-called *observable predicates* and names of observable particulars. Descriptive terms are, roughly speaking, terms whose meanings determine the content of a statement, in contrast to the *logical constants* that determine the form of a statement. For example, in the statement "All men are mortal," "men" and "mortal" are the descriptive terms, "all" and "are" the logical constants.

Now, it will generally be agreed that the descriptive terms in a statement must be meaningful if the statement is to be meaningful. Accordingly, one of the tasks Carnap set himself in the cited essay was to formulate a criterion of meaningfulness of descriptive terms. But it is doubtful whether this is at the same time a sufficient condition for the meaningfulness of a statement. As logical positivists, Carnap foremost, have emphasized, natural languages have a deficient syntax in that they permit the formation of grammatically correct sentences that are meaningless although the constituent terms are meaningful, e.g., "Virtue drinks

capable of being independently established as indirectly verifiable. And I can now reformulate the principle of verification as requiring of a literally meaningful statement, which is not analytic, that it should be either directly or indirectly verifiable in the foregoing sense." For discussions concerning the adequacy of this amended version, see the following articles: D. J. O'Connor, "Some Consequences of Prof. Ayer's Verification Principle," *Analysis*, 1950; R. Brown and J. Watling, "Amending the Verification Principle," *Mind*, 1951.

wine," "A dog just ate the law of gravitation." The second task, there-fore, that Carnap tackled was to formulate rules of sentence formation that are more stringent than the rules of sentence formation of natural languages; that is, the rules are to be so chosen that in the ideal language only meaningful sentences can even be sentences. Without going into the question of whether and how such an ideal language could be con-structed, our aim will be to prove the following: a statement may satisfy the conditions of an empiricist language as laid down in *Testability and Meaning* and yet fail to be verifiable or confirmable in any ordinary sense of these words.

One of the fundamental principles of logical positivism is that a descriptive term is significant if and only if it is either ostensively definable—a name of an observable particular, such as a dog or a building, or a predicate designating an observable quality or relation—or else is reducible to ostensively definable terms. This is really a semantic version of Hume's principle that every idea derives from an antecedent impres-sion or is composed of ideas that derive from antecedent impressions. It amounts to a simple principle of learning that, unfortunately, tends to be forgotten by philosophers, who are so absorbed in verbal abstractions that they lose sight of the prosaic basis of sense-experience from which all significant language originates and to which it must eventually return: You may define one word by means of other words, but unless you eventually come to words whose meanings are explained by *exhibition* of the qualities or particulars they designate, no word has been given a semantical meaning at all. You may define a square as an equilateral figure all of whose angles are right angles, then explain that "equilateral" means having sides of equal length and that a right angle is an angle of such a kind that if two congruent angles of that kind are brought together so that one arm of one angle coincides with one arm of the other angle, the other two arms will form one straight line. But unless you explain to your audience the meanings of "angle" and "straight line" by pointing at instances, they will not have been brought any closer to an under-standing of the word "square."

Now, whereas in our former approach to the formalization of the empiricist criterion of meaningfulness we began with a class of directly verifiable statements, called "observation statements," we begin in our pre-sent approach with a class of ostensively definable and relatively simple *predicates,* called by Carnap "observable predicates," such as "red," "warm," "straight," "hard," "coincides," "larger," supplemented perhaps by a set of names of observable particulars (individual constants). Our next task consists, not in specifying logical relations that must hold be-tween meaningful statements that are not observation statements and observation statements, but in specifying *definitional* relations that must obtain between a descriptive term that is not itself an observable predicate nor an individual constant, and the primitive descriptive terms, if that term is to be admitted into a scientific language. A very simple kind of definitional relation, which at an early stage of the positivist movement was considered sufficient for the definitional construction of scientific concepts, is *explicit definability*. The above definition of "square" is an example of explicit definition: the defined term ("definiendum") is declared synonymous with "equilateral figure all of whose angles are right angles" (the "definiens") in the sense that in any sentence it may be replaced by the definiens without changing the truth-value (i.e., truth or falsehood) of the sentence, or even the meaning of the sentence. The definiendum may be introduced into the language just for purposes of abbreviation, or it may already have a use before being explicitly defined. In the latter case, the purpose of the definition is to make explicit a *criterion of application;* i.e., the definition tells us exactly what observable properties, or relations to other things, a thing must have if a simple statement applying the definiendum to a thing is to be true. We have learnt the meaning of "square" by ostensive definition, i.e., by being conditioned to associate the word with a certain kind of shape; but if we came upon a borderline case where simple inspection could not decide whether the shape before us was square or not, the above definition would tell us what observations and measurements have to be made in order to decide the question. Let us call such simple statements, e.g., "This figure is square," *atomic* statements, since they are not composed of statements but constitute the building blocks for more complex statements. We can then understand Carnap's claim that in making clear to ourselves the semantical meaning of a predicate by defining it on the basis of observable predicates, we at the same time describe a *method of verification* of its atomic statements.

F.   COMPLETE AND INCOMPLETE DEFINITION

Another type of definition by means of which a method of verification for atomic statements of defined predicates may be described is *contextual definition* (also called "definition in use"). For example: x is harder than $y =_{df.} x$ can scratch y but y cannot scratch x (where x and y are crystals or stones with a sharp point); or: x has the same weight as $y =_{df.}$ if x and y are placed in the opposite pans of a beam balance, the balance will reach a state of equilibrium. Like explicit definitions, contextual definitions in terms of observable predicates not only provide criteria of application of the definiendum, but at the same time are rules for eliminating the definiendum from any sentence by translation into a synonymous sentence. There is, however, a difference: if a term is contextually defined, it cannot simply be replaced by a more complex synonym without changing the remainder of the sentence from which it is eliminated. In other words, a contextual definition is a rule for translating an entire sentence that contains the definiendum into a synonymous sentence that does not contain it. The difference will easily be grasped by comparison of an explicit and a contextual definition of one and the same term: a brother is a male sibling (explicit definition); x is brother of y if and only if x is male and has the same parents as y (contextual definition). The so-called *dispositional* predicates, i.e., predicates designating a disposition to react in a characteristic way to a certain kind of stimulus, can be contextually defined only in terms of observable predicates. Atomic statements containing the dispositional predicate thereby become translatable into conditional statements. For example: x is soluble in liquid $L =_{df.}$ if at any time x is immersed in L, then x will dissolve at that time.

The latter type of contextual definition, however, raises a delicate problem. It certainly describes a method of verification: if x dissolves after being immersed in L, then x is soluble in L; and if x does not dissolve after being immersed in L, then x is not soluble in L. But suppose x is a piece of wood that is never at all immersed in L; is it then soluble in L according to the above definition? The attempt to answer this question forces us to reflect on the meaning of "if-then." Normally one would say no, on the ground that we have reason to believe that if the piece of wood *were* immersed, it *would not* dissolve: we have observed other pieces of wood being immersed in water, say, without dissolving; hence we can infer by analogy that this piece of wood would remain solid too. Yet, for reasons we cannot detail in the present connection (cf. Chapter 6, p. 98; Chapter 15, p. 273), many logicians interpret "If p, then q" to mean "Either p is false or q is true," or equivalently "It is not the case that p is true and q is false." This relation of implication from one statement to another, which has the characteristic property that it depends only on the truth-values, not on the meanings, of two statements whether they are related by it, is called *material implication*. Nobody maintains that this relation is asserted to hold between the statements "This piece of sugar is immersed in tea" and "This piece of sugar dissolves" when one says, "If this piece of sugar were immersed in tea, then it would dissolve." But whereas the analysis of the causal relation one asserts to hold is very difficult, the logical properties of material implication are easily discovered.

In particular, it follows from its definition that a false statement materially implies any statement. Therefore our contextual definition of "soluble" entails that a match that is kept dry until it burns up *is* soluble in water if the definiens is interpreted as a material implication. Carnap, who at the time thought that the only clear meaning that can be given to "if-then" as used in a scientific language is material implication, concluded therefore—not that dry matches are soluble in water, but that dispositional predicates are not contextually definable so as to be in principle eliminable from scientific discourse. As an alternative method of introducing such predicates, which abound in scientific discourse though not all of them are directly recognizable by the ending "-uble," "-ible," or "-able," he suggested *reduction sentences.*

For example: for any time t and for any object x, if x is immersed in L at t, then x is soluble in L if and only if x dissolves in L at t. Although "if-then" is again meant in the sense of material implication, this reduction sentence does not permit us to assert that a thing which is never immersed in L is soluble in L. For, in order to be justified in asserting "x is soluble in L," we must first be justified in asserting "x dissolves in L (at some time)," but this would require an actual experiment with x. The virtue of the reduction sentence, then, is that it permits us to ascribe a disposition D to an object only if the relevant experiment has been performed and found to have a positive outcome; whereas according to the contextual definition in terms of material implication, any object has any disposition provided it is not subjected to the relevant experiment. (Note that our dry match could even be argued to be both soluble and insoluble if we defined "x is insoluble in L" to mean " 'x is immersed in L' materially implies 'x does not dissolve in L' "!) Since the reduction sentence describes a test for solubility in terms of a specific experimental condition, viz. immersion, and does not by itself enable us to decide whether an object that is not subjected to that particular condition is soluble, it may appropriately be called both a *conditional* and an *incomplete* definition.

The reader may, with good reason, protest that so far no good reason at all has been given for using reduction sentences instead of the complete definitions he is accustomed to. For surely it is a poor argument against complete definitions in terms of an "if-then" relation to say that these give rise to paradoxical consequences if "if-then" is interpreted in a way in which it just is not meant in everyday and scientific language. However, reduction sentences may nevertheless be preferable to complete definitions because of a feature of empirical concepts that may be called their "openness." Let us illustrate this feature in terms of a fundamental concept of physics: mass. A complete definition of this concept would require, first of all, a criterion of equality of the masses of two bodies. Suppose we try the following contextual definition: the mass of $A =$ the mass of $B =_{df.}$ if A and B collide directly, then their relative velocity after the collision is equal to their relative velocity before the collision.

Now, obviously this definition presupposes that the colliding bodies are of such a nature that they rebound without deformation after collision, as in the case of billiard balls, and that none of their kinetic energy is converted into some other form, say, heat. Surely, no physicist would seriously believe *this* is what he means when he ascribes equal masses to, say, two eggs!

If the definiens really expressed the meaning which the expression "equal masses" has in every context of usage, then it would under any circumstances be self-contradictory to say something like "These two bodies have equal mass, but after collision they both came to a stop." Since, on the contrary, we can obviously conceive of situations in which we would say just that, the above definition is not really a complete definition at all. It does not say, for example, what "equal mass" means in contexts where no collision experiment is possible, e.g., "The mass of the earth is not equal to the mass of Mars." For this reason, a reduction sentence would be more suitable, for a reduction sentence only formulates a criterion of application relative to a specific experimental context and does not declare the reduced term *synonymous* with any combination of observable predicates: if A and B collide directly and are the sort of bodies which rebound without deformation (elastic bodies), then the mass of A equals the mass of B if and only if their relative velocity after impact equals their relative velocity before impact. The reader may object that our counterexamples (the eggs and the planets) really would not be counterexamples to the above complete definition if the qualification that the bodies are elastic were explicitly mentioned in the antecedent of the definiens. This is true. But since the definition, even if thus amended, does not describe a test for deciding whether two eggs or two planets have the same mass, and it surely is not meaningless to ask whether two bodies of these kinds have equal mass, it still follows that the definiendum is not synonymous with the definiens in all contexts. If we use the method of reduction sentences, we replace a single definition by a set of reduction sentences, each of them describing a test procedure for different contexts in which the concept might be applied. Thus, if we ascribed equal mass to two eggs, we would probably mean that they would balance each other if placed in the opposite pans of a balance; hence we add the reduction sentence: If A and B are placed in opposite pans of a balance, then they have equal mass if and only if the balance reaches a state of equilibrium.

A very similar example is the concept of temperature. It can hardly be maintained that quite generally " x has a temperature of $y°$ at time t" means "If x were brought into contact with a mercury thermometer at t, the top of the mercury would coincide with the mark y a little later"; surely we mean nothing of the kind when we speak of the temperature of the sun, for even if we manufactured a mercury thermometer of gigantic dimensions, the mercury would vaporize long before reaching the temperature of the sun! But even if we confine ourselves to temperatures that can be directly measured, a complete definition can be seen to be inadequate. Temperature can be measured not only in terms of volume changes but also in terms of pressure changes. The gas thermometer is constructed on the basis of the linear proportionality of temperature to the pressure of a gas at constant volume, just as the mercury thermometer is constructed on the basis of the linear proportionality of temperature to the length of a liquid that is free to expand along one dimension only.

Now, suppose that a body is heated and we first try to determine the increase of temperature by means of a mercury thermometer, finding that the mercury rises to twice its original height. Thereupon we check by means of the gas thermometer and find to our amazement that the pressure of the thermometric gas has remained constant. What should we say then? Assuming that we are quite sure that no experimental error was committed, would we conclude without hesitation that the temperature did double but that the hitherto assumed law of the linear proportionality of temperature to the pressure of a gas at constant volume had been flatly refuted? This is what we should say if the definition in terms of the mercury thermometer expressed the complete meaning of "temperature," for it would then be just self-contradictory to doubt whether the temperature really doubled without doubting that the mercury doubled in length. And since it would be no more self-contradictory to say, in such a hypothetical situation, "Perhaps we were mistaken in our assumption of direct proportionality[6] of temperature to length" than to say "Perhaps we were mistaken in our assumption of direct proportionality of temperature to pressure," neither of these laws is to be regarded as a complete definition of temperature even within strictly *experimental* physics.

G. OPERATIONISM AND AMBIGUITY OF SYMBOLS

We have argued that what is commonly called an *operational* definition —so called because the definiendum is defined in terms of experimental

6. That y is directly proportional to x means that an increase in y is correlated with an increase in x, and a decrease in y with a decrease in x. The exact mathematical form of the proportionality (linear, quadratic, and so on) is another question the answer to which depends partly on conventions of measurement (cf. Chapter 8, D).

operation—is better construed as an essentially incomplete reduction sentence than as a complete contextual definition. Nevertheless, it should be mentioned that reduction sentences could—waiving the artificial argument from the definition of material implication—be dispensed with if one were willing to speak of families of distinct, though empirically related, properties or magnitudes where one normally speaks of an *identical* property or magnitude manifesting itself in different ways. To illustrate by means of the same examples: We find empirically that if in a collision of two bodies *A* and *B* the relative velocity of impact is conserved as they rebound, then *A* and *B* will likewise keep a balance in equilibrium if placed on its opposite pans, further than an elastic spring is lengthened the same amount when they are successively suspended on it. Suppose we called the magnitude that determines the relative velocity of rebound "impact-mass," the magnitude that determines the state of a beam balance "lever-mass," and the magnitude that determines the state of a spring balance "spring-mass." We could then say that the three kinds of experimental operations *completely* define, respectively, equality of impact-mass, equality of lever-mass, and equality of spring-mass, and that there is a well-confirmed empirical law to the effect that any two bodies that have equal impact-mass also have equal lever-mass and equal spring-mass. Because these differently defined properties coincide as a matter of empirical fact in their extension, i.e., any pair of bodies that are related by the one kind of equality are also related by the other kinds of equality, we use the same *symbol* "mass." Nevertheless, this symbol stands for different properties in different kinds of experimental context.

This is the point of view of Bridgman's famous operationism, the principle that "different operations define different concepts." It easily happens that we forget that the same symbol stands for different concepts because experience has disclosed an invariable, or nearly invariable, correlation. Thus we say that the straightness of a stick can be both seen and touched, as though there were an identical quality that manifests itself to different senses. Because of this empirically founded linguistic identification of visual and tactual straightness, we are shocked when we find a stick feeling straight and at the same time looking bent, as in the famous "illusion" of the stick that is halfway immersed in transparent water. We ask: How do we know whether it is really straight or really bent? Why should the sense of touch be more revelatory of the real qualities of things than the sense of sight? But had we, following Bridgman's precept, used different symbols corresponding to different operations (in this case the perceptual operations of looking and touching), we would just note that not all things that are "tactually straight" are also "visually straight" under all conditions, and the question of reality would not arise.

A less trivial illustration is the famous relativity of length. Classical physicists assumed that if a railroad car has a certain length when it is at rest, it must have the same length when it is in motion. Indeed, common sense thinks of the length of the car as an inherent property that cannot "really" change through a change of the method of measuring it. But suppose you agree with the operationist that all you could mean by ascribing to the stationary car a length of x meters is that *if* one were to apply a meter rod to it in the familiar manner, one would have to lay it off x times to get from one end of the car to the other; then you must also agree with him that it is not a priori predictable that the same car in motion will have the same length as measured from the ground on which it moves. For such a measurement of length would involve a new kind of operation: several observers on the ground would have to mark the places on the ground where the front and rear of the car passed, and then the distance between a front-place and a rear-place that were marked *simultaneously* would have to be measured in the usual way. Measurement of the length of a body in motion relative to the measuring observer, therefore, involves a determination of simultaneity. Therefore "length" as operationally defined really stands for different properties that are usually called "rest-length" and "kinetic length." That the rest-length of a body is invariably equal to its kinetic length is no more a priori certain than that tactually straight sticks are invariably visually straight. Indeed, the special thory of relativity denies this equality, and if it were not for the unconscious habit of hypostatizing measuring operations into inherent properties of the measured objects, common sense might not find this shocking at all.

H. IS A STATEMENT COMPOSED
OF MEANINGFUL TERMS
NECESSARILY CONFIRMABLE?

We shall see later that in spite of the undoubted merits of operationist analysis, such as the analysis performed by Bridgman in *The Logic of Modern Physics*, it cannot do justice to a theoretical science such as theoretical physics; and that even the technique of reduction sentences, although a genuine improvement on the technique of complete ((explicit or contextual) definition, has its limitations. But in the meantime let us stop and see how the verifiability principle of meaningfulness has fared in our new approach. Suppose we say that any sentence of accredited form[7] is meaningful provided it is composed of meaningful terms and meaningful terms only, where a meaningful term is either a logical constant or an observable predicate or a name of an observable particular or is definable by, or reducible to, terms of the latter two kinds. Does it follow, then, that every meaningful statement whose truth-value cannot be determined a priori is confirmable? It does not. In order to see that it does not follow, let us look again at the completely untestable hypothesis that every body in the universe, including our measuring rods, is constantly expanding, the rate of expansion being exactly the same for all bodies. The descriptive terms in it are easily definable on the basis of the primitives of an empiricist language, and the sentence has accredited form. The moral to be drawn is that the verifiability criterion of meaningfulness of statements is not a necessary consequence of the empiricist criterion of meaningfulness of descriptive *terms*. Our hypothesis of speculative cosmology that all solid objects are constantly expanding at the same rate[8] is not even in principle confirmable if change of size is operationally defined in the usual way, yet it need not be excluded from the kinds of empiricist languages Carnap described in *Testability and Meaning*.

Selected Readings

Ayer, A. J., "Demonstration of the Impossibility of Metaphysics," *Mind*, 1934. [Reprinted in P. Edwards and A. Pap (eds.), *A Modern Introduction to Philosophy* (New York, 1957).]

————, *Language, Truth and Logic* (2nd ed., New York, 1950), chap. 1.

Berlin, I., "Verifiability in Principle," *Aristotelian Society Proceedings*, 1938–39.

Carnap, R., "Testability and Meaning," *Philosophy of Science*, 1936–37. [Also lithographed by the Graduate Philosophy Club, Yale University (Whitlock's, Inc., New Haven, Conn.). Reprinted in part in H. Feigl and M. Brodbeck (eds.), *Readings in the Philosophy of Science* (New York, 1953).]

7. We cannot here go into the highly interesting problem in the philosophy of language of the extent to which one can formulate rules of sentence formation that will preclude the possibility of forming sentences out of meaningful vocabulary that are nonetheless nonsensical, such as "Virtue drinks wine." For the sake of the argument, let us assume that an empiricist language can be so defined that such sentences are excluded from it.

8. This hypothesis, which nobody would seriously put forth as an explanation of observed phenomena, must not be confused with the famous hypothesis of an expanding universe; the latter means that the densiy of matter decreases owing to the recession of spiral systems as evidenced by the red shift (Doppler effect).

Carnap, R., "The Elimination of Metaphysics through Logical Analysis of Language," in A. J. Ayer (ed.), *Logical Positivism* (New York, 1959).

Ducasse, C. J., "Verification, Verifiability and Meaningfulness," *Journal of Philosophy*, 1936.

Evans, J. L., "On Meaning and Verification," *Mind*, 1953.

Ewing, A. C., "Meaninglessness," *Mind*, 1937. [Reprinted in P. Edwards and A. Pap (eds.), *A Modern Introduction to Philosophy* (New York, 1957).]

Frank, P. (ed.), *The Validation of Scientific Theories* (symposium on operationism) (New York, 1961).

Hempel, C. G. *Fundamentals of Concept Formation in Empirical Science* (International Encyclopedia of Unified Science, II, no. 7, Chicago, 1952).

———, "Problems and Changes in the Empiricist Criterion of Meaning," *Revue Internationale de Philosophie*, 1950. [Reprinted in L. Linsky (ed.), *Semantics and the Philosophy of Language* (Urbana, Ill., 1952); and as "The Empiricist Criterion of Meaning," in A. J. Ayer (ed.), *Logical Positivism* (New York, 1959).]

Lazerowitz, M., "The Positivist's Use of Nonsense," in M. Lazerowitz, *The Structure of Metaphysics* (London, 1955).

Lewis, C. I., "Experience and Meaning," *Philosophical Review*, 1934. [Reprinted in H. Feigl and W. Sellars (eds.), *Readings in Philosophical Analysis* (New York, 1949).]

Marhenke, P., "The Criterion of Significance," in L. Linsky (ed.), *Semantics and the Philosophy of Language* (Urbana, Ill., 1952).

Mehlberg, H., *The Reach of Science* (Toronto, 1958), part 3.

Nagel, E., "Verifiability, Truth and Verification," *Journal of Philosophy*, 1934. [Reprinted in E. Nagel, *Logic without Metaphysics* (New York, 1956).]

Pap, A., "Reduction Sentences and Open Concepts," *Methodos*, 5 (1953).

———, "Reduction Sentences and Disposition Concepts," in P. A. Schilpp (ed.), *The Philosophy of Rudolf Carnap* (Library of Living Philosophers), forthcoming.

Reichenbach, H., "The Verifiability Theory of Meaning," in H. Feigl and M. Brodbeck (eds.), *Readings in the Philosophy of Science* (New York, 1953).

Schlick, M., "Meaning and Verification," *Philosophical Review*, 1936. [Reprinted in H. Feigl and W. Sellars (eds.), *Readings in Philosophical Analysis* (New York, 1949).]

———, "Positivism and Realism," in A. J. Ayer (ed.), *Logical Positivism* (New York, 1959).

Stace, W. T., "Metaphysics and Meaning," *Mind*, 1935. [Reprinted in P. Edwards and A. Pap (eds.), *A Modern Introduction to Philosophy* (New York, 1957).]

———, "Positivism," *Mind*, 1944.

Waismann, F., "Verifiability," in A. Flew (ed.), *Logic and Language* (Oxford, 1951).

Wisdom, J., "Metaphysics and Verification," *Mind*, 1938.

CHAPTER 3

Theoretical Constructs
& the Limitations
of Operationism

A. THE IMPOSSIBILITY OF INTRODUCING
THEORETICAL CONSTRUCTS
BY REDUCTION CHAINS

Even if, as a first liberalization of a strict operationism, reduction sentences are admitted and thus some account is taken of what we called the "openness" of scientific concepts, the empiricist criterion of meaningfulness of descriptive terms still does not do full justice to the abstract character of theoretical sciences such as mathematical physics. In order to make this limitation clear, let us return to our earlier illustration: What do we mean when we ascribe to the sun a tremendously high temperature? Suppose that, as suggested, we reformulate so-called operational definitions of temperature, in terms of operations of measuring temperature, as reduction sentences, and thus renounce the claim that the meaning of a statement of the form "The temperature of x at t is $y°$" can be completely expressed by a conditional statement containing only observable predicates, such as "coincides." Could we at least formulate a reduction sentence describing how any such hypothesis might be tested?

That even this is not feasible becomes clear if we take a close look at the method actually used by physicists to discover the sun's temperature. This method essentially involves *calculation* on the basis of laws containing temperature as a variable. The average temperature at the surface of the earth can be determined by more or less direct measurement, and thereupon a law, confirmed by independent measurements of the physical magnitudes it connects, is used to calculate the intensity of heat radiation at the earth's surface (Stefan-Boltzmann law). The next step consists in calculation of the intensity of heat radiation at the center of the sun on the basis of a law asserting that the intensity of heat radiation at a point is a definite function of the distance of the point from the source of heat (idealized as a point). Since the average distance of the earth from the sun can be calculated by means of other laws (specifically, the laws of mechanics, including the law of universal gravitation), this law enables a simple calculation of the unknown quantity, and a renewed application of the Stefan-Boltzmann law yields the degree of temperature prevailing on the sun. Now, the essential point is that for the calculation of the sun's temperature *theories* are used which connect the magnitude temperature with other physical magnitudes and which cannot plausibly be interpreted as reduction sentences connecting a theoretical term, i.e., a term designating something that is not directly observable, with observational vocabulary; in fact, a term such as "heat radiation" is no less theoretical than the term "temperature."

It is true that by means of what Carnap called *reduction chains* even terms designating states that cannot be *directly* inferred from experimental data are amenable to the sort of anchoring in the plane of observation that was exclusively contemplated by the earlier empiricists. For example, one might first introduce the term "electric current" by the reduction sentence: If a wire is connected with a galvanometer, then electrical current flows through the wire at t if and only if the galvanometer needle is deflected at t. And then the term "magnetic" might be reduced to the term "electrical current" as follows. If x moves through a closed wire loop at t, then x is magnetic at t if and only if an electric current exists in the loop at t.[1] But the process of confirming the hypothesis about the sun's temperature cannot be represented by such a reduction chain. For the confirmation of this hypothesis involves calculations by means of laws expressing functional relations between magnitudes, and this process is quite different from the reduction of the confirmation of "x is magnetic" to the direct confirmation of such ob-

1. This illustration is borrowed from Carl G. Hempel, *Fundamentals of Concept Formation in Empirical Science* (Chicago: University of Chicago Press, 1952), p. 27. It should be noted that a reduction chain cannot be contracted by elimination of connecting links, such as "electric current" in the above illustration, because a reduction sentence, unlike a complete definition, does not assert an equivalence between the reduced term and some combination of those terms to which the latter is reduced.

servation statements as "*x* moves through a closed wire loop which is connected with a galvanometer whose needle is deflected simultaneously."

One or two additional illustrations may be in order to bring out the limitation of the method of reduction chains. Reduction sentences must, like complete definitions, be subjected to the requirement of noncircularity. An explicit or contextual definition is said to be circular if the definiendum occurs among the terms used to define it. If, like Newton, you define the mass of a body as the product of its density times its volume ("bulk"), this may be all right if you can define "density" without using "mass" in turn. But if density is, as usual, defined as the ratio of mass to volume, then "mass" has been defined in terms of itself though the use of the abbreviation "density" disguised this fact. A definition that is circular in this sense is, of course, futile. Similarly, a reduction sentence would defeat its purpose if the term to be reduced were included in the set of basic terms to which it is to be reduced. With this warning in mind, let us see how the term "root-mean-square velocity of a gas molecule (symbolized by $\bar{v}$), which occurs in the postulates of the kinetic theory of gases, could be reduced to observables. The symbol $\bar{v}$ is explicitly definable as the square root of the arithmetic mean of the squares of the velocities of the individual molecules,

$$\left(\frac{v_1^2 + v_2^2 + \cdots + v_n^2}{n} \right)^{1/2}$$

but this is not, of course, a reduction sentence; a reduction sentence would have to describe a method for inferring the value of $\bar{v}$ for a given mass of gas under determinate pressure and temperature conditions. Could we not, as follows, reduce this construct quite easily to the observables pressure and density in terms of whose values it is actually computable: if operations for measuring pressure and density of a gas at constant temperature are performed, then, if the measured pressure is p and the measured density is d, $\bar{v} = (3p/d)^{1/2}$? But suppose we were asked how we know that the average molecular velocity is related to the mentioned observables in just this way? Would this question be as naive as the question how we know that two bodies that are capable of balancing each other have the same weight, or that a liquid that burns when exposed to high temperature is inflammable? Certainly not.

In fact, a physicist would answer the question by deducing the equation linking our construct to the observables from the postulates of the kinetic theory together with explicit definitions of the molar magnitudes pressure and density in terms of such molecular magnitudes as velocity and mass of a molecule. It is only if we accept the assumptions of the kinetic theory, which are formulated in terms of the very concept to be reduced to observables that we arrive at the conclusion that $\bar{v}$ can be experimentally determined in just that way. If these assumptions are not incorporated into the reduction sentence, then the latter cannot plausibly be claimed to *de-fine* even partially, the construct. For whereas it would be absurd to doubt whether a thing that actually dissolves in a liquid L is soluble in L, if indeed the reduction sentence for "soluble" is a (conditional) definition of this predicate, it is not at all the same sort of absurdity to doubt whether $\bar{v}$ really has the value computed by means of the formula "$\bar{v} = (3p/d)^{1/2}$" from accurately measured values of p and d. To assume that this "unobservable" magnitude had a significantly different value would not be *self*-contradictory, it would only be contradictory to the assumptions of the kinetic theory, which are not by any means self-evident. On the other hand, if these assumptions are explicitly incorporated into the alleged reduction sentence, then the latter is circular and forfeits its claim to explain the meaning of "velocity of a molecule" in terms of molar observables.

Exactly the same methodological moral may be drawn from the experimental determination by J. J. Thomson of the ratio of charge (e) to mass (m) of an electron. There emerges from an analysis of the experiment in terms of electromagnetic and electrostatic principles an equation expressing e/m as a function of electric field intensity, potential difference, and magnetic flux density. This equation, however, is deduced from principles involving the very magnitudes e and m: m gets into the final equation through an application of the principle of the conservation of energy to the electron's motion from cathode to anode, and this principle, of course, involves the mass; and e comes from an equation linking the deflecting electric field force Exe to the force exerted upon the electron in the opposite direction by a magnet. Again, therefore, the equation that serves to calculate the microcosmic unobservable on the basis of such observables as potential difference cannot, on pain of vicious circularity, be interpreted as a reduction sentence.

In this connection we can see the limitation of a strict operationism from still another angle. Different operations, we were told, define different concepts. We remarked in passing that this position could be consistently maintained if one were willing to follow the example of relativity theory and split supposedly inherent properties into distinct though empirically related dispositional properties[2] (kinetic length and rest-length, impact-mass and scale-mass, pressure-temperature and volume-temperature, and so on). But this concession to operationism was premature. Consider again the ascription of a tremendously high tempera-

2. We here use "dispositional property" broadly to refer to any property that is defined—completely or incompletely—by a conditional statement of the form "If such and such operations are performed, such and such results will be observable." For a detailed analysis of the concept "disposition," see Chapter 15.

ture to the sun. If the meaning of a statement is determined by the operations that are appropriate for its verification, then "temperature" cannot
mean in this context what it means when we speak of, say, the temperature of our bedroom, for the operations by which the statement about the
sun is established are partly calculations (Bridgman calls them "pencil
and paper operations," suggesting that one does not have to have a mind
in order to do mathematical physics) on the basis of laws that have been
extrapolated beyond the range within which they were experimentally
confirmed. Suppose that, as consistent operationists, we accordingly
denote temperatures that can be determined only by calculation by a
symbol different from the one we use for temperatures that can be
determined by measurement:

$$T^c \text{ (sun)} = x^\circ \text{ K}$$
$$T^e \text{ (surface of the earth)} = x^\circ \text{ C}$$

or

$$\text{mass}^e \text{ (billiard ball)} = x \text{ g}$$
$$\text{mass}^c \text{ (earth)} = x \text{ kg}$$

But we deduce the values of T^c (sun), mass^c (earth), mass^c (electron),
and so on from experimentally verified statements about observables by
means of equations whose variables range over both measurable and only
computable values of *one and the same magnitude*. If the Stefan-Boltzmann law, for example, were formulated in terms of T^e, then it could not
be used to calculate T^c (sun); if the laws of mechanics were formulated
in terms of mass^e, as direct inductions from experiments with manipulable
bodies, then they could not be used to calculate mass^c (earth) and mass^c
(electron). In sum: if we don't want to admit that mass (earth), mass
(electron), and mass (billiard ball) are in some sense determinate forms
of *one and the same* determinable property, then we cannot logically
justify our calculations of unobservable quantities by means of extrapolated laws. In just which sense we can speak of identity here, is a
question that will be answered in due course.

B. THE ARGUMENT FROM THE
APPLICATION OF MATHEMATICS

Another argument against reducibility of theoretical concepts to observables is based on the application of mathematics in quantitative sciences. Suppose we attempt to define rest-length (i.e., length as measured
from a system relative to which the measured body is at rest) operation-

ally in terms of yardsticks or more sensitive instruments for measuring length. Such a definition would, if complete, describe in terms of observables necessary and sufficient conditions for all statements of the form "length $(x) = y$ cm," and if incomplete, it would at least describe sufficient conditions in terms of observables for all statements of that form.[3] However, no matter how sensitive a measuring instrument may be, it cannot distinguish more than a finite number of values of the measured magnitude, since it has a finite "least count." For example, suppose that the smallest difference of length that can be detected by a given instrument is 0.001 mm; then this is called the least count of the instrument. On the other hand, if we wish to apply mathematics, specifically the calculus, to such physical magnitudes as length, then we must conceptualize them as continuous variables, i.e., variables such that between any two rational numbers which they may assume as values there is still another rational number which is also a value of the variable. Thus, no measurement with the above-described instrument could discover whether the true length (whatever may be meant by that) of a rod is 85.55678 cm or 85.55679 cm. Yet, both of these statements are legitimate substitution instances of the statement form "length $(x) = y$ cm" if y is, as required by application of the calculus, a continuous variable ranging over all the infinitely many rational numbers (fractions); and what is worse, whereas any proposed translation into the language of performable measurements yields *operationally equivalent* statements (i.e., any operation of measurement that would verify the one would verify the other too), the translated statements are *logically* incompatible.

Could we circumvent this difficulty by declaring statements such as "The length of this rod is 85.55678 cm" to be meaningless in case the last decimal place, or even several decimal places, are "experimentally insignificant," as laboratory scientists say? This would be equivalent to replacing such statements by apparently less precise statements in which only experimentally significant decimals are used, say, "The length of this rod is 85.5568 ± 0.00005 cm." But that this solution is untenable may be shown as follows. It will surely be agreed that a true statement cannot have any false consequences, and that equivalent statements cannot have incompatible consequences. Now, suppose that "weight" were operationally defined by reference to a fairly insensitive platform balance whose least count is a tenth of a gram. According to the suggestion that we are criticizing, the statements that a body weighs 12.19 grams and that the same body weighs 12.10 grams would then be equivalent. Similarly, the statements that another body, B, weighs 6.29 grams, respectively, 6.20 grams, would be equivalent. But according to the law

3. Cf. Hempel, *op. cit.,* p. 30.

that the weight of a body is equal to the sum of the weights of its parts[4] the statements which we supposed to be experimentally equivalent entail consequences which are experimentally incompatible: If B weighs 6.29 grams and A weighs 12.19 grams, then A and B together should weigh 18.48 grams; if A weighs 12.10 grams and B weighs 6.20 grams, then A and B together should weigh 18.30 grams. But these consequences are experimentally incompatible, since 0.18 grams is a difference that could be detected even by the insensitive platform balance at our disposal.

This illustration shows that even if the mathematics applied in quantitative science were so rudimentary as to involve only rational numbers (i.e., fractions, whether or not they be expressed in decimal form) it is doubtful whether the exclusion of quantitative statements that have no direct experimental significance could even be *consistently* enforced. Every measuring instrument is less sensitive than it might, theoretically, be—though it is even logically impossible that an instrument could be so sensitive as to detect a physical difference corresponding to any mathematical difference, however small. But a physical difference that is so small that it is not directly detectable even by means of the most delicate measuring instrument may none the less be *indirectly* detectable through mathematical deduction of consequences. If we weigh a number of bodies separately, then weigh them all together and find that the weight of their physical sum differs detectably from the arithmetic sum of their individual weights, we do not abandon the principle of the additivity of weight (the weight of a physical whole is equal to the sum of the weights of its parts) but conclude that the balance employed is insufficiently sensitive. If "true weight" were operationally defined with reference to the most delicate balance available at the time, it would be meaningless to say that the latter might not, after all, indicate the true weights of bodies. Yet, such a statement would not be at all unreasonable if the described sort of situation (apparent breakdown of the principle of additivity of weight) were to arise. And if "true weight" is defined as the result yielded by an infinitely sensitive balance, the definition is, of course, far from operational.

The case for operational definitions of what we shall henceforth call *physical functors* (expressions designating physical magnitudes) becomes especially weak if we consider that even elementary mathematics involves irrational numbers, i.e., numbers that, like the square root of two, cannot be expressed as fractions of integers. For surely no conceivable measurement could disclose whether the "true" value of a physical magnitude is a given irrational number that differs from it by less than, say, a billionth. Should we say, then, that two such statements have the same

4. This is an *empirical* generalization, not an a priori truth. See Chapter 8, C.

meaning? But then we would have to deny that the Pythagorean theorem —which implies that the diagonal of a square whose side has unit length (say, one meter) has a length of $\sqrt{2}$ meters—says anything about physical, measurable space; for it would be equally true to say that the length of the diagonal is some *rational* number that is very, very close to the square root of two. It may be replied that the theorems of *physical* geometry, i.e., geometry considered as the science of measurable spatial relations, must be formulated in terms of error-intervals anyway: if the length of the side of a physical square is within ϵ of unity, then the length of its diagonal is within τ of the square root of two, where τ is a function of ϵ. But if the expression "length of $\sqrt{2}$ m" were meaningless, how could the expression "length differing from $\sqrt{2}$ m by τ" be meaningful? And if the former expression were synonymous with "length differing from $\sqrt{2}$ m by less than τ," then it would reduce to a meaningless stutter: length differing from length differing from length differing . . . . Indeed, here again mathematically formulated physical laws serve as directives for increasing the precision of our measurements: we find that with increasing precision in the measurement of length, the diagonal of a square of unit side measures out as increasingly close to the square root of two; henceforth we do not abandon the Pythagorean theorem as not true of physical space if we find that the diagonal of a square we supposed to have unit side is significantly different from $\sqrt{2}$ m: we conclude rather that we made an error in measuring the side of the square, or in supposing the figure to be a square, perhaps owing to physical influences that affected the length of the measuring rod.

C. POSTULATIONAL DEFINITION
AND PARTIAL INTERPRETATION

If physical functors such as "mass (of an electron)," and "velocity (of a molecule)," are not definable by reduction to observable predicates, and if common nouns denoting micro-objects such as "electron," "atom," and "photon" are not so definable, what then is the form of the rules governing their usage? The answer is that they are defined by postulates that link them to other terms of equally abstract character. The method of *postulational definition* (also called *implicit* or *axiomatic* definition) is used especially in formal sciences such as number theory or formal geometry. Its underlying idea is this: In order to deduce theorems from a set of postulates by application of principles of formal logic, it is not necessary to suppose that the primitive (undefined) terms have any specific meanings; they may be supposed to denote anything at all, and still the theorem follows from the postulates in the sense that any entities of which the postulates are true are entities of which the theorem is true also. For example, we can say that "All A are C" follows from "All A are B" and "All B are C" though we do not know what A, B, and C stand for. What we are asserting is that any *interpretations* of A, B, and C that make the premises true, also make the conclusion true.

Now, we can say that the postulates "All A are B" and "All B are C" define A, B, and C as denoting any classes A, B, and C such that A is included in B and B is included in C. It is, perhaps, an initially puzzling use of the word "define," but we are, after all, saying something, though not very much, about the meanings of the symbols in saying that they mean classes that are related in the specified way. Notice that we have not given a postulational definition of A in isolation, nor of B in isolation, but of the entire set A, B, C. This is of the essence of a postulational definition: a set—more exactly, an ordered set—of entities is defined by the logical relations expressed by the postulates, but nothing is thereby said about the specific nature of the entities. In formal geometry, for example, one is not interested in the specific natures of points, straight lines, and planes, but only in their relations, such as expressed by the following postulates: For any two points, there is exactly one straight line that contains both of them; for any two straight lines, there is at most one plane that contains both of them; for any straight line S, for any plane P, and for any point O, if P contains S and contains O and S does not contain O, then there is exactly one straight line that is contained in P and that contains O and that contains no point that is contained by S. (With some effort, the reader may recognize in the latter postulate the famous "parallel axiom," formulated with reference to three-dimensional space.) If a formal geometrician were asked what he meant by "point," "straight line," and "plane," he would be likely to reply: Any entities of which the postulates are true, i.e., elements of classes S, P, and O such that if "straight line" denotes a member of S, "plane" a member of P, and "point" a member of O, then all the postulates are true. In this sense the postulates define an ordered set of classes. Such an ordered set is often called a *model* for the postulational system.[5]

Consider, now, a set of postulates for Newtonian dynamics (it is not claimed to be complete in any sense):

1. If and only if a net (resultant) force F acts on a particle P, then P accelerates in the direction of F, and the magnitude of the acceleration equals the ratio of F to the mass of P (second law of motion).

5. It should be noted that the classes in question may be classes of any type of entities, e.g., classes of relations. On consistency proofs by models, see Chapter 7, B.

2. If a particle P exerts a force on another particle P', then P' exerts an equal force on P in the opposite direction (third law of motion: equality of "action" and "reaction").

3. Any two particles exert on each other a force (gravitational attraction) that is directly proportional to the product of their masses and inversely proportional to the square of their distance apart (law of gravitation).

4. Any set of forces that act either concurrently or successively on an identical particle have the same effect on the particle's acceleration as a single force that is the resultant (vector sum) of all of them (law of the independence of forces).

5. Every particle has a constant mass.

Not all of the terms that occur in these postulates are primitive; specifically "acceleration" is explicitly definable in terms of "displacement" and "time interval." Some physicists would say that "force" is likewise eliminable, since it is definable as the product of the mass of a particle times its acceleration. If this view—which, incidentally, entails that it is meaningless to speak of forces as causing accelerations—were accepted, postulate (1) would be redundant. But as it is a controversial interpretation of mechanics, let us treat "force" here as a primitive term of Newtonian dynamics, along with "mass," "displacement," "time interval," and "particle." The last term denotes whatever entities can be characterized as having a constant mass, whether they be planets or atoms. These postulates, then, constitute in their entirety a postulational definition of the primitive terms. They tell us, for example, that the time required for a given particle P to gain a definite velocity from rest is related in a definite mathematical way to the mass of P and the forces acting on P, whatever mass and force may be intrinsically. It may be frustrating not to know what exactly we are talking about, but such knowledge would be mere excess baggage from the point of view of the purely theoretical physicist who is not interested in experimental verification (though in this respect he is a mathematician rather than a physicist). He can deduce from these postulates, for example, that a particle that falls under the sole influence of gravitational attraction, falls with an acceleration that is independent of its mass. On the other hand, as long as our primitive terms are but postulationally defined, they cannot meaningfully be used in *singular* statements, such as "The mass of particle A is twice the mass of particle B." The postulates do not even tell us what sort of things may be called "particles"; they tell us at most, hypothetically, that anything that has mass, and can be acted on by forces, is a particle. But what things have mass? Particles? Obviously we turn in a fruitless circle if we attempt to determine the application of the primitive terms without going outside the postulational system. That is, if we wish to do empirical science with the help of formal logic and mathematics, we must supplement the postulational definition with an *interpretation*.

Even though the technique of reduction sentences cannot, as we have seen, provide a *complete* interpretation of the functors, it is indispensable for the sort of *partial* interpretation without which a statement such as "The mass of this body is 5 kg" would be meaningless. That is, we must give interpretations in terms of procedures of measurement for instances of the statement form "Mass $(A) = x$ grams" (where A is an unde-termined particle), "The distance of A from B at time $t = x$ cm"; or rather, we must formulate rules for such interpretations by reference to standards of measurement. But as we have dedicated a special chapter to the logical analysis of measurement (Chapter 8), let us skip this problem now and return to the difficulty that motivated our discussion of postu-lational definition. We pointed out that it does not seem possible to give any interpretation in terms of observables for such terms as "mass of an electron," "average distance of two molecules," or indeed "electron" and "molecule." Before we explain what we mean by "partial" inter-pretation of such terms, let us remind the reader of the distinction be-tween an interpretation of a theoretical term and a definition of a theo-retical term within the theoretical system on the basis of other theoretical terms. For example, the physicist defines acceleration as the rate of change of velocity with respect to time, and velocity as the rate of change of spatial position with respect to time. He further defines "instantaneous" velocity (which is what "velocity" means in the above definition of acceleration) with the help of the mathematical concept of the "limit," but as long as no interpretation in terms of standards of measurement that define the units "second," "centimeter," and so on is forthcoming, a statement about the actual acceleration of a car, for example, is devoid of meaning. It is as though I introduced a new word "klupper" by means of the impressively precise definition "A klupper is a popper containing two blue gooms and two red fooms," and then attempted to decide on the basis of the definition whether there are any kluppers and if so, whether this or that object is one.

Now, take our primitive term "force." There is no doubt that we can give rules of *indirect* measurement of force: Force is measurable in terms of its effects, viz. accelerations, and accelerations are measurable in terms of displacement and time. Even a balanced force can be measured in terms of displacements, e.g., the displacement of the pointer of a scale. When we speak of nonuniform displacements of particles as afford-ing indirect measures of force, we think of force as the *cause* of acceler-ated motion. If there were no other way of explaining the meaning of "acceleration" except as that which is produced by unbalanced forces, then of course the statement that unbalanced force is the cause of acceleration would be utterly uninformative. But since "acceleration" has been explicitly defined in terms of primitive terms that can be directly interpreted by reference to procedures of measurement, such a vicious circle is avoided. The definition of force as something that causes acceleration, therefore, amounts to a partial interpretation of the term "force," though it leaves the question as to the intrinsic nature of force (if, indeed, that is a meaningful question) unanswered. Or let us look at it this way: We can interpret the functors "mass," "displacement" (or, to resolve the latter magnitude, "length" and "angle"), and "time interval" directly in terms of appropriate methods of measurement. Our postulates express mathematical connections between these magnitudes and force. Thereby "force" has been partially and indirectly interpreted. It is not the postulates by themselves, nor the reduction sentences by themselves, but the two together that effect a partial interpretation.

In passing we may also answer the question what sort of things electrons, electromagnetic waves, fields of force, and so on, into which the physicist resolves the physical world, *are*—at least in the physicist's conception. No other definition is possible here but postulational definition. The physicist formulates equations describing the motions of particles, or waves, or the distribution of fields of force in terms of functors that are, directly or indirectly, interpreted in terms of rules of measurement. The abovementioned entities are then defined simply as the entities that move in the described way or, in the case of fields, have the described dynamic structure.

One must be careful, however, to formulate this conception accurately. We should not, for example, define the class of Newtonian particles *explicitly* as the class of entities that satisfy the postulates of Newtonian dynamics. For if so, the latter either would be no propositions at all, i.e., they could not significantly be called true or false, confirmed or disconfirmed, or else they would be mere tautologies and as such have neither predictive nor explanatory power. The former would be the case if they were formulated by means of free variables: If a force F acts on x, then x undergoes an acceleration that is equal in magnitude to the ratio of F to the mass of x; whether or not x and y accelerate relative to an inertial system, x exerts a force on y (which is such and such a function of the distance between x and y), and y exerts an equal force on x in the opposite direction; and so on. Can we say that these postulates are true, or false? Certainly not as long as the range of the variables x and y remains unspecified; just as there would be no sense in asking whether the equation "$y = 2x^2$" is true or false; one can only ask whether it is *satisfied* by this or that ordered pair of numbers. Similarly we could not ask whether the dynamic postulates are true, but only whether they are satisfied by such and such objects.

Now, suppose we formulate them as universal propositions about particles, thus: If an unbalanced force acts *on a particle*, then that particle undergoes an acceleration . . . ; similarly, let the other postulates be formulated as universal propositions explicitly about particles. But if a particle is defined as anything that, if acted on by an unbalanced force, undergoes an acceleration . . . , then each postulate reduces to the tautology that particles are particles. What has happened is that postulational definitions have been misunderstood—in fact have been treated as though they were *explicit* definitions. As we pointed out previously, a postulational definition is essentially a definition of an ordered set of terms, not of a single term. If a set of postulates contains only one primitive term, then the alleged postulational definition of that term is easily replaced by a straightforward explicit definition. For example, suppose we laid down three postulates for a relational predicate $R:$ For any x and y, if x has R to y, then y does not have R to x; for any x, y, and z, if x has R to y and y has R to z, then x has R to z; for any x and y, if x is distinct from y, then either x has R to y or y has R to x. The properties of relations that are expressed by these postulates are called asymmetry, transivity and connexity, and a relation that has all of them is called an ordering relation. But there is no point here in speaking of a postulational definition of the concept "ordering relation"; an ordering relation may be explicitly defined as a relation that satisfies the above postulates. Now, it will be recalled that in our formulation of the dynamic postulates the term "particle" occurred as one of the primitives along with primitive functors such as "mass" and "force." It would be a mistake to suppose that we already understand the latter terms independently of an understanding of "particle," then to formulate postulates by means of these understood terms, and finally to define particles as entities satisfying the postulates. The point is rather that "particle" is postulationally defined *together* with the primitive functors that designate measurable properties of particles.

What, now, remains of the empiricist criterion of significance of descriptive terms? Has it suffered shipwreck because we must recognize that a term may have legitimate status in a science though it cannot be tied to observables either by complete definitions or by reduction chains? Not at all. It just has to be refined to take account of the contribution of postulational definitions to the specification of meanings. Suppose somebody confronts you with a childlishly simple postulate: $A = (B \cdot C)$, where the letters stand for classes, and $(B \cdot C)$ means that class whose members belong to both B and C. As long as B and C remain uninterpreted, so does A. If he tells you that B denotes the class of dogs and C the class of blue things, you then understand that A denotes the class of blue dogs. The postulate together with the interpretations of B and C by means of observational vocabulary has provided a complete interpretation of A. On the other hand, he might interpret A, say, as the class of women. Does the postulate now tell you what B means? Well, it tells you at least that it means a class that includes the class of women: perhaps the class of human beings, perhaps the class of bipeds, but not the class of tables, say. In this sense the postulate leads to a partial interpretation of B. According to the liberalized empiricist criterion of significance, B is a meaningful term within a theory including our "postulate" and our interpretative sentence, though there be no interpretative sentence for B itself. In no deductively formulated science, such as Newtonian particle mechanics, is the situation as simple as this, but the principle remains the same.

We are also in a position now to justify the scientist's assumption that he means the *same*, numerically determinable property by the term "mass" when he speaks of the mass of the earth or the mass of a rifle bullet or the mass of an electron—an assumption which is incompatible with strict operationism. It is justified to the extent that the use of the term is regulated by the same *postulational* definition in these diverse contexts. Thus the revolving motion of an electron is supposed to be governed by the same laws as the revolving motion of the planets according to Bohr's theory of the atom as a microcosmic solar system. On the other hand, to the extent that the dynamic laws of quantum mechanics are radically unlike the laws of classical particle dynamics, subatomic particles are "particles" in a different sense, and the masses ascribed to them are a different, though analogous, sort of property.

D. RELATIVIZATION OF SIGNIFICANCE TO THEORIES

It should be obvious now that the empirical significance of a scientific term depends on the theoretical network in which it is embedded. A partially interpreted deductive theory, such as classical particle mechanics, is comparable to a net only some of whose knots are anchored to the ground by posts: these knots correspond to the theoretical terms that are directly interpreted, the posts to the interpretative sentences (variously called "rules of correspondence," "coordinative definitions," "reduction sentences," "operational definitions"), the ground to the plane of observation, the freely floating knots to those theoretical terms which owe their empirical significance only to the postulates (including definitions) that connect them with interpreted terms. However, this "liberalization" of the criterion of significance is not as revolutionary as metaphysicians who are hoping for their enemies' defeat may be inclined to make out. For there is no essential difference between indirect interpretation through explicit or contextual definitions, which had always been considered indispensable, and indirect interpretation though postulates. Indeed, if it were not for the desire to reduce the number of primitive terms to the indispensable minimum, definitions could be replaced by postulates. For example, instead of explicitly defining "momentum" as "mass times velocity," we could add the postulate that the momentum of a moving particle at time t is equal to the product of the particle's mass times its velocity at t.

Sometimes the scientist himself is undecided whether a general statement that he uses as premise in his deductions has the status of a definition or of a postulate. For example, in order to deduce the general gas law from the postulates of the kinetic theory of gases, one must assume that the absolute temperature of an ideal gas is proportional to the average kinetic energy of its molecules ($\frac{1}{2}m\bar{v}^2$, where m is the mass of a gas molecule). Some say this is a definition of "absolute temperature," some that it is a postulate connecting different magnitudes. Actually, the latter interpretation is more plausible, since it would hardly make sense to speak of an "explanation" of the general gas law in terms of the kinetic theory unless the functor "temperature" had the same meaning in the premises as it has in the deduced conclusion, and it obviously did not mean "average kinetic energy (of translation) of a molecule" for the experimental physicist who established the general gas law by induction from measurements. But if the constituent symbols in "average kinetic energy of a molecule" were directly interpreted, then the equation under discussion would lead to an indirect interpretation of "absolute temperature" no matter whether it appear in the formalization of the theory as a definition or as a postulate.

The same example, however, serves to bring out what is really novel in the relativization of the significance of terms to deductively formulated theories. It is not the admission of terms that are but *indirectly* interpreted, but the admission of terms that are but *partially* interpreted. Obviously, if a term A is explicitly defined by means of terms B, C, combined in a definite way (say, by conjunction, or by disjunction, or by conjunction and negation, then interpretations of B and C will uniquely determine the interpretation of A; but the converse does not hold. I might, for example, define A as the sum of the class B and the complement of class C (i.e., to be an A is to be either a B or a non-C); if I then interpret A as the class of dogs, I have partially interpreted B as a class that is included in the class of dogs, but the question is left open *which* of the many classes that are included in the class of dogs is meant. Now, no direct interpretation for "mass of a gas molecule" and "$\bar{v}$" can be given. To define "$\bar{v}$" in terms of "average displacement per second of a molecule" is not to interpret it, for there is no such thing as a direct measurement of a displacement of a single gas molecule in random motion. What has to be directly interpreted by rules of measurement, then, is "absolute temperature." Similarly, gas pressure, which is definable within the deductive theory in terms of change of momentum of gas molecules, can be directly interpreted in terms of manometer readings. Thereby the constructs of the kinetic theory are indirectly but only partially interpreted: experimental data, such as results of measurement of gas pressure and gas temperature, will be relevant to the question whether the postulates containing these constructs are true, and in this sense the constructs are empirically significant. Similarly, if I find an object that is a dog, this discovery has some bearing on the question whether the object belongs to class B; I can at least say that there is a finite probability that it belongs to B, whereas the hypothesis "x is a B" would be refuted if x turned out to be, say, a cat.

A sentence that in isolation is neither confirmable nor disconfirmable by experience, and is *in this sense meaningless*, may, as we have seen, acquire empirical significance once it becomes part of a partially interpreted theory. This is clearly recognized by contemporary logical positivism[6] (or "logical empiricism"). But there is another sense in which the significance of a sentence may be relative to a physical theory: a sentence that in isolation from physical theories may seem perfectly meaning*ful* may be meaning*less* in the context of a theory T, because in conjunction with T a meaningless or self-contradictory sentence is deducible from it. Thus, is it meaningless to suppose that there occur, or may occur, motions exceeding the velocity of light? It seems to be a perfectly meaningful supposition, for even if it be true that the velocity of light is the upper limit for all physically possible velocities, this is a physical fact; in other words, what we suppose to be the case is at most *empirically* impossible, not *logically* impossible, hence it must be allowed to be a significant supposition. But once we incorporate the hypothesis of the limiting character of the velocity of light into the special theory of relativity, we obtain the consequence that a body moving with a speed exceeding c (the speed of light *in vacuo*) would acquire a length expressed by an imaginary number! For if in

$$l_k = l_0 \left(1 - \frac{v^2}{c^2} \right)^{1/2}$$

where l_k is the kinetic length, l_0 the rest-length (i.e., the length when $v = 0$), v the velocity of the body relative to an inertial system, and c the

6. It is therefore somewhat of a caricature of logical empiricism to accuse it of the "dogma" that statements are empirically confirmable or disconfirmable *in isolation* from a system of statements [see Willard Quine, "Two Dogmas of Empiricism," in *From a Logical Point of View* (Cambridge: Harvard University Press, 1953)]. Of course, *some* statements are confirmable in isolation from all theories: basic observation statements, such as statements of pointer coincidences in physics.

constant velocity of light, we substitute for v a number greater than c, then l_k acquires an imaginary value. And since every conceivable measurement yields a rational number, no operational meaning can be attached to "length represented by an imaginary number." One may say that the above equation cannot legitimately be used to deduce a meaningless sentence, since the length-variables range only over *real* numbers representing lengths. But if the length-variables are thus restricted, then in consistency the variable v must be restricted to real numbers, representing velocities, that are not greater than c—and this is just another way of saying that it is meaningless within the context of the special theory of relativity to speak of velocities exceeding c.

A similar example is the question whether we can meaningfully suppose that there are temperatures below the "absolute zero," i.e. $-273°C$. According to experimental thermodynamics, $V_t = V_0(1 + \beta t)$, where V_0 is the volume of a heated gas at some arbitrary initial temperature, t the temperature change to which it is subjected, V_t the volume acquired after the temperature change is over (i.e., after thermal equilibrium with the surroundings is restored), and β the rate at which the volume changes with the temperature. β (the so-called coefficient of thermal expansion) has been found to be equal to $\frac{1}{273}$ for all gases; i.e., if the gas is heated $1°C$, its volume increases by $\frac{1}{273}$ of its original volume; if the gas is cooled $1°C$, it contracts by $\frac{1}{273}$ of its original volume. It follows that if V_0 is the volume at $0°C$, and the temperature of the gas is reduced to $-273°C$, its volume must shrink entirely (on the assumption, indeed, that condensation does not occur before such a low temperature is reached). Were it to cool still further, again without condensing, its volume would become negative! A truly nonsensical consequence! Here again it might be replied that the equation has been misused, because it asserts a functional relationship between volume and temperature only for positive values of volume. But this is to say that it is a meaningless question to ask what would happen to the volume of a noncondensable mass of gas (if there were such a thing) if the latter were cooled below $-273°C$. Yet, since it is surely a contingent law of nature (a state of affairs whose contradictory is conceivable) that the coefficient of thermal expansion is no smaller than $\frac{1}{273}$, the meaninglessness of the question is relative to a contingent law.

Laymen in science may, in their rare moments of speculation, ask themselves whether electrons, or atoms, or molecules are red or blue or green, hot or cool or cold. After all, they are supposed to have size, to move, and to be impenetrable so as to be capable of colliding; and can anyone imagine things having these "primary qualities" (as Locke called them) without having any color nor any degree of temperature? (No, said Berkeley, and concluded that both Locke and Newton were just talking nonsense.) But suppose we incorporate the assumption that a molecule has some degree of temperature into the kinetic theory of heat. According to that theory, temperature is a property of an *aggregate*, just the way in statistics "average income" and "average age" are terms used to characterize groups, not individuals. For example, it would be nonsense to ask about the average age of John Smith. Similarly, it can be shown to be nonsense to speak of the temperature of an individual molecule, but only relative to the kinetic theory. For according to that theory a statement about the temperature of a physical object x implies a statement about the average kinetic energy of the particles composing x; hence, speaking of the temperature of a particle constituent of x would be like speaking of the average age of John Smith. Yet, should scientists some day abandon the kinetic theory, new arguments would have to be advanced against the meaningfulness of discourse about the temperature of molecules.

Nevertheless, the layman would do well to note in the meantime that as the terms "molecule," "atom," "electron," and others denoting microcosmic particles are used in the context of physical theories, they cannot be meaningfully combined with predicates designating temperatures or colors—or even smells! This shows that such particles should not be conceived as things that differ only in minuteness from the macrocosmic things of daily life. For whereas a man who affirmed the existence of tiny pebbles that are colorless and devoid of temperature could justly be accused of talking nonsense, the analogous affirmation of the existence of colorless and temperatureless atoms will appear nonsensical only if one confuses the theoretical language of the scientist with the "thing-language" of everyday life and accordingly thinks of atoms as tiny—just very, very tiny—pebbles.

Selected Readings

Beck, L. W., "Constructions and Inferred Entities," in H. Feigl and M. Brodbeck (eds.), *Readings in the Philosophy of Science* (New York, 1953).

Bergmann, G., "Sense and Nonsense in Operationism," *Scientific Monthly*, 1954.

Braithwaite, R. B., *Scientific Explanation* (Cambridge, 1953), chap. 3.

Bridgman, P. W., *The Logic of Modern Physics* (New York, 1927).

———, *The Nature of Physical Theory* (Princeton, N.J., 1936).

———, "Operational Analysis," *Philosophy of Science*, 1938.

———, *Reflections of a Physicist* (New York, 1950).

———, "The Operational Aspect of Meaning," *Synthese*, 1950–51.

———, "The Nature of Some of Our Physical Concepts, I and II," *British Journal for the Philosophy of Science*, 1950–52.

Bures, C. E., "Operationism, Construction and Inference," *Journal of Philosophy*, 1940.

Campbell, N. R., *Physics: The Elements* (Cambridge, 1920), chap. 5, 6. [Reprinted as *The Foundations of Experimental Science* (New York, 1957).]

Carnap, R., "The Interpretation of Physics," in H. Feigl and M. Brodbeck (eds.) *Readings in the Philosophy of Science* (New York, 1953).

———, "The Methodological Character of Theoretical Concepts," in H. Feigl and M. Scriven (eds.), *Minnesota Studies in the Philosophy of Science* (Minneapolis, 1956), vol. I.

Cohen, M. R. and E. Nagel, "The Nature of Mathematical Systems," in M. R. Cohen and E. Nagel, *Introduction to Logic and Scientific Method* (New York, 1934. [Reprinted in H. Feigl and M. Brodbeck (eds.), *Readings in the Philosophy of Science* (New York, 1953).]

Craig, W., "Replacement of Auxiliary Expressions," *Philosophical Review*, 1956.

Feigl, H., "Operationism and Scientific Method," *Psychological Review*, 1945.

Hempel, C. G., "The Concept of Cognitive Significance: A Reconsideration," *Proceedings of the American Academy of Arts and Sciences*, 1951.

———, "A Logical Appraisal of Operationism," *Scientific Monthly*, 1954.

———, *Fundamentals of Concept Formation in Empirical Science* (Chicago, 1952).

———, "The Theoretician's Dilemma," in *Minnesota Studies in the Philosophy of Science* (Minneapolis, 1958) vol. II.

Kaplan, A., "Definition and Specification of Meaning," *Journal of Philosophy*, 1946.

Margenau, H., *The Nature of Physical Reality: A Philosophy of Modern Physics* (New York, 1950), chap. 4, 5.

Nagel, E., "Operational Analysis," *Journal of Philosophy*, 1942.

———, *The Structure of Science* (New York, 1961), chap. 5, 6.

Pap, A., "Are Physical Magnitudes Operationally Definable?" in C. W. Churchman and P. Ratoosh (eds.), *Measurement: Definitions and Theories* (New York, 1959).

Reichenbach, H., "Are There Atoms?" in H. Reichenbach, *The Rise of Scientific Philosophy* (Berkeley, Calif., 1951).

Scheffler, I., "Prospects of a Modern Empiricism: I and II," *Review of Metaphysics*, 1957.

Schlesinger, G., "P. W. Bridgman's Operational Analysis," *British Journal for the Philosophy of Science*, 1959.

CHAPTER 4

The Principle of Verifiability in Physics & Psychology

A. THE LAW OF INERTIA AND ABSOLUTE TIME

One of the most illuminating applications of the principle of verifiability in physics is the relativistic critique of the Newtonian concepts of *absolute* space, time and motion. This critique was initiated by Ernst Mach, the great positivistic philosopher of science of the nineteenth century, and perfected by Einstein. One quickly reaches the heart of this critique, and therewith the essence of one of the greatest revolutions in the history of science, if one attempts to understand clearly what is asserted by the law of inertia, or Newton's first law of motion. "An isolated particle, i.e. a particle on which no external force is acting, either continues in its state of rest or continues to move with uniform speed in a straight line (eternally, as long as it remains isolated)." The critical question usually raised is: What empirical criterion is there for the presence of a force? If it is just a change in the particle's velocity (i.e., speed or direction of motion), isn't this great law a mere tautology? The physicist uses the law in arguing from the observed change of direction of the planets' movements to the action of a force (gravitation) as the cause of acceleration; but if the only evidence for the existence of the cause is just the observed acceleration, is he really explaining anything at all?

But let us disregard this problem now and concentrate on other, no less striking, difficulties. What is to be understood by "uniform speed"? A body moves with uniform speed, we may be told, if it traverses equal distances in any equal time intervals, however small they may be.[1] But this theoretical definition does not make "uniform speed" an operationally meaningful concept unless the physical operations are specified by which equality of spatial distances and equality of time intervals may be determined. Let us concentrate on the meaning of "time-equality." Assuming that we have a well-defined method of measuring length, the verification of time-equality can be reduced to the verification of equality of length. We select some standard clock, in the generalized sense of "clock," i.e., a system in periodic motion, such as an oscillating pendulum or the rotating earth, and define as equal times, times during which this clock undergoes equal displacement (equal arcs rotated through, in the case of the earth). But how do we know that the clock itself moves, or oscillates uniformly? Surely, if it does not, then our "operational" definition of time-equality in terms of the standard clock provides us with no true measure of time-equality. The earth, for example, is known not to rotate with exact uniformity, owing to centrifugal effects, and any actual pendulum describes smaller and smaller arcs per unit time, owing to frictional dissipation of mechanical energy. Accordingly Newton said: Time can be measured only in terms of uniform motions, but since absolutely uniform motion presupposes absolutely isolated and internally frictionless physical systems, which do not exist, the time we measure ("sensible" time) must be distinguished from *absolute* time, which "flows equably." Newton did not notice that this description of absolute time amounted to the nonsensical statement that absolute time moves uniformly, i.e., traverses equal distances in equal times. What he probably meant was that absolute time is the time that would be measured by an absolutely uniform motion (whether translational or rotational) if such existed. But such a definition is, of course, circular: before we could recognize an absolutely uniform motion, we would have to be able to recognize absolutely equal time intervals. Since no method for determining such "absolute" equality can be described, the concept of absolute time, said Mach, is operationally meaningless. And he rejected it on this ground, as a metaphysical fiction that is useless for physics.

However, for one who recognizes the fruitfulness of theoretical concepts that have no direct empirical interpretation, perhaps there is another way of looking at the matter. Perhaps the concept of absolute

1. Galileo first called attention to the necessity of the qualifying phrase "however small they may be." For the *average* velocity in an accelerated motion may be constant if suitably large time intervals are chosen.

time-equality serves a regulative function, as an ideal guiding measurements to increasing precision, somewhat the way the Pythagorean theorem, involving irrational numbers, was explained to motivate checking and rechecking of measurements of length. The physicist begins with a fairly crude clock, such as Galileo's "water clock" or the earth considered as a rotating system, by means of which he establishes the law of inertia to a first degree of approximation. He finds that a particle that is sufficiently far from other matter to be considered practically isolated does not traverse *exactly* equal distances in times that are equal by this crude standard. This does not lead him to question the law of inertia, but to question the accuracy of the clock. Replacing it by a better clock, he finds the law of inertia to be more nearly true, and this very law is used as a criterion of accuracy of a clock. That is, an absolutely accurate clock, or a clock measuring absolute time, can be defined as a clock relative to which an isolated particle traverses exactly equal distances in equal times. This conception harmonizes with Poincaré's statement that the physicist chooses his physical definition of time in such a way that the laws of mechanics become as simple as possible. We could, as Schlick once pointed out, define as equal the time intervals separating the successive pulse beats of some oriental prince. But such a definition would have the inconvenient consequence that each time our prince grew unduly excited or lay in a fever, all physical processes would become accelerated in a perfectly inexplicable way. It should be noted, however, that if absolute time is thus defined as a regulative concept, the law of inertia turns into a tautology. It remains an empirical question to what degree a given physical system satisfies the definition of absolute time (so as to be eligible as standard clock), but the statement that an isolated particle is at rest or in absolutely uniform motion (relative to inertial systems) turns into a tautology even if an independent criterion of "isolation" can be given.

B. EINSTEIN AND SIMULTANEITY

Einstein continued Mach's line of empiricist critique of Newtonian mechanics by reflecting on the method of verifying *simultaneity* of spatially separated events. If two sounds are emitted at places A and B, sufficiently distant, and they are heard simultaneously by an observer stationed midway between A and B, they will not be heard simultaneously by an observer at A, nor by an observer at B. Were they emitted simultaneously or not? He who has never reflected on the conceptual foundations of physics may think it simple-minded even to raise the question. Why, of course they were emitted simultaneously, provided the medium of sound propagation was homogeneous and at constant temperature, for in such a medium sound waves propagate themselves with constant speed in all directions. But how do we know that the velocity is constant? The determination of such constancy involves the timing of at least three spatially separated events, and hence we need three observers equipped with clocks at three places. Clearly, their timings are acceptable as evidence relevant to the question of constancy of velocity only if their clocks are *synchronized*. But to say of two clocks that they are synchronized is to say that they are in the same state *at the same time*. Thus the attempt to verify simultaneity of spatially separated events by means of an assumption of constancy of velocity of a signal (such as sound or light) leads back to an assumption of just such distant simultaneity. We can, of course, directly verify that two contiguous clocks are in the same state at the same time, but to assume that they remain synchronized when they are spatially separated is to assume that the state of the clock does not depend on its spatial location. How would we verify that? We would just have to see whether two clocks that were synchronized when contiguous remain synchronized when they occupy different places, which is the question at issue. It is clear that the circle can be broken only by *postulating* some signal velocity, such as the velocity of light in a vacuum, as constant. From this point of view, which was unambiguously expressed by Einstein himself, and expertly defended especially by Reichenbach,[2] the question whether the velocity of light is "really" constant is just as meaningless as the question whether the standard meter, by reference to which the meaning of statements of the form "the length of $x = y$ m" is defined, really has a constant length.

It would, however, be inaccurate and confusing to say flatly that the famous principle of the constancy of the velocity of light is simply a result of the application of the verifiability theory of meaning to the concept of distant simultaneity. To begin with, "constancy of the velocity of light" is ambiguous: it might mean constancy of the speed with respect to change of direction, or independence of the velocity of light from the velocity of the light source relative to the observer. Only the former kind of constancy is relevant in this context. Einstein defines distant simultaneity as follows: E_1 and E_2 are simultaneous if and only if light-signals emitted from the place of E_1 to the place of E_2, or from the place of E_2 to the place of E_1, simultaneously with the occurrence of these events, arrive simultaneously at the midpoint between the places of

2. Hans Reichenbach, *Philosophy of Space and Time* (New York: Dover Publications, Inc.), 1957.

E_1 and E_2.[3] On the basis of this definition it is a tautology to say that two light rays emitted simultaneously toward each other from two places reach the midpoint between these two places at the same time; and accordingly it is a tautology to say that they move to the midpoint with the same average velocity. It would be an empirical question whether the velocities are equal only if the question of distant simultaneity could be decided without making use of light signals. But it does not, of course, follow that the following proposition (which is what is usually meant by the postulate of the constancy of the velocity of light) is not empirical: if c is the velocity of a light ray relative to its source O, and O moves with finite velocity relative to a system S, and c' is the velocity of the light ray relative to S, then $c = c'$. Secondly, whether even the assertion of constancy of the velocity of light in the explained restricted sense is a tautology, such that no conceivable physical facts have a bearing on the question of its truth, depends on how we interpret a "physical definition" such as Einstein's. Consider the physical (or "operational") definition of "The length of x at time $t = y$ m" as meaning "If x were measured at t with the standard meter, or a meter of the same length as the standard meter, the latter would have to be laid off y times from one end of x until the other end of x was reached." A formal consequence of this definition is, of course, that the standard meter itself has the same length at all times (if indeed the expression "length of the standard meter" is conceded to be meaningful at all relative to this definition).

But how can this result be reconciled with the belief that owing to uncontrollable temperature fluctuations even the standard meter may slightly change in length? Only by construing the alleged definition as an *interpretive postulate* connecting the theoretical term "length" with the laboratory language and thereby making statements containing that term empirically testable; but as such it is not exempt from revision in the light of new experience. What in fact happens is that the choice of a standard measuring rod enables formulation to a first approximation of laws connecting length with other magnitudes, such as temperature, whereupon those very laws may point to indirect evidence that the chosen standard has a variable length: it may be found that other ma-

3. Note that this definition is, appearances notwithstanding, not circular, because what is defined is distant simultaneity whereas the concept of simultaneity by which it is defined is the concept of *contiguous* simultaneity (i.e., simultaneity of events at the same, or nearly the same, place). According to relativity theory, there is no *generic* relation of simultaneity of which distant and contiguous simultaneity are special cases the way motherhood and fatherhood are special cases of parenthood (or rather, it is physically meaningless to speak of such a generic relation). Note further that the defined concept of simultaneity refers to pairs of events in the same physical system; it is not relevant, e.g., to the question whether an event in some moving train happened at the same time as some event outside the train.

terials have smaller coefficients of thermal expansion, and the original standard may be replaced by a more accurate one. In the same way, Einstein's "definition" is best construed as an interpretive postulate connecting statements about distant simultaneity with directly verifiable statements about contiguous simultaneity. This postulate serves, together with postulates concerning equality of time intervals and therewith the measurement of duration, as a basis for measurement of velocities; by means of such measurement kinematical laws (i.e., laws connecting the magnitudes length, time, velocity, acceleration) are established. But it is not inconceivable that such laws might someday point to indirect evidence *against* the postulated constancy of velocity, in much the same way in which the laws of mechanics enabled physicists to interpret certain observed facts as evidence against the initially postulated uniformity of rotation of the earth.

C. FORCE AND ABSOLUTE MOTION

The name "Einstein" may bring to the layman's mind the sentence, "All motion is relative," but few know what this sentence means. One interpretation, which we have already touched upon, is that as far as physics is concerned statements of the form "*x* moves" are meaningful only if they mean "*x* changes position relative to *y*" where *y* is some *other body*. If this is what the theory of the relativity of motion amounts to, then, indeed, it is not a physical theory at all but an application of the verifiability theory of meaning to physics; for the only ground on which this semantical principle has ever been asserted, implicitly or explicitly, is that only changes of *relative* position of bodies are verifiable: a statement to the effect that a body changes its *absolute* position in space, in other words, that a body moves in *absolute space*, is purely metaphysical, i.e., unverifiable. It was in this sense that Mach rejected the Newtonian concepts of absolute space, and of motion in absolute space, as useless appendices of the organism of physical science.

In order to determine, however, whether the concept of absolute motion and the concept of absolute space in terms of which it is defined can be banished from physical science on these grounds, we must acquaint ourselves with the way Newton proposed to distinguish between absolute and relative motion. Newton was well aware of the fact that there is no physical criterion for distinguishing between absolute and relative motion in the case of *uniform* motions, i.e., the sort of motions that, according to the law of inertia, do not require to be sustained by forces.[4] If balls were dropped in a uniformly moving train or ship, for example, they would be found to fall in accordance with the same law as if the vehicle were stationary. In general terms: let L be a law of mechanics that is valid relative to measurements made in a system S, and let S' be a system that moves uniformly relative to S; then L is also valid relative to measurements made in S'. In Newtonian mechanics this is usually called the principle of restricted relativity. To put it somewhat more intuitively, it asserts that it is impossible to discover by means of mechanical experiments and measurements within a system S whether S is at rest or in uniform motion relative to some other system (and a fortiori, of course, whether S is at rest or in uniform motion in absolute space—if we may, for the sake of the argument, talk as though "absolute space" had a meaning). If your train moved with complete uniformity, and you could not look out of the window, it would be impossible for you to discover by means of mechanical experiments in the train that it moved at all. It should be noted that the principle of restricted relativity is a physical law, and the impossibility in question therefore is physical, not logical. It is logically conceivable that there exists a "privileged" system S_0 such that the laws of mechanics verified in a system S assume an especially simple form when S is at rest relative to S_0. If we then defined "absolute" rest as rest relative to S_0, we *could* verify whether the system in which we experimented was in a state of absolute rest or in a state of absolute uniform motion without "looking out of the window."

Accelerated motion, on the other hand, manifests itself within the accelerating system through "inertial" forces: when the train accelerates, you feel a backward pull; and if mechanical experiments were performed in an accelerating train, their results would differ from the results of the same experiments performed in a uniformly moving train, since the motions of the bodies would also be affected by the inertial force produced by the train's acceleration. Since uniform motion in absolute space, if there be such a thing, does not have any observable effects different from those of uniform motion relative to an inertial system—i.e., a physical system that is approximately at rest relative to the fixed stars —Newton conceded that as far as uniform motion is concerned, no physical proof for the existence of absolute motion is possible. However, he described two experiments, both involving rotating systems.[5] which

4. The discovery, by Galileo, that there are motions that do not require dynamic causes, so that what requires a dynamic explanation is not the existence of motion but *changes* of motion, marks the end of Aristotelian physics and the beginning of modern physics.

5. Rotation is a case of accelerated motion even if it is "uniform," because the direction of motion of the constituent particles of the rotating system changes, and change of direction implies change of velocity. (Velocity is a "vector," a magnitude that has direction.)

seemed to him to afford conclusive evidence for the existence of absolute accelerated motion. You fill a bucket with water, suspend it by means of a rope, then twist the rope and let it untwist itself. The bucket is set into rotation, and after a while the bucket's rotation is communicated, through adhesive forces, to the water in it. One can then observe a depression of the water surface, of paraboloidal form (i.e., the line of intersection with a flat disk would be a concave segment of a parabola). This depression of the water surface is usually explained as the effect of the centrifugal forces that pull on the water particles in proportion to their distance from the axis of rotation. Now, the fact that seemed to Newton to prove that these centrifugal forces are produced by the water's absolute rotation, not its rotation relative to the containing bucket, is that the water surface remains depressed after the bucket has stopped rotating, as long as the water continues to rotate. For the same deformation exists when the water does not rotate *relative* to the bucket at all, i.e., when both bucket and water rotate with the same speed relative to the earth. The logic of Newton's argument is simply that A cannot be the cause of B if B occurs in the absence of A. As evidenced by the form of the water surface, the centrifugal forces operate both when there is relative rotation between water and bucket and when there is not; hence they cannot be caused by the relative rotation; hence, Newton concluded, they are caused by the water's rotation in *absolute space*.

It would require a very strong prejudice against relativity to be convinced by Newton's argument, for it is so obvious that his conclusion does not follow: as long as the water surface is deformed, the water is rotating relative to the earth; why then could not this relative rotation be the cause? Or, as Mach pointed out, the cause might be the rotation relative to the fixed stars. It may seem incredible that bodies at such an immense distance should have any causal influence, yet, said Mach, this hypothesis is at any rate not any less verifiable than Newton's hypothesis of a causal influence of (unobservable) absolute space. Either hypothesis is unverifiable—the hypothesis that the change of position relative to the fixed stars is the cause, because we cannot annihilate the stars and then see whether the effect still occurs, and Newton's hypothesis because rotation in absolute space is unobservable anyway. Evidently it was Occam's "razor" ("do not multiply entities beyond necessity") which induced Mach to prefer the explanation in terms of relative rotation though it admittedly could not be put to an empirical test.

We shall come closer to an understanding of the logical issue involved if we take a look at Newton's second example of allegedly absolute rotation. If a heavy globe is attached at each end of a stretched rope, and this system is set into rotation around the center of the connecting rope, the centrifugal force manifests itself as tension in the rope. As this tension is proportional to the square of the angular velocity of rotation, a hypothetical observer sitting on one of the globes could verify changes of speed of rotation by measuring the tension in the rope. He would not have to look outside the system, as we have to in order to verify that our uniformly moving train is moving fast or slow or, indeed, is moving at all. Here again, it is obvious that the principle of Newtonian relativity cannot be extended to accelerated motion: it seems that it *is* possible to discover a system's state of acceleration within the system. But this is not all that Newton meant to prove; he meant to prove that only accelerations in absolute space have the sort of dynamic effects that enable one to detect acceleration from within the system. Take some other system, said Newton, and rotate it relative to the first; the first system, then, is equally rotating relative to the second, but that this rotation is merely "apparent" is shown by the absence of the centrifugal effect.

Now, here again Newton's argument is not convincing because there happens to be a physical, visually observable system such that centrifugal effects are uniquely correlated with rotation relative to it: the system of coordinates whose origin is defined by a fixed star, or indeed any system that is not accelerated relative to this system ("inertial system"). One could, therefore, explain centrifugal effects in terms of *real* acceleration without violating the requirement of verifiability, by defining real acceleration as acceleration relative to an inertial system. But suppose that no such unique correlation existed; that is, suppose that there existed no "privileged" class of physical systems S such that every centrifugal effect was correlated with acceleration relative to a member of S, and every variation in the intensity of centrifugal force with a corresponding variation in this relative acceleration. Would it then be logically permissible to invoke absolute acceleration, in the sense of acceleration in absolute space, as the cause? Or would the verifiability theory of meaning disqualify it?

The answer is surely that it would be impermissible if "cause" is meant —in the sense of everyday life and experimental science—as an antecedent *observable* event which is regularly correlated with the effect (cf. Chapter 14). Newton's inference from centrifugal force to absolute rotation is radically unlike the inference from smoke to fire, or from wet ground to rain. Here the causal antecedents are observable kinds of events. Even though we may not be able to witness the particular instance of rainfall that caused the observed wetness of the ground, or the particular fire that caused the observed smoke, we have directly observed events of the same kind in the past, and hence we can say that the observational evidence makes the causal hypothesis probable in the sense that the latter is a member of a class of hypotheses most of which have turned out to be true when similar effects were observed ("frequency interpretation" of probability; cf. Chapter 11). But since absolute rotation in Newton's sense is not a directly observable kind of event, we cannot say that an observed centrifugal effect is probably caused by it *if* we mean "cause" and "probable" in the above senses.

The qualified way in which we have answered our logical question indicates, however, that the concept of absolute motion cannot be eliminated as meaningless so easily.' Anticipating a later analysis (cf. Chapter 18), we must distinguish causal explanation in terms of empirical laws from *theoretical* explanation, i.e., explanation in terms of theoretical constructs. After all, is Newton's explanation essentially different from the explanation of an observed irregularity in the motions of heavenly bodies in terms of the theory that light is something that travels with finite, though enormous, speed, or from the explanation of an observed deflection of a galvanometer needle in terms of the passage of electrons? Here, too, we are *postulating* events of (directly) unobservable kinds, we are not *inferring* antecedent or simultaneous events of observable kinds. That the pointer of a galvanometer is deflected whenever there is an electrical current in the coil connected with it is not an empirical law that has been directly confirmed by *separate* observations of quickly moving electrons and simultaneous movements of a pointer. Absolute acceleration may not be a predictively fertile construct, and it may be dispensable in the sense of Occam's razor. (It *is* dispensable, if the general theory of relativity is true.) But that is different from saying that it is inadmissible on empiricist principle. If it is embedded into the postulates of a partially interpreted theory of mechanics, it is a significant construct whether or not it be also predictively fertile and indispensable for the explanation of phenomena. It is true that an admissible theoretical concept must be such that statements containing it are confirmable *independently* of any particular phenomenon for whose explanation they are formulated, but this does not mean that they must be confirmable independently of *any and all* such phenomena.[6]

D. BEHAVIORISM AND THE POSTULATE OF PUBLIC VERIFIABILITY

It has been remarked that if ceremonial language were reformed in the light of behaviorist psychology, "How are you?" would be replaced by "How am I?" For if my feelings, emotions, and sensations are nothing

6. The precise sense in which theoretical explanations must be "independently confirmable" will be discussed and illustrated in Chapter 18.

but forms of my bodily behavior, then other people are in a better position to know about them than I myself. However, we must distinguish *reductive* behaviorism, which denies that there are mental events or "private" states of consciousness as distinct from physiological processes and ways of overt behavior, from *logical* behaviorism. A logical behaviorist (or "physicalist," in the terminology of the Vienna Circle) is not concerned with the question whether there are mental events, in the sense of "inner" states of an organism which may manifest themselves in physiological states or overt behavior yet are not identical with any physical events. He is concerned rather with psychological *statements*. Specifically, he holds that psychological statements are scientifically meaningful only if they are translatable into the physical language, into statements about physiological processes or overt reactions to external stimuli, or dispositions to such reactions. Since he arrives at that view by the consideration that only such physical statements are publicly verifiable, that a "mentalistic" statement such as "The rat is now in the conscious state of expecting to be fed," or "When other people look at the traffic light they have similar color sensations as I experience when I look at it," is not verifiable by anyone except the subject it is about, logical behaviorism is obviously an application of the principle of verifiability. In this connection two questions should be distinguished:

1. Is it possible to analyze the intuitive meanings of mentalistic statements, i.e., statements like the above examples, in terms of a physical language?

2. Does the principle of verifiability entail that such statements are either semantically meaningless or else translatable into physical language?

It is easy to show that the answer to (1) is negative; indeed, this is so obvious that it must be assumed that what led logical behaviorists to demand that psychologists who wish to do science define their concepts in behavioristic—or, more broadly, physical—language, was the belief that the answer to (2), not the answer to (1), is affirmative. Carnap, for example, a vigorous advocate of physicalism, did not deny that words such as "angry," "anxiety," "feeling sad," "desiring water" have subjective meanings that cannot be expressed by any combination of physical terms. What he denied was that statements containing such words in their subjective senses assert anything that is true or false. If I say, "The rat expects to be fed now," I may imaginatively project my own mental states into the rat: this is what I would experience if I were in a similar situation! But if the statement has only this subjective meaning, said Carnap and the physicalists, it does not assert any possible fact, because it is not verifiable (note the underlying assumption that "*p* is a factual statement" entails "*p* is verifiable"!). In order to be a factual, verifiable statement it must mean something like "The rat now moves towards a place where food was presented to it at regular intervals, and so and so much time has elapsed since its last feeding."

It can be shown, however, that what was thus dismissed as merely "subjective" meaning is actually the semantical meaning, the truth-condition of such a psychological statement; and that consequently the principle of verifiability would be simply false if it entailed that psychological statements are neither true nor false to the extent that they have only "subjective" meaning. Suppose, for example, that when I say about another organism O, whether rat or human being, that it is now hungry, I am referring to the time that has elapsed since its last feeding, the present contents of its stomach, its food-seeking behavior (e.g., its grabbing a loaf of bread and proceeding to devour it) and other physical facts which are normally said to be "expressions" of hunger, in the same sense in which I refer to the fact that X is a woman who has no husband now but had a husband who died when I say, "X is a widow." In that case all of the following statements would be *self-contradictory:* O is now hungry though it ate a lot just until a minute ago and is not at all acting now so as to secure more food; O has an empty stomach now but is not hungry at all; O is eating a loaf of bread now as though it had not eaten for a day, but actually O is not hungry, it just eats the bread because somebody who said, "Eat that bread or I'll shoot you," is pointing a gun at its back. But though we may under some circumstances find it hard to believe such statements, they are not self-contradictory. If a man were to ask, "Is a woman who is now unmarried but was married to a man who died really a widow?" we would infer that he was unsure about the meaning, in English, of the word "widow," for if he did understand that meaning, he would in effect be asking the silly question whether a widow is really a widow. Now, no matter how many physical expressions, as one normally says, of hunger the physicalist may enumerate in his physicalistic definition of "hunger," the analogy will not hold. If one asks, "Does it necessarily follow from the fact that O has not eaten for 12 hours and is now eating in a way in which I eat when I am starved, that O is hungry how?," one does not thereby betray ignorance of the conventional meaning of the word "hungry," nor does one ask the silly question, "Does 'O is hungry' entail 'O is hungry'?"

To put it formally: if a mentalistic statement M had the same semantical meaning as a conjunction of physical statements $P_1 \& P_2 \& \cdots \& P_n$, then to accept the conjunction $P_1 \& P_2 \& \cdots \& P_n$ while doubting M would be self-contradictory, and it would be self-contradictory to say "P_1 is false (where P_1 is some part of the conjunction) but M may be true just the same." Yet, an impartial introspection of meanings will show that such statements make perfectly good sense. It will not do to reply that in feeling that they make sense we are unconsciously shifting from the semantical to the pragmatical meaning; that M fails to be synonymous with P_1 & P_2 & $\cdots$ & P_n only in the sense in which "nigger" fails to be synonymous with "Negro," or perhaps "educator" with "teacher." For it is the supposition of M's being *true* while P_1 is false that makes sense; hence P_1 cannot express even a part of the *truth-condition* of M. That P_1 may nevertheless express perfectly good *evidence* for the proposition designated by M is a different matter entirely.

A point of logic should be noted here. Logical behaviorists sometimes concede to their critics that the meaning of a psychological statement cannot be *completely* expressed by a finite conjunction of physical statements, just as a statement of theoretical physics, say, "An electromagnetic field of such and such distribution exists in such and such a region," cannot be completely translated into the language of observables. If so, it ceases to be a relevant criticism to point out that "P_1 & P_2 & $\cdots$ & P_n but not M" is not self-contradictory. But it remains relevant to point out that statements of the form "M but not P_1" are logically consistent; for if so, then not even a part of the meaning of M can be expressed in physical language. Could the behaviorist circumvent these difficulties by defining psychological terms by means of *disjunctions* of possible physical symptoms, thus: $M = P_1$ or P_2 or $\cdots$ or P_n? What must be kept in mind here is that a disjunction does not entail any member of itself but is entailed by any member of itself. If so, then the behaviorist who shifts to this form of definition cannot be criticized by pointing out that "M but not P_1" describes a logical possibility. Yet, he would then be committed to the absurd consequence that M follows necessarily from any particular P_1. When one says that anger, for example, may manifest itself by a flushed face *or* by the face growing pale *or* by a trembling voice *or* by clenched fists, one only means that any of these expressions makes the hypothesis that the subject feels angry probable, not that the psychological hypothesis is entailed by any one of them.

At this point the logical behaviorist may retreat to the less daring position of merely *methodological* behaviorism. He may say: "You may well be right. And the principle of verifiability, construed as the *assertion* that all and only verifiable statements describe possible facts (are true or false), may well be untenable. Yet, though mental states and processes such as I, the psychologist, experience may well occur in other organisms too (in fact, I strongly suspect that they do, though I could not logically justify this belief), their very privacy makes an intersubjective science of them impossible. It is only connections between publicly observable stimuli and publicly observable responses that can be scientifically investigated. Whether or not private states of consciousness intervene between these physical events, and if so, what they are like, is a question beyond the domain of empirical science." The methodological behaviorist, in other words, holds that psychology is either a *natural* science, or no science at all—where "natural science" is defined as a science of some aspect of the physical world. It cannot be denied that the swing from introspective psychology to the experimental science of behavior has been fruitful from the point of view of empirical science. But as philosophers of science we must scrutinize the arguments by which the methodological behaviorist justifies his exclusive concern with stimulus-response connections. Specifically, we must ask whether this restriction is really dictated by the maxim, "Investigate only subject-matters about which you can make publicly verifiable statements!" After our analysis of the meanings of "verifiable" (Chapter 2, A, B), it should be obvious where the methodological behaviorist has gone wrong: he has failed to distinguish conclusive verification from confirmation.

In order to confirm the hypothesis that you sometimes see red when you look at the traffic light, and that this visual sensation is a partial cause of your publicly observable reaction, viz. stopping the car, I need only construct an *argument from analogy*, which is an argument of the following form: objects $a, b, c, \ldots, n$ have properties $P_1, P_2, \ldots, P_m$ in common; $a, b, c, \ldots, m$ further have property P_n; therefore n likewise has P_n. This is, of course, only a form of probable reasoning, not of deductive (demonstrative) reasoning. That is, it can be supposed without contradiction that the premises of an argument of this form are true while the conclusion is false. To determine the criteria of soundness of such arguments— to determine, in other words, under what circumstances such reasoning leads to a fairly probable conclusion—is a task of inductive logic. We are not concerned with it at the moment. We only wish to show that hypotheses about the occurrence of mental states in other organisms (or, if you are less naturalistic, in other minds) are in principle confirmable by an argument from analogy, no matter whether their degree of confirmation relative to physical evidence be low or high. For this purpose we consider the special case that the set of objects $a, b, c, \ldots, n$ comprises just two objects a and b. We then obtain the following form of argument: a and b have $P_1, P_2, \ldots, P_m$ in common; a further has P_n;.therefore b has P_n. Now, let a and b be two organisms that are similar in appearance, physiology, and behavior. One of these organisms knows by introspection that it has the disposition, say, to feel a certain kind of pain when affected in a certain way; hence it concludes by the argument from analogy that the other organism has the same disposition. And from the inferred proposition that the other organism feels a similar pain when affected similarly, together with the observation statement that it is now affected that way, it follows that it now feels that kind of pain.

Can a verify his inference that b feels pain? Not conclusively, the way b can verify it by just attending to the pain he feels. Indeed, such conclusive verification by a is logically impossible, since if a had this kind of *direct* evidence he would have to feel pain himself; the statement which he would conclusively verify, then, would not be a statement about *another* mind. However, since *a* has been able directly to confirm the law that a certain kind of physical stimulus gives rise to a certain kind of pain, by attending to the pain *he* feels on such occasions, the very physical evidence from which he infers that *b* feels pain *confirms* that hypothesis, makes it probable to some degree. The verifiability theory of meaning, therefore, does not entail that statements about other minds must be interpreted physicalistically in order to be semantically meaningful. Some logical behaviorists have argued that if the physical premises (i.e., premises describing physical facts) from which the conclusion about the other mind is inferred constitute the only evidence for it, then there is no genuine inductive inference; and to *explain* the observed behavior, such as screams, in terms of a hidden state of consciousness, such as a pain, is as circular a procedure, they say, as to explain the observed fact that people usually fall asleep after consumption of opium in terms of the "dormitive virtue" of opium. But this argument overlooks that the hypothesis about the other mind is further confirmable *independently* of the physical evidence that suggested it. *a* has verified that when he is very hungry he has not eaten for at least four hours and further has the disposition to eat very fast (to the neglect of good manners) when he has an opportunity to eat. Now *a* verifies that *b* has not eaten for five hours and infers that *b* is very hungry. Since *a*, like a good scientist, makes inferences only with great caution and subject to revision, he decides to put this inference about *b* to a test: he offers *b* a substantial steak, and finds that *b* gulps it down within five minutes. To be sure, if *a* puts enough trust in people's autobiographical reports, he might just ask *b* whether he is hungry, and the verbal response "Yes, I am hungry" would be perfectly good independent evidence. But this kind of evidence is unavailable if, for example, *b* is *a*'s faithful dog. At any rate, it should be perfectly clear that on the basis of analogical argument hypotheses about other minds are confirmable in terms of publicly observable stimuli and responses, though their meanings cannot be expressed in physicalistic language.

Selected Readings

Ayer, A. J., "Our Knowledge of Other Minds," in A. J. Ayer, *Philosophical Essays* (London, 1954).

Bergmann, G., "Logic of Psychological Concepts," *Philosophy of Science*, 1951.

———— and K. W. Spence, "Operationism and Theory in Psychology," *Psychological Review*, 1941.

Borel, E., *Space and Time* (New York, 1960).

Born, M., *Einstein's Theory of Relativity* (London, 1924).

Carnap, R., "Logical Foundations of the Unity of Science," in H. Feigl and W. Sellers (eds.), *Readings in Philosophical Analysis* (New York, 1949).

———, "Psychology in the Language of Physics," in A. J. Ayer (ed.), *Logical Positivism* (New York, 1959).

d'Abro, A., *The Evolution of Scientific Thought from Newton to Einstein* (2nd ed., New York, 1950).

Einstein, A., *Sidelights of Relativity* (New York, 1923).

———, and L. Infeld, *The Evolution of Physics* (New York, 1954).

Frank, P., *Relativity, a Richer Truth* (Boston, 1950).

———, *Philosophy of Science* (Englewood Cliffs, N.J., 1957), ch. 4, 5.

Grünbaum, A., "The Clock Paradox in the Special Theory of Relativity," *Philosophy of Science*, 1954.

———, "Logical and Philosophical Foundations of the Special Theory of Relativity," *American Journal of Physics*, 1955.

Hempel, C. G., "The Logical Analysis of Psychology," in H. Feigl and W. Sellars (eds.), *Readings in Philosophical Analysis* (New York, 1949).

Hochberg, H., "Physicalism, Behaviorism and Phenomena," *Philosophy of Science*, 1959.

Israel, H. E., and B. Goldstein, "Operationism in Psychology," *Psychological Review*, 1944.

Kris, E., "The Nature of Psychoanalytic Propositions and Their Validation," in S. Hook and M. R. Konvitz (eds.), *Freedom and Experience, Essays Presented to Horace Kallen* (Ithaca, N.Y., 1947).

Lundberg, G. A., "Operational Definitions in Social Science," *American Journal of Sociology*, 1941–42.

Mach, E., "Newton's Views of Time, Space and Motion," in E. Mach, *Mechanics* (Chicago, 1942). [Reprinted in H. Feigl and M. Brodbeck (eds.), *Readings in the Philosophy of Science* (New York, 1953).]

Margenau, H., and R. A. Mould, "Relativity: An Epistemological Appraisal," *Philosophy of Science*, 1957.

Newton, I., "Absolute and Relative Space, Time and Motion," in I. Newton, *Philosophiae Naturalis Principia Mathematica*, Book I, rev. trans. by F. Cajori (Berkeley, Calif., 1934). [Reprinted in A. Danto and S. Morgenbesser (eds.), *Philosophy of Science* (New York, 1960).]

Pap, A., "Other Minds and the Principle of Verifiability," *Revue Internationale de Philosophie*, 1951.

Pratt, C. C., "Operationism in Psychology," *Psychological Review*, 1945.

———, *The Logic of Modern Psychology* (New York, 1948), chap. 3, 4.

Poincaré, H., *The Foundations of Science* (New York, 1929).

Reichenbach, H., "The Philosophical Significance of the Theory of Relativity," in H. Feigl and M. Brodbeck (eds.), *Readings in the Philosophy of Science* (New York, 1953).

———, *Philosophy of Space and Time* (New York, 1958).

Schlick, M., *Space and Time in Contemporary Physics* (Oxford, 1920).

———, *Philosophy of Nature* (New York, 1949), chap. 7–9.

———, "Are Natural Laws Conventions?" in H. Feigl and M. Brodbeck (eds.), *Readings in the Philosophy of Science* (New York, 1953).

Skinner, B. F., "Operational Analysis of Psychological Terms," *Psychological Review*, 1935.

Stevens, S. S., "The Operational Basis of Psychology," *American Journal of Psychology*, 1935.

——, "Operational Definition of Psychological Concepts," *Psychological Review*, 1935.

Waters, R. H., and L. A. Pennington, "Operationism in Psychology," *Psychological Review*, 1938.

Whitehead, A. N., *The Principle of Relativity* (Cambridge, 1922).

Wisdom, J., *Other Minds* (New York, 1952).

Part Two

MATHEMATICS,
LOGIC,
AND EXPERIENCE

CHAPTER 5

The Nature of Arithmetical Statements

A. A PRIORI KNOWLEDGE AND ANALYTIC STATEMENTS

In groping for an adequate formulation of the verifiability theory of meaningfulness, we restricted its scope to statements claimed to express *factual* knowledge, in contrast to statements claimed to express a priori knowledge. The reason was that it is doubtful whether the notion of empirical confirmability can be applied to statements that can be known to be true independently of experience, without "looking at the world," through the "mere operation of thought" (as Hume put it). Thus it would be peculiar to say the proposition that whatever is colored is spatially extended had been confirmed by observing that colored things are also spatially extended, since such language suggests that conceivably some colored thing might not be spatially extended. In other words, "p is empirically confirmable" entails "The falsehood of p is logically possible."

It is especially the logical positivists who use the term "factual knowledge" in the sense of "knowledge about the world" as contrasted with knowledge of the meanings of words or symbols and of logical consequences of definitions by means of which such meanings are fixed. They maintain that without experience it is impossible to acquire any knowledge about the world, though the laws of logic and mathematics are indispensable tools for the organization of our empirical knowledge.

[77]

Their opponents, however, maintain that the laws of logic and mathematics are not just rules concerning the use of symbols but describe the logical structure of the world, and since these laws can be known a priori, antipositivists hold that a priori knowledge about the world is possible. That two things plus two things make four things, that anything that is red is either red or round, that nothing is both a telephone and not a telephone, that two quantities that are equal to a third are equal to each other: such propositions, say the antipositivists, are absolutely *necessary* and no experience could possibly refute them, yet they do describe the world, they are not just linguistic conventions.

But it is inadvisable to formulate the issue between logical positivists and their critics in terms of the phrase "about the world," for it is not clear what this phrase means. We can distinguish statements about language from statements which are not about language: " 'Table' is an English word" is a statement about language that is itself in the *metalanguage*, i.e., the language used to speak about language. On the other hand, "There is a table in my study" is a statement about the world—if that means that it is not about language, that it is in the *object-language*. According to this criterion, the statement "The table in my study is a table" is likewise about the world though it is hardly necessary to examine the table in my study before assenting to it. And so is the statement "If there are at this time two tables and two chairs in my study and no other pieces of furniture, then there are at this time four pieces of furniture in my study." The metastatement " 'The table in my study is a table' is a trivial statement, it conveys no information about the table" is not about the world, in this sense, but the statement it mentions is. A second interpretation of "about the world" is this: A statement is about the world if it is *empirical*, i.e., if its truth or falsehood can only be discovered by looking at the world, by making observations. Now, since positivist and antipositivist are agreed that the cited necessary statements are not about the world in *this* sense, this can hardly be the intended sense of the phrase "about the world." In denying that statements that can be known to be true a priori convey any information about the world, the positivist surely is not just asserting the tautology that a statement that can be known to be true a priori is not empirical.

In order to come closer to the real issue, we must add a technical distinction to the distinction between a priori and empirical knowledge (cf. Chapter 1, D): the distinction between *analytic* and *synthetic* statements, which was first explicitly made by Kant though it may be found in Locke and Leibniz. It is perfectly natural to say that the statement "All bachelors are unmarried," for example, does not tell us anything about bachelors though it is undoubtedly in the object-language; that it rather tells us something about the *meaning* of the word "bachelor." All that is required to see that it is true, indeed necessarily true, is an understanding of the meaning of words. Not so in the case of the grammatically similar statement "All crows are black": here we do not just make explicit a part of the meaning of the word "crow"; we can imagine a crow that is not black; only experience can tell us whether or not there are crows that are not black. Statements of the first kind, which, though belonging to the object-language, merely unfold the meaning of a word or symbol, are analytic in a broad sense ("broadly analytic"); statements of the second kind are synthetic. If we can rest satisfied with the positive definition of "analytic" just given, we can define "synthetic" simply as "neither analytic nor self-contradictory." A self-contradictory statement results when an analytic statement is denied: "Some bachelors are married," for example, says that some people are both married and not married at the same time. Analytic statements are often said to be true by virtue of the meanings of their constituent terms. By "body" we mean a spatially extended thing that has mass, hence "All bodies are extended and have mass" is an analytic statement about bodies; on the other hand, Newton's law, "All bodies attract each other with a force that is directly proportional to the product of their masses and inversely proportional to the square of their distance," is a synthetic statement about bodies whose truth cannot be seen a priori.

Now we can formulate as follows the positivist thesis against metaphysicians who claim that man is capable of a priori knowledge of necessary facts: Whatever statements can be known to be true a priori are analytic, i.e. they only make explicit meanings that have been conventionally assigned to words or symbols. This thesis is, of course, equivalent to denying that any synthetic statements can be known to be true a priori. It might be combined with the verifiability theory of meaning in the succinct thesis: a statement that is neither analytic nor self-contradictory is (semantically) meaningful if and only if it is empirically verifiable. It should be noted, however, that "empirically verifiable" in this context is so meant that a statement that does not need to be empirically verified because reflection on its meaning is sufficient to reveal its truth, is not empirically verifiable. Indeed, when positivists insist on empirical verifiability as a necessary condition for the significance of statements that are neither analytic nor self-contradictory, they mean by "empirically verifiable statement" nothing else than "empirical statement." They deny that there can be synthetic statements that are semantically meaningful and can be established a priori.[1]

---

1. In this introductory discussion we use the term "analytic" as broadly as it has come to be used by logical positivists. A narrower concept of analytic truth (called "strictly analytic truth"), which leaves room for perfectly harmless "synthetic a priori" propositions, will be defined in Chapter 6, A.

B. ARE THE EQUATIONS
OF ARITHMETIC ANALYTIC?

Kant took it for granted that arithmetic is a "pure" science, i.e., that arithmetical statements are established a priori, not through the sort of empirical generalization that makes us believe the law of gravitation and the law that cats give birth to cats, not to dogs or any other kind of animal. But what led him into a philosophical puzzle was his belief that these propositions are also synthetic. "7 + 5 = 12," he argued, does not just explicate the meaning of "7 + 5" the way "All triangles have three angles" just explicates the meaning of "triangle." Indeed, it could not be maintained that "7 + 5" is synonymous with "12" the way "triangle" is by definition synonymous with "closed rectilinear figure with three angles"; nor would it be plausible to hold that anybody who understands the expression "the sum of seven and five" thereby already knows the equation to be true, for undoubtedly he first had to learn by counting that seven and five add up to twelve.

Kant unfortunately confused the issue by defining analytic subject-predicate statements obscurely as statements whose subject "contains" the predicate. If the criterion of such "containment" is the psychological one that a person who thinks of the subject at the same time thinks of the predicate, then one and the same statement that was synthetic for a person when it was first considered may be analytic for that person at a later time. Thus it is conceivable that a child learn the meanings of "seven," "five," and "sum" before even learning to count up to twelve; surely he can understand "seven plus five" without knowing that "seven plus five make twelve." Furthermore, even if he already can count up to twelve, it will take him a while to find out that seven and five add up to twelve; hence the thought of twelve will not instantly follow the thought of seven plus five. But anybody who is capable of reading this book with understanding will be able to answer the question "How much is seven plus five?" instantly. This psychological criterion of containment, then, is utterly useless.

But Kant himself gave another criterion of analyticity which—at first glance at any rate—is purely logical and independent of learning background and mental associations: a statement is analytic if its negation is self-contradictory. To be sure, the negations of analytic statements usually are not self-contradictory in themselves, but are rather translatable into self-contradictions with the help of definitions. Thus "some bachelors are not unmarried" is translatable into "Some unmarried men are not unmarried" with the help of the definition "bachelor = unmarried man." But while the question whether a given definition adequately expresses the meaning of the defined term in such and such contexts of usage is a question beyond logic in the strict sense, the question whether a statement can be denied without self-contradiction *given* such and such definitions is purely logical. And that true arithmetical equations are analytic in that sense may seem to be undeniable. The relevant definitions of the numbers take the form "$n = m + 1$," i.e., each number, with the exception of the "first" number, zero, is defined as the immediate successor of some other number. Thus "$2 = 1 + 1$," "$3 = 2 + 1$," "$4 = 3 + 1$," and these equations are all definitions, not theorems of which it would be reasonable to demand a proof. Now, a series of substitutions that are legitimized by these definitions transforms "$2 + 2 = 4$" into "$1 + 1 + 1 + 1 = 1 + 1 + 1 + 1$," i.e., into an identity. Were we to deny the equation, while abiding by the stipulated definitions, we would deny that the number 4, defined as $1 + 1 + 1 + 1$, is equal to itself. If we agree to call the statement "Everything is identical with itself" a law of logic, are we not driven by this analysis to admit that the laws of logic are sufficient to guarantee the truths of arithmetic, and that the latter are therefore analytic?

But this picture is oversimplified. In fact, we have been led into confusion by a loose use of the word "definition." When an analytic statement is described as a statement which is true by virtue of the definitions of constituent terms ("true by definition"), "definition" is meant in the sense of "statement explaining the meaning of a word or symbol." Is "$2 = 1 + 1$" a definition in that sense? Only if the symbols constituting the definiens, viz. "1" and "+," have a meaning. Now we may be told that these symbols have the precise meaning that is expressed by the explicit definition "$1 = 0'$" and by the recursive definition of "+": $x + y' = (x + y)'$,[2] $x + 0 = x$. But thus we are led to "0" and "$'$" as undefined (primitive) symbols and as long as no meanings are assigned to them, the defined symbols are meaningless too. The definitions are only rules for transformation of symbolic formulae. They regulate the manipulation of symbols within a deductive system of arithmetic, but they do not tell us how the symbols might be *applied* to anything outside the system. For example, the above definition of "2" is useless for deciding whether or not a given collection has two members as long as the primitives "0" and "$'$" remain uninterpreted. And since sentences containing uninterpreted symbols are obviously neither true nor false, we cannot call the theorems of uninterpreted arithmetic true, hence we cannot call them analytic in the specified sense. The sentences of an uninterpreted deductive system can be classified into those that are provable on the basis of the axioms (including definitions), those whose negations are

2. "$. . . '$" reads: the successor of . . . .

provable, and so-called "undecidable" sentences, i.e., sentences belonging to neither of the former classes. But they cannot be classified into *true* and *false* because only meaningful (interpreted) sentences can be true or false. And since analytic statements are statements whose *truth* can be ascertained in a special way, viz. by sole reference to analysis of meanings and laws of logic, it is a mistake to call the theorems of an uninterpreted deductive system "analytic."

C. THE LOGICIST INTERPRETATION OF ARITHMETIC

However, according to the *logicist* philosophy of mathematics, as developed by Gottlob Frege and more or less independently by Bertrand Russell, it is possible to interpret arithmetical terms, such as "0," "successor," "2," by means of *logical constants* in such a way that the sentences of arithmetic turn into statements that are formally deducible from laws of logic. The arithmetic of natural numbers had been axiomatized by the Italian mathematician and logician Peano in such a way that "number," "0," and "successor" were the three primitive terms occurring in five axioms:

1. 0 is a number.
2. The successor of any number is a number.
3. No two numbers have the same successor.
4. 0 is not the successor of any number.
5. If P is a property such that (*a*) 0 has the property P, and (*b*) if a number n has P, then the successor of n has P, then every number has P.

Axiom 5 is the famous principle of mathematical induction which is best conceived as a concentrated statement of an infinite chain of implications of the form "if $[p$ and (if p, then $q)]$ then q": suppose that for every n, if n has P, then n' has P; then in particular if 0 has P, then 1 has P; but 0 has P; therefore 1 has P; but (*b*) having been proved with complete generality, we can apply it to 1: if 1 has P, then 2 has P; therefore 2 has P; and so on. Since induction is commonly contrasted with deduction, it is therefore confusing that this sort of inference is called "induction" at all. Now, these axioms can be formalized, with the help of symbolic logic, in such a way that "0," "number," and "successor" occur as free variables and all other expressions are either logical constants or bound variables:

1. $N(a)$
2. $(x)(y)(Sxy \cdot Ny \supset Nx)$
3. $(x)(y)[Nx \cdot Ny \cdot x \neq y \supset (z)(v)(Szx \cdot Svy \supset z \neq v)]$
4. $(x)(Nx \supset -Sax)$
5. $(P)\{[Pa \cdot (n)(m)(Pn \cdot Smn \supset Pm)] \supset (z)Pz\}$

In order to deduce theorems from these postulates[3] we do not need to assume that the primitives mean anything more specific than entities satisfying the postulates. For example, we can deduce from the first two postulates, together with explicit definitions of specific natural numbers in the form "*n* is the successor of *m*," that for every number there is a number which is its successor, and the third postulate then leads to the conclusion that there are infinitely many numbers. But if we took "*a*" to denote the number 1,000, and "number" the class of numbers that are equal to or greater than 1,000, the proof would go through just as well. In fact, any progression of natural numbers, regardless of the identity of its first element, satisfies Peano's postulates. One might attempt to characterize the unique meaning of "zero" in terms of some unique mathematical property of this number, e.g., that the sum of zero and any other number is equal to that other number. But since "sum" is re- cursively defined in terms of "zero," this leads us nowhere.

Now, Russell derived the unique meanings of the primitives by re- flecting upon the language of applied arithmetic. It makes a big difference whether we say the number of a man's sons is zero or one or two, and this difference cannot be explained within the language of uninterpreted arithmetic. We begin contextual definitions, i.e., rules for eliminating the arithmetical terms from certain kinds of contexts, especially from state- ments ascribing a number to a given class: the number of class *A* is zero = there is no *x* such that *x* is member of *A;* the number of class *A* is one = there is an *x* such that *x* is member of *A*, and for any *y*, if *y* is member of *A*, then $y = x$;[4] the number of class *A* is two = there is an *x* and a *y* such that *x* is distinct from *y* and both *x* and *y* are members of *A*, and for any *z*, if *z* is a member of *A*, then $z = x$ or $z = y$; and so on. A contextual definition, of course, is limited because it fixes the use of the definiendum only relative to a special form of sentence. What does "two" mean in the purely mathematical statement "Two is a prime number," for example? The above contextual definition does not tell us. But Russell,

---

3. Clue to symbols: $Nx = x$ is a number; $(x) =$ for every *x*; $Sxy = x$ is the suc- cessor of *y*; $\cdot = $ and; ... $\supset$ ... $=$ if ... then ... ; $Pa = a$ has property *P*.

4. The definition may appear to be circular if "there is an *x*" is taken in the sense of "there is at least *one x*." But "there is an *x*" can be defined as synonymous with "it is not the case that there is no *x*," and if this roundabout locution were used even the appearance of circularity would be destroyed.

like Frege before him, adds an explicit definition which is aimed at the language of pure arithmetic, in contrast to applied arithmetic: two is the class of all classes that have two members. This definition is not circular, because in the definiens "two" has no independent meaning; it is part of the expression "have two members" which has already been defined in terms of logical constants. If the reader finds it intuitively more intelligible if two is defined as the *attribute* of being a class with two members, and analogously for the analogous explicit definitions of the other natural numbers, he may substitute that conception with impunity.

The successor relation is definable in terms of logical constants as follows: The successor of a number n is the class of all classes that arise when to a class with n members exactly one element is added. The notion of addition involved in this definition is purely logical: what is in question is the logical sum of a class and a unit class (class with exactly one member), where the logical sum of two classes is the class of those entities that are members of one *or* the other. It should again be noted that this definition of "successor" is not circular because, although "one" is defined within the uninterpreted system of arithmetic as the successor of zero, the *interpretation* of "one" by means of logical constants makes no use of the notion of successor. Finally, natural numbers are defined as numbers satisfying the principle of mathematical induction, i.e., numbers that have all those properties of zero which are "hereditary" (in Russell's phrase) with respect to the successor relation, i.e., those properties which the successor of n has, provided n has them. The general notion of "number" is defined in terms of the notion of similarity of classes: a number is a class of all classes similar to a given class, and two classes are said to be similar if their elements can be matched one by one (the notion of "one-by-one matching" in turn is defined in terms of "one-one relation" which is definable in terms of logical constants alone). It is obvious right away that these definitions turn axiom 1 into a tautology: 0 has all the hereditary properties of 0. That axiom 2 becomes a tautology is also fairly obvious, for it now says the following: suppose that y has all the properties that 0 has and that the successor of any n has provided n has it; and suppose that x is the successor of y; then x has all the properties that 0 has and that the successor of n has provided n has it. At any rate, this proposition is formally demonstrable by means of symbolic logic (the proof does not depend on the definition of "successor").[5] The formal proof of axiom 4 is a little complicated, but the

---

5. To be established: (x) (y) $(Sxy \cdot Ny \supset Nx)$. Proof on the basis of the definition:
$$Nx = (P) \ [Py \cdot (n) \ (m) \ (Pn \cdot Smn \supset Pm) \supset Px$$
1. $(P) \ [P_o \cdot (n) \ (m) \ (Pn \cdot Smn \supset Pm) \ P_y]$ premise
2. Sxy premise
3. $Po \cdot (n) \ (m) \ (Pn \cdot Smn \supset Pm)$ subordinate hypothesis

logical validity of this postulate in Russellian interpretation is again obvious: the definition of "successor" is such that only a number that is the number of a class containing at least one element can be successor of some number; but zero is defined as the number of the null class, therefore zero by definition cannot be a successor.[6] The fifth postulate, of course, turns into the barest tautology, which is no surprise since the natural numbers were deliberately defined as entities that satisfy it: if a given property, *P*, is a hereditary property of zero, then everything that has all the hereditary properties of zero has *P*.

The third postulate, however, which guarantees that the sequence of natural numbers is open at one end, i.e., does not return into its starting point, was a serious obstacle to the program of reducing arithmetic (and the higher branches of mathematics built upon arithmetic) to pure logic. For suppose that the number of concrete individuals in the universe were finite, say *n*. Then no classes with $n + 1$ members would exist, hence the number $n + 1$, being defined as the class of all classes with $n + 1$ members, would be the null class; hence $n + 1$ would equal $n + 2$, whereas *n* would be distinct from $n + 1$ since by hypothesis there are classes with *n* members; hence there would be two distinct numbers with the same successor, which contradicts Peano's postulate. Russell saw no logically consistent way out of this difficulty except to lay down an *axiom of infinity:* there are infinitely many concrete individuals in the universe. Since obviously the truth of this axiom cannot be guaranteed by logic (it is not even self-evident), this ad hoc device made the claim that all arithmetical theorems can be demonstrated by means of pure logic untenable.

Would it be possible to guarantee the infinity of the sequence of natural numbers without an axiom of infinity and without abandonment of the Russellian definition of number? Some logicians claim that this can be done, that in fact not a single concrete entity needs to be presupposed—as it should be from the point of view of mathematicians

---

4. $Py \cdot Sxy \supset Px$	3, simplification and universal instantiation
5. $Sxy \supset (Py \supset Px)$	4, commutation and exportation
6. $Py \supset Px$	2, 5, modus ponens
7. $Po \cdot (n) (m) (Pn \cdot Smn \supset Pm) \supset Py$	1, universal instantiation
8. Py	3, 7, modus ponens
9. Px	6, 8, modus ponens
10. $Po \cdot (n) (m) (Pn \cdot Smn \supset Pm) \supset Px$	3–9, conditional proof
11. $(P) [Po \cdot (n) (m) Pn \cdot Smn \supset P_m) \supset P_x]$	10, universal generalization

6. The student might object that 0 is the successor of -1. But -1 is a negative integer, whereas what is here in question is the logical foundation of the theory of *natural numbers.*

who regard numbers as abstract entities whose existence does not pre-suppose the existence of concrete objects in space and time ("Plato-nism"). We just construct conceptually an unending sequence of distinct classes: the null class, the unit class whose only member is the null class, the unit class whose only member is the foregoing class, and so on. To prove the distinctness of all these classes, we need only the definition of class identity according to which A and B are the same class if and only if anything that is a member of A is a member of B, and conversely. For consider, for example, the first two elements of our sequence: the second element is a class with one member, the first class is the null class, hence they have different membership. Now, all the following classes are unit classes, but the fact that the first two classes are distinct guarantees that they all differ in membership too: the solitary member of the third class, for example, differs from the solitary member of the second class, be-cause the latter is the null class, whereas the former is a unit class; the solitary member of the fourth class differs from the solitary member of the third class because the latter is the second element of our sequence and the former the third, which elements have already been shown to be distinct; and so on. Since the sequence is infinite, any class of similar classes composed of such elements will be nonempty.

Russell, however, could not accept this solution of the difficulty be-cause of his own prohibitive *theory of types*. The latter is a stipulation of a criterion of significance of sentences, designed to avoid logical paradoxes such as the famous "Russell paradox" of the class of all classes that are not members of themselves. Most classes we can think of seem not to be members of themselves, i.e., not to have the properties by which they are defined: for example, the class of men is not a man, the class of dogs is not a dog. Consider, now, the class of all such classes, i.e., classes that are not members of themselves. Is it a member of itself or not? A moment's reflection will reveal that if it is, then it is not, and if it is not, then it is. By the law of logic that if p implies not-p then not-p is true, and if not-p implies p, then p is true (in other words, if a proposition implies its own negation, then it must be false), we must conclude that the class of all classes that are not members of themselves both is and is not a member of itself: a contradiction.

The theory of types consists in the stipulation that sentences of the form "x is a member of y" are meaningful, and thus true or false, only if the type of y is $n + 1$ provided the type of x is n. This entails that the sentence whose truth-value we tried to determine, viz. "The class of all classes which are not members of themselves is a member of itself," has no truth-value at all, for it has the form "x is a member of x." The type of class y is said to be higher by one than the type of x if x is either a member of *y* or a member of the complement of *y*, where the complement of a class is the class of all those entities that are not members of it (but could significantly be supposed to be members of it). For a detailed exposition of the theory of types the reader must be referred to other sources,[7] but this brief explanation should suffice for our purposes. Consider, for example, the number two, defined as the class of all classes that contain exactly two elements out of the described sequence of ghostly classes. Any such couple is a class whose members differ in type—for example, the couple consisting of the null class and the unit class whose only member is the null class. Let us call the first member of the couple *a*, the second *b*, and the couple itself *C*. Then we are supposing that *a* is a member of *C* and that *b* is a member of *C*, but since *a* and *b* differ in type, it cannot be the case, as required by the theory of types, that the type of *C* is higher by one than the type of *a* and also higher by one than the type of *b*.

Since the time when Russell regretfully rejected this way out of the difficulty posed by Peano's third postulate for a reduction of arithmetic to pure logic, several logicians have shown that the theory of types is not the only way in which logical paradoxes such as Russell's paradox can be avoided. One such alternative stipulation consists in admitting sentences containing descriptions of such troublesome classes as the class of all classes that are not members of themselves as significant, but characterizing the troublesome classes as "nonelements," i.e., classes that are not members of any class.[8]

It should be noted, however, that one could consistently retain the theory of types and avoid the axiom of infinity if one construed numbers as special kinds of *attributes* instead of construing them, as Russell did, as special kinds of *classes*. What distinguishes an attribute from the class of all those entities that have the attribute is that different attributes may correspond to the same class. For example, anything that is an equilateral triangle is also an equiangular triangle, and conversely, hence the class of equilateral triangles is identical with the class of equiangular triangles; yet the attribute of being an equiangular triangle seems clearly distinct from the attribute of being an equilateral triangle; "equiangular" and "equilateral" are not synonyms. Again, the attribute of being a regular solid with square faces is distinct from the attribute of being a regular

7. A. N. Whitehead and B. Russell, *Principia Mathematica*, 3 vols. (2nd ed., New York: Cambridge University Press, 1925–1927), Vol. I, introduction, Chap. 2; C. I. Lewis and C. H. Langford, *Symbolic Logic* (New York: Dover Publications, Inc., 1959), Chap. 13; I. M. Copi, *Symbolic Logic* (New York: The Macmillan Company 1954), Chap. 5 and App. B.

8. This solution was first suggested by J. von Neumann, and is worked out in detail in W. V. Quine's *Mathematical Logic* (rev. ed.; Cambridge: Harvard University Press, 1951).

solid with twelve equal edges such that any two edges that have a point in common form a right angle, yet whatever has the one has the other and conversely; they are alternative ways of defining the class of cubes. The pairs of coextensive attributes considered so far may be said to be logically equivalent relative to the system of Euclidean (plane or solid) geometry, in that the axioms of the system permit us to prove that nothing could possibly have the one without having the other. But the concomitance of distinct attributes may be purely contingent: it is, for example, a contingent fact, not a logically necessary fact, that anything that is a living organism containing a kidney is a living organism containing a heart, and conversely.

The most striking proof, however, of the distinctness of class and attribute is afforded by the null class itself. We cannot but speak of *the* null class, because of the already given definition of class identity: $A = B =$ df. there is nothing that is a member of A and not a member of B, and there is nothing that is a member of B and not a member of A. Clearly, the truth of "$A = B$," so defined, follows from the emptiness of A, or of B. We therefore must identify, for example, the class of unicorns with the class of mermaids and the class of golden mountains. Yet, since the predicates "is a unicorn," "is a mermaid," "is a golden mountain" have *incompatible* meanings, they must *a fortiori* connote distinct attributes. Accordingly we may with propriety speak of *an* empty attribute, whereas it is proper to speak of *the* empty class.

Now, we have seen that "$n + 1 = n + 2$" follows from the assumption that the number of individuals is n together with the Russellian definition of numbers as *classes* of similar *classes*. But if the number $n + 1$ is defined as the *attribute* (of a class) of having $n + 1$ members, and similarly $n + 2$ as the attribute (of a class) of having $n + 2$ members, Russell's conclusion does not follow. For though, on that assumption, both attributes would be empty they would remain just as distinct as the attribute, say, of being a mermaid and the attribute of being a golden mountain, and for just the same reason: they are defined as incompatible attributes. For example, the expressions "A has two members" and "A has three members" are so defined in *Principia Mathematica:* that it would be contradictory to suppose that the same class had both (exactly) two and (exactly) three members. Therefore, even if just one concrete object existed (whatever "concrete object" may exactly mean), the number two would retain its conceptual distinctness from the number three; and this argument, obviously, can be generalized for any finite number n and its successor.

In this way the logicist interpretations of Peano's primitives do indeed, enable a deduction of the laws of arithmetic from purely logical axioms by means of principles of formal deduction.[9] At the same time, they account for the empirical use of the laws of arithmetic as instruments of deduction of empirical propositions from empirical propositions. Suppose you have verified by counting that you have three nickels and four dimes in your pocket and no other coins. Unless you are wholly ignorant of arithmetic, you will not go through a separate process of counting in order to find the answer to the question how many coins you have in your pocket; you will simply use the equation "3 + 4 = 7," and if you were to check the calculation by actually counting out the total number of coins, it would not be because you were unsure of the validity of the equation but because you considered the possibility that the empirical premises might be false, i.e., that you made a mistake in counting or overlooked some other coins in your pocket. But how is it that such an equation can be applied to such empirical situations if it is not simply an empirical generalization, highly probable but not absolutely certain, about the results of counting operations? The answer that the equation is formally provable within a formal system of arithmetic, such as Peano's, is completely beside the point, because it can be applied as a rule of deduction to empirical statements containing the symbols "3" and "4" only if the same symbols as used in formal arithmetic *refer* to verifiable attributes of collections, whereas they refer to nothing at all in that context. One of the chief virtues of the logicist interpretation is that it provides a satisfactory answer to this question. For, if A and B are mutually exclusive classes (like the class of nickels now in my pocket and the class of dimes in the same pocket), and the statements "The number of A is 3" and "The number of B is 4" mean what they mean according to the logicist interpretation, and further "The number of coins in A *or* B is 7" means what it means according to the logicist interpretation, then the latter statement is a logical consequence of the former two statements. The law of arithmetic is a universal statement about any classes: for any classes A and B, if A has three members and B has four members and A and B have no members in common, then the logical sum of A and B (i.e., the class of things that are members of A or B) has seven members. It warrants the deduction of "The logical sum of A and B has seven members" from "A has three members and B has four members and A and B have no common members."

It is important to understand that the arithmetical equation, so interpreted, says nothing about the relationship of the numbers of elements in two separate collections to the number of elements in the collection

<hr />

9. In connection with the definition of multiplication, however, a set-theoretical existence postulate becomes necessary, the "axiom of choice" (or "multiplicative axiom"), whose purely logical character has been disputed.

resulting from their *physical* addition. For example, it does not permit us to deduce from the statements "There are three coins in my left pocket" (*p*) and "There are four coins in my right pocket" (*q*) the conclusion "If the coins in my right pocket are put into my left pocket, there will be altogether seven coins in the latter." What can be tautologically deduced from the conjunction of *p* and *q* is only this: the number of coins that are either in my left pocket or in my right pocket is seven. For this reason it is sheer confusion to say, as is sometimes said, that the laws of arithmetic are not necessarily conformed to by the physical world: mix two gallons of water with two gallons of alcohol and you will get three, not four gallons of the mixture! The point is that the arithmetical concept of sum must not be confused with any kind of physical joining. What is necessarily true is the following proposition: If bottle A contains at time *t* two gallons of water and bottle B contains at *t* two gallons of alcohol, then there are four gallons of liquid that are contained in *either* A *or* B at time *t*.

D. MILL'S EMPIRICISM

John Stuart Mill is usually cited as an extreme empiricist who denied that the laws of arithmetic are known a priori and maintained that they derive their certainty simply from the fact that they are the most comprehensive generalizations about any kinds of countable objects that have been empirically confirmed much more extensively than, say, the laws of physics. However, the propositions that Mill regarded as empirical are different from the propositions that according to the logicist school are logically true. He seems to have had in mind such propositions as "If in counting the pebbles at one place I get three, and in counting the pebbles at another place I get four, then, if I pile the pebbles all together and count them, I shall get seven." This proposition about the results of counting processes is, indeed, not analytic and can be established only empirically. There is no contradiction involved in the supposition that the total number of pebbles that are counted after the spatially separate collections are united should turn out to be, say, six. And this is the case even if no mistake in counting were made, for it is not self-contradictory to suppose that a physical object just vanished.

To see the great difference between a proposition of applied arithmetic such as the above and an arithmetical proposition which is, in the explained sense, logically true, it is sufficient to grasp the difference between a number concept that is defined in terms of a counting procedure and a number concept that is defined by means of purely logical concepts. To say that a collection contains three elements in the former sense of "three" is to assert the following: If a one-one correspondence were established between the collection and a subclass of the class of numerals, starting the matching process with the numeral "1" and continuing with immediately succeeding numerals, the last numeral would be "3." To say that it has three elements in the logicist sense is to say: There are distinct elements x, y, z that belong to the collection and for any element u, if u belongs to the collection then u is identical with x or with y or with z. It is true that in order to formulate the latter proposition one has to count variables, but the proposition does not *mention* any counting procedure.

It is particularly important to keep in mind that insofar as propositions of applied arithmetic are necessary (a priori) they have no predictive content. It may well be that the following proposition is necessary: *if* (if the apples on the table were correctly counted at time t, they would be found to be three; and if the pears on the table were correctly counted at t, they would be found to be four), *then* (if the apples and the pears were correctly counted together *at t*, they would be found to be seven). But it is essential that the three counting operations mentioned by this hypothetical proposition occur at the same time. For this very reason we cannot deduce from it what the counted number of the sum of the collections would be if the latter were counted a little later. If a later count of the sum yielded, say, the number six, and a careful recount confirmed the result, one would not question any law of arithmetic but assume that one piece of fruit disappeared mysteriously during the time separating the three counting processes. This is to say that any predictive use of an arithmetical equation presupposes the empirical premise that the counted objects continue to exist as separate, distinguishable objects. The principle emphasized by logical empiricists, that from necessary propositions alone no predictions are derivable, is therefore confirmed by a close analysis of the application of arithmetic. We cannot deduce with theoretical certainty from what we have counted what we *shall* count.

It thus appears that there need not be any disagreement between the logicist and the Millian interpretation of arithmetical equations since the same string of symbols may in one context be used to express a logically necessary proposition and in another context to express an empirical proposition referring to counting operations. But the issue of the correct interpretation of arithmetical sentences is even less clear-cut than is suggested by this statement, for there are two kinds of necessary propositions that may be expressed by a sentence such as "2 + 3 = 5." The first is the sort of logical truth that can be expressed in terms of class variables and the logical constants of *Principia Mathematica*. But suppose that cardinal numbers were defined, in analogy to measurable traits of objects, as dispositional properties of collections, i.e., in terms of the outcomes of counting operations consisting in an ordered assignment of numerals to the elements of the counted collection. Consider now two nonoverlapping collections A and B and their sum $A + B$. Suppose that we assign the task of counting A to *observer* O_1; the task of counting B, *beginning simultaneously with* O_1, to observer O_2; and the task of counting $A + B$, *again beginning simultaneously with* O_1, but without using any law of arithmetic, to observer O_3. Then we assert the following hypothetical proposition: If no mistake in counting is made, and the collections remain unchanged during the counting process (i.e., no elements disappear, none are added, none split up), then, if O_1 counts n, and O_2 counts m, then O_3 counts $n + m$. The provisos in the antecedent were, indeed, so chosen as to guarantee the necessity of the proposition. But do they render it logically true?

The proposition is not a logical truth, since it mentions counting operations, and therewith assignments of numerals; it does not contain exclusively logical concepts. Still it might be argued to be analytic on the ground that one would unhesitatingly infer that at least one observer made a mistake in counting if the results did not conform to the conventional laws of arithmetic, or that in such a case one would infer that at least one collection changed in number. But it is not clear that the sort of analyticity that is established by this argument is anything else than indubitability, in the sense of a proposition one cannot conceive to be false. If one cannot conceive the falsehood of "If p, then q" and finds "q" to be false, then one is of course compelled to question "p." If, to be sure, the laws of arithmetic were our *only* criteria for judging whether a counting operation was correct or mistaken and whether a collection remained constant in number, then such hypothetical propositions would be empty tautologies. But this is by no means the case: we can check a counting operation directly, by repeating it and having others repeat it, and take the consistency of the results as establishing its correctness; and in the case of sufficiently small collections we can verify without using arithmetic that their number remained constant, by direct observation. If so, then the Kantian doctrine of the *synthetic a priori* character of simple arithmetical judgments is not obviously false, as maintained by Russell and the logical empiricists who accepted his logicism. O_1 counts a collection of apples and finds there are seven; he recounts several times, all the while making sure that no apples disappear and none are added; O_2, taking similar precautions, counts five apples in a different collection; does it not *follow* that O_3, who counted the sum of these collections of apples in one single counting operation, and who counted correctly by the same criterion of consistency (which does not presuppose the use of "7 + 5 = 12"!), must have counted twelve?

Selected Readings

Ayer, A. J., *Language, Truth and Logic* (rev. ed.; New York, 1950), chap. 4. [Reprinted in P. Edwards and A. Pap (eds.), *A Modern Introduction to Philosophy* (New York, 1957).]

Behmann, J., "Sind die mathematischen Urteile analytisch oder synthetisch?," *Erkenntnis*, 1934.

Black, M., *The Nature of Mathematics* (New York, 1933).

Broad, C. D., "Are There Synthetic A Priori Truths?," *Aristotelian Society Proceedings*, supp. vol. 15 (1936).

Carnap, R., *Foundations of Logic and Mathematics* (International Encyclopedia of Unified Science, I, no. 3, Chicago, 1939).

——, "Formal and Factual Science," in H. Feigl and M. Brodbeck (eds.), *Readings in the Philosophy of Science* (New York, 1953).

Frege, G., *The Foundations of Arithmetic*, trans. J. L. Austin (New York, 1950).

Gasking, D., "Mathematics and the World," in A. Flew (ed.), *Logic and Language* (Oxford, 1955), vol. 2.

Hempel, C. G., "The Nature of Mathematical Truth," in H. Feigl and W. Sellars (eds.), *Readings in Philosophical Analysis* (New York, 1949), and in H. Feigl and M. Brodbeck (eds.), *Readings in the Philosophy of Science* (New York, 1953).

Hospers, J., *An Introduction to Philosophical Analysis* (Englewood Cliffs, N.J., 1953), chap. 2.

Lewis, C. I., "The Pragmatic Conception of the A Priori," in H. Feigl and W. Sellars (eds.), *Readings in Philosophical Analysis* (New York, 1949).

Mill, J. S., *A System of Logic* (London, 1893), Book II, chap. 6.

Pap, A., "The Different Kinds of A Priori," *Philosophical Review*, 1944.

——, "Mathematics, Abstract Entities, and Modern Semantics," *Scientific Monthly*, 1957.

Popper, K., G. Ryle, and C. Lewy (symposium), "Why are the Calculuses of Logic and Mathematics Applicable to Reality?," *Aristotelian Society Proceedings*, supp. vol. 20 (1946).

Ramsey, F. P., "The Foundations of Mathematics," in F. P. Ramsey, *The Foundations of Mathematics and Other Logical Essays* (New York, 1950).

Russell, B., *Introduction to Mathematical Philosophy* (London, 1948), ch. 1–3, 13, 18.

Schlick, M., "Is There a Factual A Priori?," in H. Feigl and W. Sellars (eds.), *Readings in Philosophical Analysis* (New York, 1949).

Sellars, W., "Is There a Synthetic A Priori?," *Philosophy of Science*, 1953.

Wittgenstein, L., *Remarks on the Foundations of Mathematics* (New York, 1956).

CHAPTER 6

The Laws of Logic

A. TAUTOLOGIES AND ANALYTIC STATEMENTS

The statement that arithmetic is, with the help of adequate definitions, reducible to logic hardly clarifies the nature of arithmetic as long as we do not know what a logical truth is. The philosophers of science who have contributed the lion's share to the clarification of mathematics, logic, and the relation of these formal sciences to experience, are the logical positivists. And it is one of their characteristic tenets that the laws or truths of logic are tautologies and thus have no "factual content"; another terminology often used to make the same claim is that they are "analytic," in contrast to the synthetic propositions established by the factual sciences. It is also not uncommon to pass from this assertion to the conclusion that the allegedly inexorable necessity of the laws of logic is somehow reducible to linguistic conventions. The latter thesis is sometimes called *logical conventionalism*. In order to make up our minds about its merits, we must first attend carefully to the meanings of the key terms in this important controversy in the philosophy of science—"tautology" and "analytic."

The simple prototype of a tautology is any statement of the form "*p* or not *p*," where "*p*" represents a statement; such as "that man is a banker, or else he isn't." Such a statement is obviously true regardless of whether its component statement "*p*" is true or false. For a disjunction, i.e., a statement of the form "*p* or *q*," is true provided at least one component statement is true. So, if "*p*" is true, "*p* or not *p*" is true; and if "*p*" is false, then by the very meaning of "not," "not-*p*" is true, so again the disjunction is true. Generalizing from this simple example, we call a tautology any compound statement that is true regardless of whether its component statements be true or false. Sometimes the computation that establishes that a given compound statement is a tautology is quite complicated, just as it may be complicated to prove that a mathematical equation reduces to an identity. The appropriate methods of computation are explained in numerous textbooks of symbolic logic; hence they need not be explained here in detail. Let us just illustrate this concept of tautology in terms of a slightly more complicated example: If p, and (if p, then q), then q. This statement form corresponds to the principle of deduction, "Whatever statement is implied by true statements, is itself true." In order to show that any compound statement of that form must be true, regardless of the truth-values of the statements replacing the variables "p" and "q," we show that it could not possibly be false. In order for it to be false, the antecedent "p and (if p, then q)"—which corresponds to the two premises of a deductive argument of that form— would have to be true while the consequent "q" is false. But in order for the antecedent to be true "p" must be true, and "if p, then q" must be true. But if "p" is true and "q" false, then "if p, then q" cannot be true. In other words, if the consequent is false, the antecedent is bound to be false—which is equivalent to saying that if the antecedent is true, the consequent is bound to be true.

By contrast, consider: If q, and (if p, then q), then p. It is possible for a true implication to have a false antecedent, hence it is possible that q and (if p, then q) be true and p be false. Hence it is possible for the above complex implication to be false, hence it is not a tautology. Again, "If not-q and (if p, then q), then not-p" is a tautology because in order for the implication to be false p would have to be true while q is false (i.e., not-q true) and (if p, then q) true, which is impossible. It may be left to the reader to apply the same method to establish that "If not-p, and (if p, then q), then not-q" is *not* a tautology.

These illustrations bring out an important connection between the concept *tautology* and the concept *valid deductive argument*: suppose that an implication "If P_1 and P_2 and . . . and P_n, then C" is a tautology in the explained sense; then an argument (or inference) whose premises are P_1, P_2, . . . , P_n and whose conclusion is C, is valid, in the sense that C must be true if P_1, P_2, . . . , P_n are all true. The converse of this conditional statement, however, does not hold. Thus, consider a valid syllogism, say, one of the form "All M are P, all S are M, therefore all S are P." Here the corresponding implication is not a tautology. For, since the three statements here do not have statements, but rather terms, as parts, each is to be represented by a simple statement variable and the corresponding implication has the form: If p and q, then r. And clearly not all implications of this form are true. Generally speaking, the tautological character of a compound statement depends upon the meanings of the logical connectives, which are particles used to form compound statements out of statements that do not contain statements as parts: "not," "if-then," "or," "and" (and certain others that are definable on the basis of these). The validity of a syllogism, as well as of many other forms of deductive inference, does not, however, depend just on the meanings of logical connectives. Here the logical constants whose meanings are decisive are "all," "some," and "are" as used to express inclusion of one class in another.

In the light of this distinction, the statement that the laws of logic are simply tautologies must be condemned as either false or trivial. It is false if "tautology" is meant in the restricted sense explained above. Let us add an example of a law of logic that is not a tautology in the restricted sense, and which moreover is beyond the scope of Aristotelian logic, which dealt exclusively with syllogistic reasoning: Whatever relation R may be, if something has R to everything else, then everything has the converse of R to something or other (where the converse of R is that relation which x has to y if and only if y has R to x). However, since all tautologies are formal truths, and it is often uncritically assumed that all formal truths are tautologies, the word, "tautology" has also come to be used in the broader sense of "formal truths." But since "formal truth" in any precise sense turns out to be synonymous with "law of logic" (or "logical truth") it is then trivial to say that all laws of logic are tautologies. A "formal truth" or a "law of logic" is a statement that is true by virtue of its logical form, and this means that its truth depends only on the meanings of the *logical constants* it contains, not on the meanings of the *descriptive* terms. "John is tall or John is not tall": clearly you can replace "John" by "Plato" and "tall" by "fat," and the resulting statement will be just as true. Similarly, any statement of the form "If all M are P and some S are M, then some S are P" is true, regardless of what descriptive terms may be substituted for "M," "P," and "S" (provided, of course, that no equivocation is committed). What is usually called a "law of logic" is a purely abstract, universal statement devoid of descriptive constants, such as: For all classes M, P, and S, if all M are P and some S are M, then some S are P. A substitution instance of a law of logic, such as "if all Negroes have black skin and some Americans are Negroes, then some Americans have black skin," is called a *logically true* statement.

Teachers of elementary logic explain to their students that one of the most frequent sources of fallacious reasoning is illicit conversion: from all A are B it does not follow that all B are A. Although philosophers are supposed to know elementary logic, they too sometimes commit illicit conversions. Passing from "all tautologies are formal truths, and hence logical truths," to "All logical truths are tautologies" is one illustration. Another instance of illicit conversion is the argument leading from the valid premise "all logical truths are true by sole virtue of the meanings of their constituent terms (in particular of the logical constants)" to the thesis that all statements that are true just by virtue of the meanings of the terms (hence, that do not require empirical verification and that cannot be empirically falsified) are logical truths. Obviously, "All bachelors are unmarried" is true by virtue of the meaning of "Bachelor," but since the word "bachelor" does not belong to the vocabulary of logic, the statement is not logically true. Now, this counterinstance is relatively trivial, since with the help of the definition "A bachelor is an unmarried man" (which fairly accurately expresses the meaning of "bachelor" in English) the above statement is translatable into a logically true statement: All unmarried men are unmarried. Such statements, which are translatable into logically true statements with the help of definitions that express the ordinary meanings of the defined terms, we call *strictly analytic.*

But not all statements that are commonly accepted as necessary, or a priori, truths, are strictly analytic. For example: No event precedes itself. That this is not a logical truth is evident from the fact that the verb "to precede" does not belong to the vocabulary of logic—it designates something we find in the world, a temporal relation—and yet it occurs essentially in the statement, i.e., you cannot substitute in the universal statement "For any event x, x does not precede x" any other grammatically admissible expression for "precede" without changing the truth-value of the statement. For example, if we substitute "occur at the same place as" we obtain a plain falsehood. In other words, the statement has the form: For any x, not-(xRx), and since some statements of that form are false, the statement in question is not a formal, or logical, truth. Now, it yet might be strictly analytic. It would be strictly analytic if it were possible to analyze the familiar relation of temporal precedence in such a way that the statement could be translated into a logically true statement—in somewhat the way in which "All uncles have siblings" can be revealed as analytic by the definition "An uncle is a human male who has a sibling who is a parent. "But precedence seems to be a simple relation that does not admit of further analysis. And if so, we have here a *synthetic* statement that is necessarily true (a priori). It has empirical content, if you wish, in the sense that it is about an empirically given relation—unlike logical truths, which do not contain descriptive terms essentially, and in that sense are not "about" the world of experience. But it is not an empirical statement, because an empirical statement, as we use this term, is a statement whose truth or falsehood depends on facts of experience. To be sure, a being who never experienced temporal succession could not possibly understand the meaning of such words as "before," "earlier," "to precede." It does not follow that the assertion we make about this nonlogical relation when we say that it is irreflexive and asymmetrical (and, for that matter, transitive) is subject to the test of experience.

B. TAUTOLOGIES AND LINGUISTIC CONVENTIONS

We have seen that the claim of logical positivism, which derives from Wittgenstein, that systems of logic are systems of tautologies, must be taken with at least one grain of salt. But let us assume, for the sake of argument, that all the laws of logic, including those of the so-called theory of quantification, are in some way reducible to tautologies, as was believed by Wittgenstein. Why did this seem to have great philosophical significance to the logical positivists, as well as to some of their critics? Because it was believed that a tautology owes its *necessity* to the force of linguistic conventions, and that therefore such a reduction would *explain* logical necessity without any metaphysical assumptions. Consider again the prototype of tautology, "*p* or not-*p*," which corresponds to the law of the excluded middle: For any proposition *p*, either *p* or the negation of *p* is true. That any statement of this form must be true follows from the definitions of "or" and "not," given in the form of statements of the truth-conditions of disjunctions and negations. Similarly, the principle of deductive inference, that whatever proposition is implied by true propositions is itself true, would seem to owe its validity to the very rule governing the use of "implies": to say that *p* implies *q* though *p* is true and *q* false, is just as self-contradictory as to say that *X* is a bachelor and married at the same time. If so, it looks as though the compulsion we feel to assent to these laws of logic is simply the ingrained habit of abiding by the linguistic conventions we were educated to conform to when we were taught the language. But linguistic conventions, after all, *may* be changed. Therefore, say the logical conventionalists, systems of logic may be changed; there is no absolute logical necessity; the logical necessity of a proposition is entirely relative to linguistic conventions, which it is possible to change.

The test of tautology by means of truth tables consists in computing the truth-values of the statement-form in question corresponding to all possible combinations of truth-values of the elementary statements. If and only if the statement-form comes out true in all cases, then it (or its substitution instances) is a tautology. But the outcome of the computation depends, of course, on the definitions of the connectives, such as "or," "and," "if, then." Thus, having laid down for "or," "and," "if, then" the truth-conditions tabulated in Tables 6.1, 6.2 and 6.3, we find in Table 6.4 that "If [p and (if p, then q)], then q" is a tautology. but suppose

Table 6.1

p	q	p or q
T	T	T
T	F	T
F	T	T
F	F	F

Table 6.2

p	q	p and q
T	T	T
T	F	F
F	T	F
F	F	F

Table 6.3*

p	q	If p, then q
T	T	T
T	F	F
F	T	T
F	F	T

* This table defines the so-called material, or truth-functional, meaning of "if, then." Its causal meaning is discussed in Chapters 15 and 16.

Table 6.4

p	q	p and (if p, then q)	If [p and (if p, then q)], then q
T	T	T	T
T	F	F	T
F	T	F	T
F	F	F	T

we defined "If p, then q" as a compound statement that is true if p is false and q is true, and false in all other cases. On the basis of this definition, "If [p, and (if p, then q)], then q" would not express a tautology, as shown by Table 6.5. More obviously still, if we defined "not" as

Table 6.5

p	q	If p, then q	p and (if p, then q)	If [p and (if p, then q)], then q
T	T	F	F	T
T	F	F	F	F
F	T	T	F	T
F	F	F	F	F

signifying a contrary, not the contradictory, of the proposition on which it operates, the law of the excluded middle would cease to be a tautology: since contrary propositions (such as "All alcoholics are unhappy" and "No alcoholics are unhappy") may both be false, "p" and "not-p" may now both be false, in which case "p or not-p" would likewise be false. And so on, for any law of logic that might be cited.

If by saying that no law of logic has *absolute* validity we mean that whether or not a given formula or sentence expresses a law of logic (in either the narrower sense, viz. truth-functional tautology, or the broader sense of "formal truth") depends on the interpretation of the logical constants, the claim is undoubtedly correct. But once it is clearly understood that the truth or falsehood of *any* sentence depends on its interpretation, such a "relativism" appears to be quite innocuous. At any rate, in this light the controversy between the conventionalist and the rationalist regarding the necessity of the laws of logic appears rather futile. What one ascribes truth to, be it formal or empirical truth, is never a bare sentence (string of marks, or sequence of noises), but a statement that is made by means of a given sentence, and what that statement is depends on the *meanings* that are assigned to the constituent symbols. Clearly the truth of a statement I am making by the use of a sentence p cannot be converted into falsehood by putting upon some symbol contained in p an interpretation different from the one I intended. And this is the case whether the statement be necessary or contingent. What I mean by saying "There are no squares that are not equilateral" is necessarily true and will remain so even if the word "square" should come to be used in the sense in which "triangle" is used at present. If at such a later time, at which we are supposing the relevant linguistic conventions to be different, the same words were used in accordance with what were then the linguistic conventions, they would be used to make a false statement. But that does not mean that the statement I am *now* making by means of that sentence would have been falsified.

It is hard to believe that the conventionalist interpretation of the laws of logic, which has been advocated by acute, sophisticated philosophers, amounts to just a gross failure to distinguish between a bare sentence (a certain kind of sequence of linguistic signs) and an assertion made by means of a sentence. Some conventionalists have meant to say, indeed have said explicitly, that the rationalists err in regarding the traditional laws of logic as necessary truths apprehended by reason, because they are "laws" in a prescriptive rather than a descriptive sense. When we speak of the laws of nature, such as the law of freely falling bodies, the law of gravitation, the laws of chemistry, we mean universal statements that *describe* the world, the course of nature as it happens to be. Now, the laws of logic do not describe any contingent features of the world that can be conceived to be different. They do not even describe mental phenomena, e.g., men's habits of drawing such and such conclusions from such and such premises. For if we find a man reasoning fallaciously, i.e., inferring from propositions assumed to be true a proposition that just does not follow from them, we do not say that the relevant law of logic has been refuted. We are prepared to describe conceivable observations that would refute certain presumed laws of nature, including laws of mental association, but it would be even absurd to suppose that any observations, whether of physical or of psychological facts, might ever refute a law such as "If a thing has either property P or property

Q, and it does not have P, then it has Q." According to the conventionalist's diagnosis of rationalism, the rationalist has been led to postulate a mysterious realm of necessary truths apprehended by reason because, while realizing that the valid sentences of logic do not describe empirical facts, he makes the mistaken assumption that they do describe facts of some kind. But, says the conventionalist, they are not descriptive sentences at all, they are *rules*. In particular, they are rules for the use of logical constants. Naturally, a rule cannot be refuted by any facts, because it does not make sense to speak of "refuting" a rule; a rule can only be violated.

In order to understand this conception of laws of logic as linguistic rules, we should reflect on the method of specifying the meanings of logical constants, i.e., such expressions as "and," "or," "not," "if, then," "all," which are involved in scientific discourse about any subject-matter. The validity of a statement of logic depends only on the meanings of logical constants, but how are the latter to be specified? Explicit definition is not possible. Some logical constants, on the other hand, can be contextually defined in terms of others. Examples:

all things have property P = *not-*(*some* things do *not* have P)
$$p \text{ and } q = \text{not-}(\text{not-}p \text{ or not-}q)$$
$$p \text{ or } q = \text{if not-}p, \text{ then } q$$

Let us assume that in our logical system the logical constants here used to define contextually "all," "and," and "or," viz. "some," "not," and "if, then," occur as primitives. How are we to explain their meanings, their rules of usage? Superficially it seems that this can easily be done (at least for "not" and "if, then") by means of truth tables which stipulate the conditions under which statements of the forms "not-*p*" and "if *p*, then *q*" are true. The truth table for "not" is very simple:

p	not-p
T	F
F	T

Here "T" means true, and "F" false, and the table is to be read from left to right as follows: if *p* is true, then not-*p* is false, and if *p* is false, then not-*p* is true. But as a definition this is circular if "*p* is false" is in turn defined as "*p* is not true." More obviously still, it would be circular to attempt to explain the meaning of "if, then" by means of a truth table. Quite apart from the consideration that the truth of a conditional statement (i.e., statement of the form "If *p*, then *q*") does not just depend on the truth-values of the component statements, but rather on their meanings [technically this is expressed by saying that "if, then" is, in most uses, not a truth-functional connective (cf. Chapter 15)], it is clear that we use "if, then" in interpreting any truth table. For a truth table says that a given kind of compound statement, such as conjunction, disjunction, negation, is true *if* the combinations of truth-values of the component statements are such and such. We must have recourse, then, to another method of formulating the rules of use of the primitive logical constants. The method in question differs fundamentally from *definition* in the usual sense, i.e., formulation of rules of substitution or translation by virtue of which the defined expression is theoretically eliminable. It is the method of *postulates*.

Thus we might explain "if, then" by stipulating that all statements of the following forms are to be true (note that this is different from *asserting* that all such statements *are* true, for according to ordinary usage of "assert," "I assert that p is true" makes sense only if it makes sense to doubt whether p is true, but such doubt is senseless if "p" just serves to specify, partially, the meanings of constituent terms):[1] if (if p, then q), then, if (if q, then r), then (if p, then r); if p, then, if (if p, then q), then q. Then we might add postulates introducing "not" along with "if, then": if p, then not-(not-p); if not-q, then, if (if p, then q), then not-p; if p, then (if not-p, then q). We have postulated, then, that all statements derivable from these schemas by substituting statements for the statement variables (in such a way that the same statement replaces the same variable within a given schema, though the same statement may be substituted for different variables) are to be true. The schemas correspond to the following principles of logic: the principle of the hypothetical syllogism (corresponding to *barbara* in the theory of categorical syllogisms); a statement implied by a true statement is true (*modus ponens*); the principle of noncontradiction; a statement that implies a false statement is false (*modus tollens*); from a contradiction any proposition follows.

The conventionalist, now, maintains that it is senseless to speak, in the manner of rationalists, of insight into the necessary truth of such principles, because they are nothing but conventional assignments of meanings to the logical constants "if, then" and "not." It does not make sense to ask how we know, indeed know for certain, that every substitution instance of these schemas is true, because no cognitive claim is involved in stipulations of rules of usage. You can say, "I do not wish to use 'if, then' in such a way that every substitution instance of this schema is

1. Readers who are untrained in formal logic will find it easier to grasp the sense of these postulates if they occasionally replace "if p, then q" by "p implies q"—though this is technically inaccurate inasmuch as grammar requires "p" and "q" to be quoted when they are connected by "implies." The first postulate, for example, is then recognizable as the principle of the hypothetical syllogism in the form: if "p" implies "q," then, if "q" implies "r," then "p" implies "r."

true," but it would be nonsense to say, "I do not believe that all substitution instances of this schema are true." In the same way, if one were to stipulate, " 'Green' is to be used to designate the color of these objects," he might be opposed by one who, for whatever reason, did not wish to use the word "green" that way. But one cannot sensibly counter: "Before accepting your rule I want to make sure that those objects really are green."

To be sure, if the expression for which a rule of usage is laid down already has a prior use, one can sensibly ask whether the rule conforms to that prior use. In the case of our logical schemata, it is clear that if any logician were to "postulate" them (in the explained sense), he would be guided by his familiarity with the already existing rules of usage of the logical constants. He would not, for example, postulate that all substitution instances of "If q, then (if p, then q), then p" are to be true, because if he did, he would require us to use "if, then" differently from the way it is in fact used. In other words, according to the actual use of "if, then" in English not all substitution instances of this schema are true. Whether or not the stipulations accord with actual linguistic usage is a question of empirical fact. But what the conventionalist is out to refute is the view that our knowledge of logical truths amounts to a priori knowledge of necessary propositions. Our knowledge that, say, the logical constants "if, then" and "not" are so used by English-speaking people that all substitution instances of, say, "If p, then not-(not-p)" are true, is just plain empirical knowledge. It is, of course, conceivable that a man might deny a statement of that form, but in that case we would just have to conclude that his speech habits are different: perhaps he uses "if, then" the way "either-or" is ordinarily used, for example. But to tell him "You cannot deny it, *because it is necessarily true*" is, according to the conventionalist, like saying "You must speak the way we speak, because you have to speak that way."

Yet, the conventionalist cannot get around the admission that there is such a thing as a priori knowledge of logical truths, which is in no intelligible sense reducible to stipulation of, or acquaintance with, linguistic rules. In the first place, it is a meaningful question to ask whether it is possible, say, to define "if, then" on the basis of "not" and "or" in such a way that (*a*) the definition accords approximately with ordinary usage, (*b*) our postulates are transformed into truth-functional tautologies if "not" and "or" are defined as truth-functional connectives in the usual way. The definition that fulfills these requirements is: If p, then q = not-p or q. We know, for example, on the basis of truth-table analysis, that any statement of the form "not-p or not-(not-p or q) or q" (the transform into primitive notation of "if p, then, if (if p, then q), then q") is a tautology. Surely it does not make sense to say *it is a linguistic rule* that in a language containing the mentioned rules for the use of "not" and "or" any statement of the above form is a tautology. Indeed, this metastatement is a necessary statement, not a contingent statement about linguistic usage. That is, it is inconceivable that, while the rules for the use of "not" and "or" remain the same, a statement of the above form should fail to be a tautology.

Secondly, logicians usually lay down their postulates, not in order to prescribe a usage for logical constants or to describe how they are in fact used, but in order to construct a system, and this means that they intend to deduce a lot of theorems from the postulates. These deductions are, of course, guided by rules of deduction. Two of the most important rules of deduction (whether or not they be absolutely indispensable) are the rule of substitution and the rule of detachment (or "modus ponens"). The rule of substitution says with reference to our postulates: any formula obtainable from a postulate by substituting for a statement variable another statement variable or a truth-function of a statement variable, the same substitution being made for each occurrence of a given variable, is a theorem (and any formula derivable from a theorem in the same manner is also a theorem). The rule of detachment says: if A and (if A, then B) are postulates or theorems, then B is a theorem (here A and B are syntactic variables ranging over formulae of the system). Without raising the question of the justification of these rules of deductive proof, we wish to insist on the following simple point: a metastatement to the effect that such and such a formula is a theorem in the system that is characterized by such and such postulates and such and such rules of deduction is not a "rule" of any kind. It is, if true, *necessarily true*. It is a fact that cannot be altered by changing rules, that in a deductive system with specified formation rules, postulates, and rules of deduction, such and such a formula is a theorem whose proof involves such and such a minimal number of elementary steps. That the discovery of such "facts" by mathematicians and logicians involves the manipulation of symbols in accordance with rules is entirely consistent with its being an intellectual discovery—even if it is a proposition about symbols and not about intangible and invisible abstract entities. Even if algebra were construed as a science whose subject-matter consists of symbols, not of abstract entities such as numbers, it would be a meaningful question whether, say, Fermat's "last theorem" (for $n > 2$, there are no solutions for the equation: $x^n + y^n = z^n$) is really a theorem in such and such a system of algebra. Mathematicians have not found the answer yet, but most of them regard it as a serious and meaningful question. And the proposition in question is either necessary or impossible; it is not an empirical proposition. It would be silly to say that the question here is whether such and such rules ought to be adopted. The question is not like the question whether there is a number that satisfies the equation "$x^2 = 2$"; it is rather like the question whether there is a rational number that satisfies that equation. It was, indeed, no discovery that there is an irrational number that satisfies it. This was a matter of decision, of deciding to broaden, by fiat, the extension of the term "number," whatever the reasons motivating the decision may have been. But Euclid did not *stipulate* that the equation has no rational solution; he *discovered* it by a well-known indirect proof.

We conclude that though logical conventionalists have rendered a valuable service in focusing attention on the role played by linguistic conventions in the acquisition of logical and mathematical knowledge, they have not shown that there is no such thing as a priori knowledge of necessary propositions and that the necessity of the laws of logic "depends" in some intelligible sense on linguistic conventions. In particular, to say of a certain complicated statement that it is a tautology, is not to deny that it is necessarily true nor that it makes sense to speak of "discovering" its truth; it is rather to explicate what the necessity and its discovery consist in. The thesis of Whitehead and Russell that all mathematical propositions are tautologies is still acutely controversial; and the thesis that all necessary propositions are tautologies is certainly false. But whether it be true or false has no bearing whatever on the question whether there is such a thing as purely intellectual discovery of necessary truths. Of course there is such discovery. And the discovery by means of some mechanical decision procedure (such as the use of "truth tables") that a certain complicated form of deductive argument is valid because the corresponding implication is a tautology is not the least useful and respectable among such intellectual discoveries.

Selected Readings

Carnap, R., *Meaning and Necessity* (Chicago, 1956).

———, "The Old and the New Logic," in A. J. Ayer (ed.), *Logical Positivism* (New York, 1959).

Ewing, A. C., "The Linguistic Theory of A Priori Propositions," *Aristotelian Society Proceedings*, 1940.

Goodman, N., "On Likeness of Meaning," *Analysis*, 1949–50. [Reprinted in M. Macdonald (ed.), *Philosophy and Analysis* (Oxford, 1954); and in a revised version in L. Linsky (ed.), *Semantics and the Philosophy of Language* (Urbana, Ill., 1952).]

Grice, H. P., and P. F. Strawson, "In Defense of a Dogma," *Philosophical Review*, 1956.

Hahn, H., "Logic, Mathematics, and Knowledge of Nature," in A. J. Ayer (ed.), *Logical Positivism* (New York, 1959).

Hardie, C. D., "The Necessity of A Priori Propositions," *Aristotelian Society Proceedings*, 1937.

Kneale, W., "Are Necessary Truths True by Convention?," *Aristotelian Society Proceedings*, supp., 1947.

———, "The Truths of Logic," *Aristotelian Society Proceedings*, 1945–46.

Lewis, C. I., *An Analysis of Knowledge and Valuation* (La Salle, Ill., 1946), chap. 5.

Malcolm, N., "Are Necessary Propositions Really Verbal?," *Mind*, 1940.

———, "The Nature of Entailment," *Mind*, 1940.

Mises, R. von, *Positivism, a Study in Human Understanding* (Cambridge, Mass., 1951).

Nagel, E., "Some Theses in the Philosophy of Logic," *Philosophy of Science*, 1938.

———, "Logic without Ontology," in H. Feigl and W. Sellars (eds.), *Readings in Philosophical Analysis* (New York, 1949); and in E. Nagel, *Logic without Metaphysics* (New York, 1957).

Pap, A., *Semantics and Necessary Truth* (New Haven, Conn., 1958), ch. 5–8.

Quine, W. V., "Truth by Convention," in H. Feigl and W. Sellars (eds.), *Readings in Philosophical Analysis* (New York, 1949).

———, "Two Dogmas of Empiricism," in W. V. Quine, *From a Logical Point of View* (Cambridge, 1953).

Waismann, F., "Analytic-Synthetic, I–VI," *Analysis*, 1949–53.

White, M. G., "The Analytic and the Synthetic: An Untenable Dualism," in S. Hook (ed.), *John Dewey: Philosopher of Science and Freedom* (New York, 1950). [Reprinted in L. Linsky (ed.), *Semantics and the Philosophy of Language* (Urbana, Ill., 1952).]

Wittgenstein, L., *Tractatus Logico-Philosophicus* (London, 1922).

CHAPTER 7

Geometry

A. THE QUESTION OF SYNTHETIC A PRIORI KNOWLEDGE ABOUT SPACE

As in the case of the analysis of arithmetical propositions, it will help our understanding of modern discussions about the nature of geometry if we first turn to Kant and take a close look at his problem. In his time Euclidean geometry, whose propositions were presupposed without question in Newtonian mechanics, stood without alternatives. Its axioms still enjoyed the reputation of being self-evident, necessary propositions. According to this view, if you understand a statement such as "For any two points there is one and only one straight line that contains both" you will assent to it without waiting for empirical confirmation. It is a universal statement a refutation of which is inconceivable, not just for you and me but for any mind endowed with what Kant called the faculty of "pure spatial intuition" (here "pure" refers to imagination as contrasted with sense perception). In this sense our knowledge of the axiom is a priori. What puzzled Kant was not the (assumed) fact that we know a good many universal propositions a priori. What he felt called for a metaphysical explanation was that the propositions thus known a priori were, as he believed, *synthetic*. That I do not need to examine bodies in order to verify that all bodies are extended, is obvious, for I need only analyze my *concept* of a body (i.e., what I mean by "body") in order to discover that a body is extended. As Kant said, such a proposition is analytic. But how can I be sure that all *A* and *B* in advance of having examined many *A*'s if the predicate *B* cannot be simply analyzed out of the subject *A?*

[107]

We shall not be concerned with Kant's metaphysical answer to his question, "How are synthetic a priori judgments about space possible?" This very question presupposes an affirmative answer to the prior question whether we do have a priori knowledge of synthetic propositions about space. Logical empiricism emphatically denies this. A leading theme in a popular exposition of logical empiricism by a reputable philosopher of science (Hans Reichenbach, *The Rise of Scientific Philosophy*) is that "scientific philosophy" has risen to its present height through a "dissolution of the (Kantian) synthetic a priori": that is, as we have reported already, logical empiricists deny that we can know any propositions a priori except analytic propositions and claim that analytic propositions convey no information "about the world" at all. As we have pointed out already, the phrase "about the world" has a most uncertain significance; hence it had best be avoided in an exact discussion. We shall accordingly restrict ourselves to the question whether given statements are analytic or synthetic a priori or empirical, without asking whether they "convey information about the world."

Among the axioms required for a strictly formal proof of the theorems of Euclidean geometry[1] are several concerning the properties of a Euclidean straight line:

1. For any two points A and B there is one and only one straight line that contains both A and B.

2. Given any three points on a given straight line, one and only one of them is between the other two. That is, if we call the three points A, B, C, then either A is between B and C, or B is between A and C, or C is between A and B; and if A is between B and C, then it is not the case that B is between A and C, nor that C is between A and B, and so on.

3. If A and B are on a straight line S, then there is another point C on S such that B is between A and C. (This formulation is equivalent to Euclid's postulate that a straight line can be prolonged indefinitely, except that "straight line" here denotes *infinite* one-dimensional continua of points, so that it makes no sense to speak of "prolonging" a straight line.)

No doubt these axioms explicate what we *mean* by "straight line"; one is, therefore, inclined to regard them as analytic propositions. However, we can formulate a synthetic proposition by considering that the same kind of line (using "line" in the generic sense of continuous, unlimited, one-dimensional manifold of points) satisfies each of these three axioms: any line that is uniquely determined by two points is such that of any three points on it, one and only one is between the other two, and such that for any two points A and B on it there is another point C on it such that B is between A and C. The term "straight line" is not

1. We follow here Hilbert's axiomatization of Euclidean geometry.

contained in this formulation. A philosopher who is eager to refute Kant's theory of synthetic a priori judgments about intuited space ("*Anschauungsraum*"), is likely to argue that the above axioms are analytic because they just analyze our conception of a (Euclidean) straight line in terms of the primitive concepts "point," "containing," and "between." But a synthetic and apparently necessary proposition can be formulated without employing the term "straight line" since Axiom 1 expresses a necessary and sufficient condition for the straightness of a line. On the basis of Axiom 1 we could explicitly define "x is a straight line" as follows: For any two points A and B that lie on x, there is no line y that is distinct from x, is of the same geometrical kind as x (i.e., satisfies the same axioms as x), and is such that A and B also lie on y. Our synthetic proposition, then, asserts that any line that has this property (which is a necessary and sufficient condition for straightness) *also* has the properties expressed by Axioms 2 and 3.

The same logical point can be made with respect to the concept of a Euclidean plane. This concept is introduced, in Hilbert's formulation of Euclidean geometry, by the following axioms:

4. Any three points that do not lie on one and the same straight line uniquely determine a plane.

5. If two given points, A and B, of a given straight line S lie in a given plane P, then every point of S lies in P.

6. If two planes have at least one point in common, then they have at least two points in common (in fact, they then have one straight line in common, the straight line in which they "cut" each other).

Here again it is tempting to say that the axioms just explicate our intuitive concept of a plane surface. If, for example, three points that are not collinear could be fitted into more than one two-dimensional continuum of points, the latter, by definition, would not be Euclidean planes (surfaces whose curvature is everywhere zero). But the same strategy is open to the Kantian to defend himself against the logical empiricist's challenge. Let us assume that "straight line" has been defined by Axiom 1, which does not mention planes; and let us use "point" and the relational term "lying on" (or its converse, "containing") again as primitives. Then the following proposition is synthetic (in the broader sense that is correlative to the narrowest sense of "analytic"): Any two-dimensional unlimited continua of points that satisfy one of the Axioms 4–6 satisfy the others as well.

One of the major aims of the great German mathematician Hilbert was to reconstruct Euclidean geometry in such a way that the proofs of its theorems would become strictly formal. This formulation required the explicit listing, as axioms, of many intuitively evident propositions which Euclid had tacitly assumed in his proofs. Now, if the proof of a theorem is strictly formal, then the proposition that *if* all the axioms are true, then the theorem is true, is indeed analytic. But the theorem itself has not thereby been shown to be analytic, and the very fact that a given axiom is *required* for the proof of a synthetic theorem shows that it is itself synthetic. (If a synthetic proposition follows from a set of premises some of which are analytic, it still follows from the set after elimination of the analytic members.) One of those synthetic and intuitively evident axioms that was "suppressed" by Euclid and made explicit by Hilbert is the following: Let A, B, C, be three noncollinear points and S a straight line in the plane determined by A, B, C such that none of these points is on S; then, if S intersects the segment AB, it also intersects either BC or AC.

Again, in order to prove specifically metrical propositions of Euclidean geometry, such as "The base angles of any isosceles triangle are equal," the notion of congruence—as asserted to hold between lines, angles, and closed figures—must be introduced as a new primitive by a special group of axioms, called by Hilbert "axioms of congruence." One of these self-evident axioms reads: If two segments are each congruent to a third, then they are congruent to each other. (It could in turn be proved on the basis of two axioms asserting that congruence is a transitive and a symmetrical relation.) This proposition is not logically true, for "congruent" is a nonlogical constant which occurs essentially; nor is it strictly analytic, for "congruent" is a primitive term and as such ineliminable. Another congruence axiom, explicitly listed in Euclid, says that all right angles are congruent. This appears to be analytic if we think of the concept "right angle" as metrically defined, i.e., an angle of 90 degrees. But a non-metrical definition can be given: an angle such that it is possible to make one arm of it coincide with one arm of a distinct but congruent angle in such a way that the noncoincident arms form a straight line. And that any two angles of this kind are congruent is not a logical truth, nor is it strictly analytic. To suppose that it would be established as analytic once one succeeded in formally deducing it from suitably chosen geometrical axioms containing the same primitive concepts would be to commit the very fallacy warned against above.

Logical empiricists would admit that in the restricted sense of "analytic" such geometrical axioms are not analytic. Since they are, however, dead set against the Kantian theory of synthetic a priori judgments about space, they have to choose among the following three alternatives:

1. The axioms in question are not propositions at all, but propositional functions; that is, the primitive terms are free variables in a formal calculus, susceptible of various interpretations, hence it does not even make sense to ask how the truth of the axioms is known.

2. The axioms are generalizations about physical space, though they involve idealized concepts, in much the same way as the laws of me-

chanics involve such idealized concepts as perfectly elastic particles and frictionless motions. It is not inconceivable that experience should induce a scientist to abandon such an axiom, "self-evident" though it may seem. Consider, for example, our axiom that all right angles are congruent, "right angle" being defined nonmetrically as above. This very notion of "congruence" suggests rigid rods that are movable in space. Thus we might empirically verify that vertical angles are congruent[2] by rotating an arm of one angle around the fixed vertical point until it coincides with the corresponding arm of the other angle. Suppose, then, that the congruence of angle B with angle A has been verified by superposition, and that A is subsequently shown to be a right angle in terms of our operational definition. Then an angle C is juxtaposed to A in such a way that one arm of it coincides with one arm of A, with the result that its other arm now lies in the same direction as the other arm of A. Accordingly we pronounce C a right angle. But to our surprise we find that C cannot, through a 180-degree rotation around the coincident arm, be superimposed upon A. Would not such an observation disconfirm the "self-evident" proposition that all right angles are equal? True, we might say that C did not remain congruent to itself while it was rotated and thus "save" the axiom. But the logical empiricist would be right in retorting that this possibility of saving an apparently disconfirmed hypothesis by modifying other relevant assumptions (in this case the assumption of "rigidity") does not establish that the hypothesis is more than a "hypothesis"; that is to say, it does not establish that the hypothesis is an a priori truth.

3. The primitive terms "straight line," "congruence," "between," "plane," and so on have geometrical meanings; in other words, the axiomatic system is geometrically interpreted. But the axioms, although not analytic in our restricted sense, are nevertheless *implicit definitions*. The latter term was employed by Hilbert himself, who said that the primitive geometrical terms are implicitly defined by the axioms in which they occur. According to the terminology adopted by Carnap and his followers in recent years, they might be called *meaning postulates*. We recall that the process of specifying the meanings of primitive terms incompletely, by formulating postulates to be satisfied by anything that is denoted by the primitive terms, is indeed basic in deductively formulated sciences.

2. It may seem that appeal to a congruence test by superposition is avoidable, because an analytical proof can be conducted as follows: Let A and B be the vertical angles whose congruence is to be established, and A' and B' their "supplementary" angles. We then get that $A + A'$ equals a straight angle, and $B + A'$ equals a staight angle, hence $A + A'$ equals $B + A'$, hence A equals B. But this "analytical" proof still presupposes congruence axioms, viz. all straight angles (or simply, all straight lines) are congruent, and two angles that are congruent to congruent angles are themselves congruent.

Let us briefly appraise the issue between logical empiricism and the Kantian philosophy of geometry according to each of these alternatives.

1. Kant, of course, did not mean by "pure" geometry a formal calculus. Therefore it is quite impossible to refute his conviction that we have a lot of synthetic a priori knowledge about intuited space by pointing out that formal geometry does not contain any synthetic propositions.

2. The logical empiricist has a strong case against Kant if he can show that the only interpretation of Hilbert's primitives that turns the axioms into specifically geometrical propositions, i.e., propositions about spatial configurations and relations, is a physical interpretation. For it does seem presumptuous to claim that we know a priori what the behavior and properties of rigid rods, light rays, taut strings, and so on are like. It is, for example, doubtful whether even Kant would have claimed to know a priori that measurement of the interior angles of an astronomical triangle whose sides are marked by light rays would, if only it were absolutely accurate, yield a sum of 180 degrees. A Kantian might say that if this is not certain, it is because it is not certain that the path of a light ray is exactly straight; that it is, however, a priori certain that the light triangle have the Euclidean property *if* the light rays are exactly straight. But such a defense of Kant provides the logical empiricist with a golden opportunity to make his point that only analytic propositions can be known a priori: what do you mean by "exactly straight"? Presumably you mean that the line satisfies the axioms of Euclidean geometry, e.g., that only one straight line can pass through a given pair of points. And since the Euclidean theorem is an analytic consequence of the Euclidean axioms, the proposition you claim to know a priori is then analytic, not synthetic. That is, what you know a priori is the analytic proposition that if a given physical interpretation satisfies the axioms of a formal geometry, it also satisfies its theorems.

The Kantian theory, therefore, is far more plausible if the axioms are taken to refer, not to properties of physical space, but to the spatial intuitions we have acquired in the course of our physical lives. One can consistently be an empiricist in the sense of holding that our geometrical concepts have an empirical origin and admit that there are propositions that are both synthetic and necessary. Similarly, the concepts "shade of a color" and "darker" undoubtedly have their origin in visual experience, but this need not prevent us from declaring the following proposition as both synthetic and a priori: If shade x is darker than shade y and y is darker than shade z, then x is darker than z. Suppose, then, that we construe the statement "Two straight segments[3] such that neither is a

---

3. "Straight segment" here is deliberately substituted for "straight *line*" because a line in the sense of geometry is unlimited and hence not intuitable.

proper part of the other and there is no segment that is a proper part of both either do not intersect at all or else intersect just once" as referring, not to anything physical, but to intuited, visual space. Since, as we have seen, there are other properties that are distinctive of straight segments besides the property expressed by this very statement, it can be construed as synthetic; and it would be difficult to tell just what "self-evident" could mean if it were denied that it is self-evident. The remark that we might never have acquired the notion of Euclidean straightness had we lived in a non-Euclidean world is irrelevant because to claim that a proposition is self-evident is not to deny that its constituent concepts may have an empirical origin. On the other hand, the logical empiricist is right in saying that if the geometrical terms are physically interpreted, there results a hypothesis subject to empirical test. As a matter of fact, if we could produce taut strings of such gigantic length as to equal about half the circumference of the globe, and we knotted two such strings together at the north pole, then stretched them out in divergent directions, we would find them meeting again at the south pole.

3. To say that a proposition is analytic because it is a "meaning postulate" or a formal consequence of meaning postulates, however, is to win a merely verbal victory over the Kantian. For a meaning postulate is nothing else than a statement that is "true by virtue of the meanings of its terms," which is the same as a statement expressing an a priori, or self-evident, truth. Logical empiricists tend to say that such meaning postulates, such as "If x is congruent to y and y congruent to z, then x is congruent to z" are linguistic rules, or semantic rules—and that it is accordingly inappropriate to speak of intuitive knowledge here. It is true that one would normally take a person's assent to such a postulate as a criterion of his having understood the intended meaning of the primitive term contained in it. But this does not mean that philosophers who speak here of an intuitively evident, necessary truth are wrong. For traditionally self-evident truths have been characterized precisely as propositions to which all rational beings assent as soon as they *understand them*. One wonders, therefore, whether the issue of meaning postulates versus synthetic self-evident propositions is a genuine one.

B. NON-EUCLIDEAN GEOMETRY AND THE QUESTION OF CONSISTENCY

It is widely believed that the rationalist view of the absolute necessity, or "self-evidence," of the axioms of Euclidean geometry has been decisively refuted by the development, during the nineteenth century, *non-Euclidian*

of consistent non-Euclidean geometries. This belief, however, is completely unfounded. In fact, the existence of consistent formal systems of non-Euclidean geometry has no bearing whatever on either the question whether the axioms of *interpreted* Euclidean geometry are necessary propositions or—as maintained by John Stuart Mill—empirical generalizations, or the question whether they are analytic or synthetic. A non-Euclidean geometry is a geometry based on the replacement of Euclid's axiom of parallels by an axiom formally incompatible with it. The famous axiom of parallels asserts that given a straight line S in a plane P, and a point Q in P but not on S, there is one and only one straight line in P and containing Q that is parallel to S, i.e., does not intersect S. The proof of the theorem that the interior angles of a triangle add up to 180 degrees depends essentially on this axiom. For centuries mathematicians tried, without success, to deduce this axiom from the other axioms of Euclidean geometry. In time, it was suspected to be logically independent of the latter; i.e., by replacing it with an axiom incompatible with it one would obtain a consistent set of axioms, a set from which no contradiction would be deducible. One such alternative asserts the existence of *two* parallel straight lines through Q in P (geometry of Bolyai-Lobatchefski);[4] another asserts that there is no parallel straight line through Q in P (geometry of Riemann). Some laymen try desperately to visualize two parallels through one and the same point in a given plane to one and the same straight line in that plane, and as they do not succeed they find non-Euclidean geometry wholly unintelligible. But it is imperative to distinguish between formal and interpreted geometry. What the mathematicians as such ask the layman to believe is not that a proposition incompatible with the parallel axiom of interpreted Euclidean geometry may be true, but only that a non-Euclidean system is consistent. As far as the problems of formal geometry are concerned, the geometrical primitives "straight line," "plane," and so on might as well be replaced by meaningless variables; thus this would effectively discourage attempts at visualizing the situation described by its axioms, for it would then be clear that they do not describe any situation at all.

Let A_1, A_2,..., A_n represent the axioms of a formalized Euclidean geometry (they are propositional functions, not propositions), the last corresponding to the axiom of parallels. Suppose it to have been established by mathematicians that the non-Euclidean sets corresponding to A_1, A_2, . . . , not-A_n are consistent. Now, whatever our final verdict on

4. The two parallel lines in Lobatchefski's geometry are limiting lines including between them infinitely many lines that likewise do not intersect S. This distinction between parallel and nonintersecting lines does not exist in Euclid's geometry. (For a more detailed but elementary explanation of non-Euclidean geometry, see P. Frank, *Philosophy of Science* (Englewood Cliffs, N.J.: Prentice-Hall, Inc., 1957), chap. 3.

the Kantian philosophy of geometry may have to be, such a mathematical discovery does not refute a single view of Kant's about geometry. For it only establishes that the axiom of parallels is not analytic (if it were, its negation would be self-inconsistent and hence inconsistent with any axiom) and that it is logically independent of the other Euclidean axioms. Surely, the first part of this demonstration would have been especially welcomed by Kant!

To establish the consistency of the axiomatic system, however, is not an easy task. Just because no contradictions have yet been deduced from the axioms of non-Euclidean geometry it does not follow that no contradictions will ever be deduced. An advance over such merely "inductive," inconclusive consistency proofs (called "proofs" by courtesy only) is constituted by consistency proofs by *models*. The idea underlying this method is very simple. Let $F(x, y, z), G(x, y, z), H(x, y, z)$ represent postulates, the free variables x, y, z corresponding to the primitive terms, and F, G, H representing the complex properties of ordered triples of entities that are expressed by the postulates. To illustrate, let x correspond to the primitive term "point," y to "straight line," and z to "containing" as a relation from straight lines to points. Then the axiom "For any two points there is one and only one straight line containing both points" can be considered as having the form $F(x, y, z)$, where F stands for the *constant* constituents of the postulate, for a complex logical relation between the variable constituents.[5] Now we can define the consistency of the set of postulates as meaning that there are values of x, y, z that simultaneously satisfy all the postulates. An ordered triple of entities that has this property is called a *model* of the set of postulates. For example, the primitive terms of the geometry of Riemann, in which the above axiom does not occur (but only the weaker axiom that for any two points there is a straight line containing both), may be interpreted as follows: "point" as in Euclidean geometry, "plane" as surface of a sphere, "straight line" as great arc on a sphere, and the relational primitives as in Euclidean geometry. In this interpretation it is obvious that there are pairs of points that lie on more than one straight line (polar opposites) and that any two straight lines in the same "plane" intersect. Spherical surfaces and great arcs on them, therefore, constitute a model of Riemannian two-dimensional geometry. The reader may wonder how something three-dimensional, such as spheres, can serve as a model for a two-dimensional geometry. But the difference between spherical and "flat"

5. If formalized by means of symbolic logic, the postulate looks as follows: $(x)(y)\{Px \cdot Py \cdot x \neq y \supset (\exists z)[Sy \cdot Czx \cdot Czy \cdot (u)(Su \cdot Cux \cdot Cuy \supset u = z)]\}$. Here the free predicate variables P, S, C (the first two monadic, the last dyadic) correspond to the free variables x, y, z in "$F(x, y, z)$," and F is the complex logical relation expressed by means of the logical constants: $=, \supset, \cdot, (x), (y), (\exists z), (u), \neq$.

surfaces can be described without any reference to a third dimension into which the surface is curved. Thus two-dimensional ("flat") beings inhabiting a spherical surface could find out by measurements on the surface that the latter was non-Euclidean, though they could no more imagine a third dimension into which the surface was curved than we three-dimensional beings can imagine a fourth dimension. Provided their measuring rods were rigid, i.e., remained congruent to themselves as they were moved about, they would discover that the sum of the angles of a triangle exceeds 180 degrees and exceeds it all the more the larger the triangle; and, of course, they might find that any two straight lines diverging from a common point eventually meet again.

A proof of consistency by means of physical models, however, is logically impure because it presupposes the truth of physical propositions. The fact the spherical surfaces and great arcs on them can be used to interpret a non-Euclidean geometry shows that the latter is consistent *if* the propositions of the ordinary, familiar geometry of spherical surfaces are true. But since there is no a priori proof of any empirical propositions, this kind of consistency proof does not satisfy the pure mathematician. Algebraic models are, from his point of view, preferable. And the question of consistency of ordinary geometry, both plane and solid geometry, is indeed reducible to the question of consistency of algebra because each geometrical concept can be correlated with an algebraic concept. This was first shown by Descartes, the inventor of analytic geometry, a science which enables the solution of geometrical problems by means of algebraic methods. Here is a partial dictionary for two-dimensional analytic geometry, well known to students of analytic geometry:

Point—ordered pair of real numbers (called the "coordinates" of the point)
Straight line—linear equation in two variables, of the form $ay + bx + c = 0$
Lying on (a relation whose domain consists of points and whose converse domain consists of lines)—satisfying (a relation between ordered pairs of real numbers and equations in two variables)

The equation of a given line (curve or straight line) is the equation such that if (x, y) are the coordinates of a point P, then P lies on that line if and only if (x, y) satisfy the equation. Suppose we are given two straight lines in the coordinate plane and we wish to determine their point of intersection by the method of analytic geometry. We determine their equations by finding their slopes and their intercepts with the axes (thereby we find the values of the constants in the linear equations), and then we compute by algebraic methods the common solution of the two equations, i.e., that pair of real numbers which satisfies both. Thereby we obtain the coordinates of the point of intersection.

Owing, then, to the existence of algebraic models for geometric systems, the question of the consistency of a type of geometry is reducible to the question of consistency of classical arithmetic and algebra (algebra is essentially a generalization of arithmetic, as expressed by the occurrence of number variables). There is one further step in this process of "reduction": if arithmetic and algebra are reducible to logic, in the sense of the "logicist thesis" (cf. Chapter 5, C), then the basic question of consistency is the question whether our system of logic, like the system *Principia Mathematica*, is itself consistent. If only we could restrict ourselves to the propositional calculus, the proof of consistency would be quite easy: the postulates of the propositional calculus are, in the intended interpretation, tautologies, hence necessarily true; and it can easily be proved that whatever sentence is derivable from tautologies with the help of specified rules of derivation (particularly the rules of detachment and of substitution) is itself a tautology. The question of consistency, however, becomes far more complicated for those branches of logic in which the simple, mechanical, truth-table test of logical truth is not available, and where the logician accordingly depends entirely on the method of deduction from a set of axioms whose consistency remains to be established in some other way.[6]

C. PHYSICAL GEOMETRY AND POINCARÉ'S CONVENTIONALISM

We must now address ourselves to the following question: Granted, for the sake of argument, that the formal consistency of non-Euclidean systems of geometry is established beyond doubt, are these systems empirically applicable as Euclidean geometry has proved to be in classical, Newtonian mechanics? Which geometry describes the structures of physical space? And is this a question that can be decided empirically by measurement? It does seem that once the primitive terms of formal geometry have been physically interpreted, we obtain physical propositions that are testable by measurement and whose truth or falsehood, therefore, depends upon the "real nature" of physical space, not upon any conventions. If, for example, we interpret "straight line" as denoting paths of light rays, it seems to become a question of fact whether triangles (bounded by light rays) satisfy the Euclidean theorem. Why, then, did the great Poincaré assert that the very question whether the Euclidean

6. These branches of logic are usually called "functional calculi" or "predicate calculi." For a classical discussion of consistency proofs for them, see D. Hilbert and W. Ackermann, *Principles of Mathematical Logic*, New York: Chelsea Publishing Co., 1950.

or the non-Euclidean axioms are true is nonsensical, as would be the question whether the true positions of bodies are those described by Cartesian (rectangular) coordinates or those described by polar coordinates? Poincaré further asserted that the axioms of a given geometry are mere "conventions," in particular those which are "disguised" definitions of the primitive geometrical terms. If he had in mind the axioms of a formal (uninterpreted) geometry, he was of course right in saying that they cannot meaningfully be described as true or false. But was he not plainly wrong if he referred to the axioms of a physically interpreted geometry?

Now, here as elsewhere we are faced with a dispute that can be adjudicated by locating the truth somewhere in the middle. Poincaré was right inasmuch as the decision of the question whether or not the metrical properties of space are Euclidean still depends on conventions after the primitives have been physically interpreted. In the first place, the answer to the above question depends on whether or not one postulates "universal forces" (Reichenbach's term) that can bend light rays. If we find that the sum of the angles of our astronomical triangle exceeds 180 degrees (beyond the excess that could be explained as error of measurement), we do not have to pronounce the theorem of physical Euclidean geometry refuted; we might say that the light rays were deformed by gravitational forces[7] and that space "itself," abstracted from gravitating matter, is Euclidean. This procedure, nevertheless, is hard to reconcile with the spirit of empiricism. For it would be impossible to verify empirically that the non-Euclidean character of our triangle is caused by the deforming agency of gravity. Suppose we set out to verify by measurement that the circumference of a flat disk has the Euclidean value $2\pi r$. If there is a source of heat at the center of the disk, the temperature will decrease from center to circumference according to the inverse square law of heat radiation. Accordingly, if our measuring rod is made of material that conducts heat and therefore expands and contracts as it moves about in the thermal field, the ratio of the measured circumference to the measured radius will turn out to differ from $2\pi r$. For the rod will remain congruent to itself while it moves around the circumference (where all points have the same temperature), but expand as it is transported radially toward the center. Now, nobody would say that such measurements refute Euclidean geometry, because the distorting force here is a "differential" force (Reichenbach's term): there are materials on which it does not act at all (heat insulators), and its effect on different materials varies with their intrinsic properties (coefficients

7. That light rays passing through an intense gravitational field should bend, is deducible from the general theory of relativity. This effect was predicted by Einstein and verified during a solar eclipse.

of thermal expansion). Applying the "method of difference," we can either remove the source of heat or conduct our measurements with a rod made of nonconducting material, and thus determine whether the geometrical properties of the disk are really Euclidean. But universal forces, such as gravitation, cannot be screened off—we cannot destroy matter and then measure angles of our light triangle all over again. The hypothesis, therefore, that space abstracted from gravitating matter is Euclidean, and that the observed non-Euclideanism is due to gravity, is unverifiable. It is true that one of the celebrated confirmations of the general theory of relativity consisted in the observation of the "bending" of a light ray passing through the gravitational field generated by the sun. But whereas Newtonian physicists spoke of gravitational fields superimposed, as it were, upon a causally inert absolute space with Euclidean properties, the theory of relativity has abandoned this dualism: relativistic physicists speak of a "metrical" field generated by matter, as though the distribution of matter determined the very metrical properties of space. The "bent" light rays are accordingly said to describe non-Euclidean geodesics, i.e., shortest paths; but since the Newtonian concept of absolute space is rejected, this does not imply that they *would* describe Euclidean geodesics if only they were not "disturbed" by gravity.

We conclude that a defense of Poincaré's conventionalism with reference to the possibility of postulating universal forces and thus retaining Euclidean geometry is rather weak, for the very meaning of such a postulate involves the notion of an absolute space whose metrical properties do not depend upon the distribution of matter. The postulate, therefore, appears to be purely ad hoc and unverifiable. There is, nevertheless, an important element of truth in Poincaré's conventionalism. Howsoever one may physically interpret the primitives of a formal geometry, the resulting propositions of physical geometry cannot be tested until a method of measurement has been chosen. This involves the choice of a definition of *congruence*. That is, the very meaning of "measurement of length" involves the assumption that the measuring rod remains congruent to itself (keeps its length unchanged) as it is moved from one place to another. How is such an assumption to be verified? The visual appearance of constancy of size is surely too unreliable to build a supposedly objective method of measurement upon. If we find that a second measuring rod can be exactly superposed upon the first at every place, the question is simply shifted: How do we know that this second rod remains congruent to itself? How do we know that the rods that are congruent at the same place are also congruent at different places? It seems, therefore, that in order for it to be a question of fact whether a given rod is rigid, i.e., remains congruent to itself in moving about, some rod must be simply declared rigid.[8] If we choose as our "rigid" standard rod a rod made of easily deformable rubber, our measurements are likely to yield non-Euclidean results. We have here arrived at a conclusion that is perfectly analogous to our earlier conclusion that a convention regarding *time congruence* must be made before the question of what are the true laws of mechanics makes empirical sense. In just the way in which a definition of time congruence by reference to irregular pulse beats (Schlick's example) would yield a more complicated non-Newtonian mechanics, so a definition of *length congruence* with reference to an easily deformable rubber rod would yield a non-Euclidean physical geometry.

One should not, however, exaggerate this element of truth in Poincaré's conventionalism, or in what Reichenbach has called the "relativity of geometry." In the actual development of physical geometry there occurs no such event as an arbitrary stipulation to designate a certain rod as "rigid." What was said earlier about the definition of time congruence applies, *mutatis mutandis*, to the definition of length congruence. One begins with an inaccurate perceptual criterion of rigidity: certain bodies are found, by touch, to be solid and, by sight, to keep a constant size in being transported.[9] Using them as measuring rods, the ancient Egyptians already discovered by measurement certain geometrical propositions about lengths and angles, such as the "Pythagorean theorem" ("In a right triangle of sides a, b, c, where a and b include the right angle, the square over c, the side opposite the right angle, equals the sum of the squares over a and b"), the proposition that the base angles in an isosceles triangle are equal, and several more of the propositions that appear as theorems in Euclid's deductive system. These very propositions are subsequently used to refine the concept of rigidity; that is, significant discrepancies between them and the results of measurements will be interpreted as evidence that the measuring rods were not rigid rather than as evidence disconfirming the Euclidean propositions.

A Kantian might well attempt an a priori proof of the Euclidean

8. Reichenbach uses the expression "defined as rigid," which is unfortunate, as one normally speaks of defining a concept or a general term, not a particular object. What he probably means is that the scientists' statement, with reference to the *standard* rod, "This rod is rigid," *makes* the rod rigid in the same sense in which the statement issued by a proper authority "*A* is hereby married to *B*" creates the state of legal marriage. To ask whether "This rod is rigid" is a true statement would be as senseless, on Reichenbach's view, as to ask whether the statement issued by the authority was true.

9. We need not enter, in this context, into the psychology-of-perception problem of how we perceive objects as remaining constant in size and shape through a change of perspective or distance, though our retinal images do not exhibit such a constancy.

structure of physical space along this line: that the Euclidean propositions are already contained in the usual concept of rigidity, and that it
would therefore be impossible to discover by measurement that the space
we inhabit is non-Euclidean. Two comments on such a rehabilitation of
Kant's philosophy of space are in order.

1. Even if it be analytic to say, for example, that the circumference
of a circular disk as measured by a rigid rod equals approximately $2\pi r$
(π being a mathematical constant, and the approximation being the closer,
the smaller the measuring rod in relation to the radius), it could remain
a question of empirical fact whether there are rigid rods so defined, and
whether this or that rod satisfies the definition. Instead of saying that
we can conceive of a physical space that measurements conducted with
rigid rods reveal as non-Euclidean, we would simply say that we can
conceive of a universe that does not contain any rigid rods. But further,
it is just wrong to claim that the Euclidean character of physical space
follows analytically from the very meaning of "measurement of length"
insofar as the geometrical concepts are operationally defined, i.e., with
reference to the operations of measurement. The most that could be
substantiated by this line of reasoning is that the "axiom of free mobility"
is such an analytical consequence. A space is said to satisfy this axiom if
bodies can be moved in it so as to remain congruent to themselves. Such
spaces are said, in the technical idiom of mathematicians, to have a
constant "curvature." Consider, for example, the surface of a potato. An
important way in which it differs from a flat surface but also from a
spherical surface is that if some sheet (of any material) closely fits
some part of the potato surface it cannot be made to fit any other part
of the surface by a smooth sliding movement without deformation.
Take this as a provisional "operational" definition of the distinction
between constant and variable curvature of surfaces. By analogical extension of the concept "constant curvature," a three-dimensional space
is said to have a constant curvature if a solid body can move in it without deformation (the word "can" here is essential: of course bodies
moving in a space of constant curvature *may* be deformed by differential
forces such as heat, but their size and shape are invariant with respect
to changes of place provided no differential forces act on them). Now,
since the very meaning of "measurement of length" involves the possibility of transporting a rod that remains congruent to itself from one
place to another, it may be argued that a measurable space *necessarily*
has a constant curvature.[10] But a Euclidean space is characterized not
only by free mobility but also by "flatness" (zero curvature), i.e., the
fact that the geometrical properties of regular figures and solids do not

10. This thesis was argued by Bertrand Russell in his dissertation "The Foundations
of Geometry."

depend on absolute size (for example, the sum of the angles of a spherical triangle varies with the size of the triangle, while that of a flat triangle does not.) Therefore it would still remain a question of empirical fact whether the physical space we inhabit has zero, positive, or negative curvature.[11]

2. Even if one accepted the argument according to which it would be self-contradictory to report as the outcome of measurements performed with rigid rods that the explored part of space has a variable curvature, one could not thereby be committed to a rejection of the postulates of the general theory of relativity that describe the space filled with gravitating matter as a metrical field whose curvature varies from place to place, the degree of curvature being a function of distances and masses. For these postulates are not, of course, directly verifiable by measurement. Wherever the verification of a physical theory, whether Newtonian or relativistic, involves measurements of lengths (distances), the assumption of free mobility is innocuous because Euclidean geometry, and a fortiori the axiom of free mobility, is still a correct approximative description of small spaces. In this respect the relation of Euclidean to non-Euclidean geometry is like the relation of Newtonian to relativistic mechanics. According to the special theory of relativity the distance between two points fixed in a system S as measured in a system S' that moves uniformly relative to S depends on the velocity of S' relative to S. Similarly, the time of motion of a body S as measured by means of a clock that moves uniformly relative to S (as contrasted with the time measurement by means of a clock fixed on S) depends on relative velocity. This is the meaning of the statement that distance and time are not "invariant" magnitudes in the theory of relativity. But unless the relative velocities approach the enormous velocity of light *in vacuo*, the difference between the time measured in S and that measured in S' is so small that by direct measurement it could not even be detected. And since the velocities of terrestrial macroscopic bodies are small compared with the velocity of light, the laws of Newtonian mechanics are still approximately correct within this limited range.

These remarks should make it clear that even if it be granted that the axiom of free mobility is, to use a Kantian phrase, presupposed by the very possibility of measurement of length, it does not follow that the

11. For the mathematical definition of "curvature" the reader may consult any elementary book on Gaussian and non-Euclidean geometry. It is important not to be misled by the nontechnical connotations of this word. In speaking of the curvature of an n-dimensional continuous manifold of points (line, surface, space) the mathematician does not imply the existence of an $n + 1$st dimension into which the manifold is curved. Understanding "curvature of space," therefore, does not require the ability to imagine a fourth dimension.

physical space explored by the physicist *must* be Euclidean nor even that it *must* have a constant curvature. On the other hand, we should also steer clear of the opposite extreme, viz. a naive operationalism according to which it can be discovered by straightforward experimental operations whether the curvature of space is constant or variable. The constant-variable space-curvature distinction is not operationally definable at all, and a direct test of the hypothesis of constant or variable space curvature is inconceivable. For the physical meaning of "The curvature in space volume V is constant" is that a body moved from one place in V to another remains congruent to itself *provided* it is not acted on by differential forces. But how is one to verify that this condition is fulfilled? One would have to determine, for example, that the temperature in V is constant or that the moving body is a nonconductor. This process of verification will surely involve measurement of length at some point (suppose, for example, that constancy of temperature is determined by means of a mercury thermometer), and so we return to the assumption of free mobility of the measuring rod which presupposes the hypothesis to be tested. And even if the difficulty of verifying without circularity the absence of differential forces could be solved, how is one to verify that a body's size is independent of its spatial position without assuming such independence for the measuring rod?

We conclude that the theory that physical space itself is curved in a variable way has no direct operational significance at all. It has empirical significance only in the context of the general theory of relativity—especially the latter's postulate of the equivalence of gravitation and inertia whose empirical basis is the proportionality of inertial and gravitational mass (independence of gravitational acceleration of the inertial mass of the falling body). The relevant empirical tests of this postulate (bending of light rays, the "Einstein red-shift") are highly indirect, and do not require a priori operational interpretation of "space curvature" any more than the indirect tests of the kinetic theory of gases presupposed an operational definition of "mass of a molecule."

Selected Readings

Black, M., "Conventionalism in Geometry and the Interpretation of Necessary Statements," *Philosophy of Science*, 1942.

Broad, C. D., "Is Space Euclidean?," *Mind*, 1945.

Einstein, A., "Geometry and Experience," in A. Einstein, *Sidelights of Relativity* (New York, 1923). [Reprinted in H. Feigl and M. Brodbeck (eds.), *Readings in the Philosophy of Science* (New York, 1953).]

Frank, P., *Philosophy of Science* (Englewood Cliffs, N.J., 1957), chap. 3.

Grünbaum, A., "Conventionalism in Geometry," in L. Henken, P. Suppes, and A. Tarski (eds.), *The Axiomatic Method* (Amsterdam, 1959).

Hempel, C. G., "Geometry and Empirical Science," in H. Feigl and W. Sellars (eds.), *Readings in Philosophical Analysis* (New York, 1949).

Jammer, M., *Concepts of Space* (New York, 1960).

Mach, E., *Space and Geometry* (Chicago, 1943).

Meserve, B., *The Evolution of Geometry and the Fundamental Concepts of Geometry* (Cambridge, 1957).

Mill, J. S. *A System of Logic* (London, 1893), Book II, chap. 5.

Nagel, E., "The Formation of Modern Conceptions of Logic in the Development of Geometry," *Osiris*, 1939.

——, *The Structure of Science* (New York, 1961), chap. 8, 9.

Nicod, J., "Geometry in the Perceived World," in J. Nicod, *Foundations of Geometry and Induction* (London, 1930).

Poincaré, H., "Non-Euclidean Geometries and the Non-Euclidean World," in H. Poincaré, *Science and Hypothesis*, trans. by G. B. Halsted (New York, 1905). [Reprinted in H. Feigl and M. Brodbeck (eds.), *Readings in the Philosophy of Science* (New York, 1953).]

Reichenbach, H., *Philosophy of Space and Time* (New York, 1958).

——, *The Rise of Scientific Philosophy* (Berkeley, Calif., 1951), chap. 8.

Robertson, H. P., "Geometry as a Branch of Physics," in A. P. Schilpp (ed.), *Albert Einstein, Philosopher-Scientist* (New York, 1951).

Russell, B., *The Foundations of Geometry* (Cambridge, 1897).

Schlick, M., *Philosophy of Nature* (New York, 1949), chap. 6–8.

CHAPTER 8

Logical Analysis of Measurement

A. QUANTITY AND QUALITY

Any science in which mathematics is applied involves counting and measurement. Countable subject-matters are collections of discrete objects, and to count such a collection is to establish a one-one correspondence between its members and numerals, the numerals being assigned in the order 1, 2, 3, . . . , n. The object of measurement (in a stricter sense of "measurement"), on the other hand, is always a *continuously variable property* of objects, or processes, such as length, weight, temperature, temporal duration, velocity. Whether we should call the objects of measurement "properties" or "qualities" is a trivial question of terminology. The important consideration is that "measuring" makes sense only with respect to variable properties.

To bring out the precise meaning of this, let us compare color and length. Both are *determinable* properties, which necessarily appear in some determinate form or other: a thing does not just have color, it has some specific color, and it does not just have length but some specific length. *Short* and *long* are determinate forms of length in the same sense in which *blue* and *red* are determinate forms of color. But there is a difference: a long thing is said to be longer, to have more length, than a short thing, whereas it would not make sense to say that a red thing has more color than a blue thing, or vice versa. Let us mark this important difference by saying that the qualities that are determinate forms of length can be ordered by a comparative relation ("longer"), whereas the qualities that are determinate forms of color cannot. Of

[125]

course, colors have measurable dimensions, such as brightness and saturation. But then it is the determinable properties "color brightness" and "color saturation" whose determinate forms can be arranged in an order, not "color." We can replace the dichotomy "tall or not tall" by "very tall or fairly tall or medium height or fairly short or very short," but no such disjunction of *degrees* of the determinable property corresponds to the dichotomy "blue or not blue." That we can meaningfully say that green is "closer" to blue than it is to, say, red is irrelevant. Similarly, shape is not measurable in the sense in which length is measurable. There is no comparative relation by which specific shapes can be uniquely ordered; it does not make sense to say that a circular figure has more or less shape than a triangular one or than a square figure. Or consider the genus "animals" in relation to its species— tigers, dogs, horses, and so on. It does not make sense to say that a tiger is more or less than a horse with respect to the generic, determinable property "being an animal," though there are respects in which such a comparison is possible (e.g., a tiger is more dangerous than a horse). It would not make sense, therefore, to attempt an ordering of animals with respect to their degree of animalhood, the way one might order them with respect to their size, weights, average blood temperature, and so on.

Now, the frequent use of the term "quality" in contrast to "quantity" might be explicated as follows: a quality is a determinate form of a determinable property that is not measurable. And a determinable property is not measurable if its determinate forms cannot be ordered in terms of "more" or "less" in the way that "heavy," "medium weight," "light," or "hot," "warm," "lukewarm," "cool," "cold" can be ordered. A quantity is a determinate form (a "degree") of a determinable property that is measurable; and if between any two degrees of a given determinable property an intermediate degree is conceivable, the measurable property is continuously variable. Notice that according to these definitions cardinality, a determinable property of collections of discrete objects, is measurable (by counting) without being continuously variable. As an abbreviation for "measurable determinable property" we shall use the word "magnitude." Length then is a magnitude; a length of 3 feet is a quantity. And length is a continuous magnitude, whereas cardinality (the determinable of which particular cardinal numbers are determinate forms) is a discrete magnitude.

One sometimes hears such confused statements as the following: "Qualities, by their very nature, cannot be measured. Quantitative science, therefore, is bound to ignore—if not destroy—the qualitative aspect of experience." But the simple truth is that some qualities of objects or processes can be ascertained by measurement—and it is in accord with scientific usage of the term to call such qualities "quantities" —and others cannot. Surely, quantitative science is so far from ignoring qualitative differences that it presupposes them according to the very meaning of "measurement." Unless such qualitative differences as small-large, heavy-light, hard-soft, warm-cold were encountered in the first place, measurement could not even be defined. On the other hand, such qualitative differences as that between the taste of grapes and the taste of oranges do not lend themselves to measurement simply because there is no determinable property with respect to which one taste quality could be said to be more or less than the other. And such being the case, no meaning could be attached to an assignment of different numbers to the two qualities.

B. THE TOPOLOGICAL CONDITIONS
OF MEASUREMENT

Let us consider length as a fundamental example of a continuous magnitude. What is given in perceptual experience prior to all measurement is that some objects are longer than others. In the case of rods, we can say that a rod x is longer than a rod y if y is congruent to a part of x. If neither x is longer than y nor y longer than x, then, of course x and y are congruent. To say that *longer* is a relation that can be used to order objects with respect to length is to say that it is asymmetrical, transitive, and C-connected. These technical terms are defined as follows: L is asymmetrical for any objects in the field of L,[1] call them x and y— if xLy, then not-(yLx). L is transitive for any objects x, y, z in the field of L—if xLy and yLz, then xLz. L is C-connected for any objects x and y in the field of L—either xLy or yLx or xCy. The letter C is chosen to suggest "coincidence," viz. coincidence with respect to the measured magnitude. In the case of length, the C-relation corresponding to L is, of course, congruence. In general, a C-relation must be transitive and symmetrical, i.e., such that if xCy, then yCx. Generalizing, the topological conditions of measurement of a determinable property Q are the following: there is an empirically given, asymmetrical, transitive, and C-connected relation R by means of which those objects which have R or its converse to some other object can be ordered. And if a given place in this order is occupied by more than

1. The field of a relation R is the class of those objects which have R or its converse to some other object, and the converse of R is that relation which y has to x if and only if x has R to y.

one object (e.g., several mutually congruent rods), then these bear to each other a coincidence relation that is transitive and symmetrical.

That L is asymmetrical need not be verified empirically; it is implicit in the very meaning of L. That it is transitive seems likewise to be an a priori certainty, since L is definable as partial congruence, and the transitivity of the latter relation follows from the transitivity of the part-whole relation. But it is not always possible to assert the transitivity of the ordering relation independently of empirical evidence. Take, for example, "heavier." There is nothing inconceivable about a body x feeling heavier than y when compared with it, y feeling heavier than z, yet z feeling heavier than or equally as heavy as x. Even if we assign to "x is heavier than y" the more objective meaning "x would— under appropriate conditions—outweigh y at any time at which x was placed in one pan of a balance and y in the opposite pan," it remains a question of empirical fact whether the relation is transitive. Turning to the conditions relating to the coincidence relations, we find that the symmetry is contained in the very meaning of the relational predicate. But the question whether transitivity must be verified empirically is more complicated than it looks at first glance.

Consider "x is congruent to y." What exactly does it mean? Since two objects may be congruent at one time and not at another, such a statement is really incomplete; congruence must be treated as a triadic relation involving the time variable. Now, "x is congruent to y at t" may be a statement describing an actual occurence at t—x and y are superposed at t so that their ends coincide completely—or it may be a dispositional statement: if x and y were superposed (contiguous) at t, then they would coincide completely at t. In the first interpretation it is surely inconceivable that congruence should fail to be transitive, for this would mean that at a given time x might coincide with y, y with z, yet x not with z! Even on the dispositional interpretation, failure of transitivity is inconceivable. For the best evidence that x and y are dispositionally congruent at t is, after all, that they are actually coincident at t, and similarly, the best evidence that y and z are dispositionally congruent at t would be their actual coincidence at t; and our best evidence for denying that x and z are dispositionally congruent at t would be that they fail to be congruent at t!

On either of these interpretations of congruence statements, therefore, the transitivity of congruence follows from the transitivity of coincidence, i.e., the relation obtaining between two rods when their ends coincide. The meaning of "congruence is transitive," however, may be less strict. It may just mean that if x is dispositionally congruent to y at t_0, and y to z at t_1, where t_1 is close to t_0, then x is dispositionally congruent to z at t_0 and t_1 and t_2, where t_2 is close to t_1. In some cases such small time differences must be allowed in order to make the transitivity hypothesis testable at all. Thus one cannot verify at one and the same time that *x* can balance *y*, *y* can balance *z*, and *x* can balance *z*; hence, the assertion that the relation expressed by "*x* can balance *y* at *t*" is transitive is not even testable. What is testable is that if *x* balances *y* at a given time and *y* balances *z* at a slightly later time, then *x* balances *z* at a still later time.

The first step in constituting a determinable property *Q* a magnitude consists in associating numbers with its determinate forms and the arithmetical relation expressed by ">" with the appropriate ordering relation *R* in such a way that the number associated with *x* is greater than the number associated with *y* if and only if *xRy*, and in associating equal numbers with *x* and *y* if and only if *xCy*. At this topological stage the difference between the associated numbers have no significance. For example, we might assign 1 to a certain shortest rod *x*, 2 to a longer rod *y*, and 3 to a still longer rod *z*, but there would so far be no meaning in the statement that *y* is twice as long as *x* and *z* three times as long as *x*. Of course, the assignment of numbers to the determinate forms of *Q* is usually merely a step preparatory to the *comparison of differences*, which is the very essence of measurement. We don't just want to know whether *x* is longer than *y*, but rather how much longer *x* is than *y*; hence numbers will be assigned in such a way that the arithmetical relations between the numbers reflect certain relations between the physical quantities.

C. THE METRICAL CONDITIONS OF MEASUREMENT; ADDITIVITY

To say that rod *y* is twice as long as rod *x* is to say that its length is equal to the sum of the length of *x* and the length of a rod that is congruent to *x*. In this way the notion of "so and so much more" is tied up with the notion of summing or adding quantities. In explaining the meaning of metrical statements (as we may call statements ascribing numerically definite quantities to objects and processes), we shall, for the sake of variety, turn to *weight* as our *example*. What is meant by "The weight of *x* is twice the weight of *y*"? It does not mean only that the number used to represent the weight of *x* is twice the number used to represent the weight of *y*, for it is just the belief that *x* is twice as heavy as *y* that leads the scientist to represent their weights by numbers in just that ratio. Further, there may be two liquids such that the numbers representing their densities are in the ratio 2 : 1, yet one cannot say that one is twice as dense as the other in the same sense in which one can say that one body is twice as heavy as another. Let us, then, trace the procedure by which one might actually discover that x is twice as heavy as y, thereby explaining the operational meaning of the expression. We simply find a body z that balances y, then join it to y on the same pan of the balance, and discover next that x balances the "join" (physical sum) of y and z. If we conventionally designate the weight of y, and of any body that bears the C-relation to y, as unity (say, one gram), the described experiment establishes that the weight of x is two grams, because the very meaning of "The weight of x is two grams" is: x bears the appropriate C-relation to (is equally as heavy as) the join of two bodies of unit weight. Generalizing, we obtain an operational definition schema for "the weight of x is n grams," where the variable n ranges over the integers.

Let us ask, now, whether it follows from our definition alone that the weight of the join of two bodies x and y is equal to the arithmetic sum of the numbers representing the weights of x and y. This is to ask precisely the following question: Suppose it to have been ascertained that x balances a join of n unit weights (hence, that the weight of x equals n grams) and that y balances a join of m unit weights. Does it *logically* follow that the join of x and y will balance a join of $n + m$ unit weights? The answer is surely negative; this is entirely a question of empirical fact. Since the answer given by experience is affirmative (within the limits of experimental error), weight is said to be an *additive* magnitude. It is easy to become confused about this matter, because the word "sum" and cognate expressions are sometimes used in an arithmetical and sometimes in a physical sense. Thus it may seem superficially that "The sum of 2 grams and 2 grams equals 4 grams" is just as logically true as "$2 + 2 = 4$." But it is an empirical truth if it means: the join of a body weighing 2 grams and another body weighing 2 grams weighs 4 grams. The general definition of "additive magnitude" is obviously: Q is an additive magnitude if there is a physical joining operation such that the value of Q characterizing the join to two objects x and y equals the arithmetic sum of the values of Q that characterize x and y.

The statement that the additive nature of such magnitudes as length and weight is empirically established must, however, be qualified. Because of the limited sensitivity of any measuring instrument a failure of additivity may always arise. Suppose, for example, that the measured weight of a body A is 10.5 g and that of a body B 6.6 g It may happen that the join of A and B, weighed by means of the same balance with a least count of 0.1 g, turns out to have a weight, not of 17.1 g, but of 17 g. The discrepancy would be explained if more refined measurements with a balance whose least count was 0.01 g revealed that *A* weighed 10.46 g and *B* 6.56 g. Still, for the same reason additivity may fail again when weights are measured with a more sensitive balance. The statement that magnitude *Q* is additive is strictly true only if it refers to the "true" values of *Q*. But since in the practice of experimental physics a breakdown of additivity is taken to *entail* errors of measurement, this statement is really analytic of the meaning of "true values (of *Q*)." Nevertheless, it has an empirical basis: it remains an empirical fact that relative to the usual "joining" operation weight is approximately additive, the approximation being the better, the more sensitive the balance. *Mutatis mutandis*, the same holds for other fundamental magnitudes.

Density and temperature are examples of nonadditive (also called "intensive") magnitudes. If, for example, we take mixing as the "joining" operation to be performed on liquids, we find empirically that the additive condition is not satisfied by densities; similarly for temperature. And there does not seem to be any joining operation on objects characterizable in terms of density and temperature such that the additivity condition is satisfied.

D. DERIVED MEASUREMENT

How can we meaningfully make metrical statements about density and temperature and other nonadditive magnitudes? The answer is that the measurement of such magnitudes is reducible to measurement of additive magnitudes on the basis of laws. Measurement of weight and volume of samples of a given substance reveals that the weight is directly proportional to the volume. This means that for any sample of the substance the ratio of its weight to its volume is the same. In mathematical notation,

$$W_1/V_1 = W_2/V_2$$

(where the subscripts 1 and 2 refer to any distinct samples of the same homogeneous substance), or alternatively,

$$W = k \times V$$

The constant of proportionality *k* is called *density* (or *specific gravity*). And since the physical dimensions of the numbers on different sides of the physical equation must be the same, the definition of density as such a constant of proportionality determines its dimension as grams per cubic centimeters. In the form of a dimensional equation,

$$g = g/cm^3 \times cm^3,$$

It is not arbitrary to call that constant of proportionality "density" rather than, say, velocity or viscosity or elasticity. Certain topological properties had already been connoted by "density" prior to the quantitative discovery leading to its derived measurement: if y is a liquid and x a solid or a liquid, then y is denser than x if and only if x is capable of floating on y. In this sense wood was known to be less dense than water independently of any measurements of weight and volume. It was further established empirically that this comparative relation is asymmetrical and transitive. Now, it is a contingent fact that for all homogeneous substances x and y, if x is denser than y in this topological sense, then the ratio of the weight of a unit volume of x exceeds the ratio of the weight of a unit volume of y. And this fact justifies the interpretation of the constant of proportionality in the physical equation $W = k \times V$ as density.

The example of derived magnitude just considered is an *empirical constant of proportionality*. Some other examples are: elasticity, measured in terms of Hooke's law; velocity, measured in terms of the law $S = k \times t$, where t is the time and S the distance traversed by a uniformly moving body; acceleration (proportionality of velocity to time in a uniformly accelerated motion, such as a free fall in a vacuum); coefficients of thermal expansion, measured in terms of the proportionality of changes of length to changes of temperature, or of changes of pressure to changes of temperature (in case the substance undergoing temperature changes keeps a constant volume). In all these examples the derived magnitude is explicitly definable in terms of the dimensions of the independent and dependent variables in the functional equation, specifically as a derivative, i.e., a rate of change of one magnitude with respect to another magnitude. This kind of derived measurement should be distinguished from measurement of one magnitude in terms of another magnitude of which it is an *empirical function*. A magnitude y is an empirical function of a magnitude x if under specified conditions an increase of y corresponds to an increase (or decrease) of x, a decrease of y corresponds to a decrease (or increase) of x, and y remains constant when x remains constant (and conversely). In other words, y is an empirical function of x if it is a law of nature that under specified conditions y is (positively or negatively) correlated with x. In this sense temperature is found to be an empirical function of volume (or length, in the case where the substance undergoing temperature changes can expand linearly only). The term "empirical function" is here used in contrast to "definitional function." Thus the momentum of a body is a function of its velocity, but this statement is entirely definitional since momentum is defined as the product of mass times velocity. It should be noted, however, that temperature is, topologically, an *empirical* function of volume because temperature changes can be qualitatively ascertained by "feeling," prior to the existence of thermometers. If "momentum" similarly had a qualitative meaning of *impulse* at the time of Galileo, then the statement that it is proportional to the mass and the velocity of a body was empirical, not dispositional, at that time.

Is it likewise an empirical discovery that the temperature of a body undergoing temperature changes is, under the relevant conditions, a *linear* function of its volume?—that is, for example, that the length of mercury is also doubled, when the temperature of the increased mercury is doubled? Obviously it could be physical discovery only if temperature were already measurable independently of measurements of volume. So, if the specification of the exact form of the functional dependence is part and parcel of the process of constituting temperature a derived magnitude, the above statement expresses a convention of measurement, not a confirmable empirical hypothesis. The relevant convention usually takes the form of defining equal temperature differences: $(T_2 - T_1) = (T_1 - T_0)$ is *defined* to mean that the differences in volume (length) of the thermometric substance that correspond to the temperature differences are equal. In this precise sense the measurement of temperature is reduced to the measurement of the additive magnitude length. Alternative conventions are, of course, possible. One could have defined, for example $(T_2 - T_1) = (T_1 - T_0)$ if and only if $(V_2 - V_1) = 2(V_1 - V_0)$; or $(T_2 - T_1) = (T_1 - T_0)$ if and only if $(V_2^2 - V_1^2) = (V_1^2 - V_0^2)$. It is easy to see that relative to the latter definition of equality of temperature differences the law of the linear proportionality of temperature to volume would not hold. For this law means that for any values of temperature, T_0, T_1, and T_2, the corresponding (i.e., simultaneous) values of the volume of a heat conductor, V_0, V_1, and V_2, the following equation holds:

$$\frac{T_2 - T_1}{T_1 - T_0} = \frac{V_2 - V_1}{V_1 - V_0}$$

which equation obviously entails that equal volume differences correspond to equal temperature differences. We emphasize the conventional element here because many students of physics tend to assume naively that we can test any physical equation by measuring the functionally related variables independently and thereupon "fitting" a smooth curve. Nevertheless the convention that has actually been adopted is genetically based on the fact that equal increases of the length of the mercury correspond to *sensations* of approximately equal temperature increases.

Our second example of this sort of derived measurement is the measurement of time. If time were an additive magnitude, then there would exist a joining operation such that the time of the "join" of two processes equaled the sum of the times of the joined processes. It may seem that such a joining operation is indeed definable: let t_1 be the time of a continuous uniform motion from P_0 to P_1, and t_2 the time of a continuous motion from P_1 to P_2 (where P_2 may or may not coincide with P_0); then the join (physical sum) of the two motions is defined as a continuous motion along the same path and *with the same velocities* from P_0 to P_2, and the time of such a compounded motion is found to be equal to the sum of t_1 and t_2. We may assume that the added times are measured by counting certain vibrations between the initial and the terminal instant of the motion. But, apart from other defects, such a definition of physical addition of times suffers from circularity, since velocity is defined in terms of time. It is therefore more plausible to construe physical time as a derived magnitude that is measured by means of the equation $S = k \times t$, which describes uniform linear (or angular) displacement as a linear function of time. Here again the decisive step is the definition of equal differences: we select some uniformly moving system, preferably one in periodic motion, such as a nearly frictionless pendulum or the earth considered as a uniform rotating body, and define equal time lapses as time lapses corresponding to equal (linear or angular) displacements. As we have already seen in another context, we must avoid the logical circle consisting in first defining time equality in terms of uniform motion and then defining uniform motion in terms of time equality; and we avoid it by defining equal time differences with reference to a *designated* system in periodic motion without mentioning in the definition that its motion is uniform. That the equation $S = k \times t$ describes the motion of the standard clock is a matter of convention, since it serves to constitute time as a magnitude. Whether it describes the motion of any other body, translational or angular, is a question of fact.[2] And to make this logical point is perfectly consistent with recognizing that the convention is not entirely arbitrary because (*a*) men have a rough pyschological sense of equality of durations, just as they have the ability to estimate roughly by tactile sensation whether two temperature differences are equal, and

2. Galileo, in his experiments with falling bodies, measured time by a water clock, assuming that equal amounts of water passed through a given cross section in equal times. There are other possibilities as well: the assumption of uniform velocity in the operational definition of time could be avoided by measuring time by *numbers* of equally spaced ticks, but this method would be built on the somewhat unreliable subjective sense of equal time differences.

(*b*) it is desirable to define derived magnitudes by equations that will yield descriptive quantitative laws that are as simple as possible.

A final word about *pyschophysical* measurement, which is essentially derived measurement on the basis of psychophysical laws. There is no justification for the frequent statement that psychological, or "subjective," phenomena do not admit of measurement. A sensation of hunger is no more or less "subjective" than a sensation of temperature, and degrees of hunger admit of derived measurement just as degrees of temperature do: we must first empirically discover a topological correlation between intensity of hunger and some physical or physiological variable (e.g., time elapsed since the animal ate last), and thereupon we are free to construct a metric for the psychological variable by defining equal differences as differences corresponding to equal differences in that physical or physiological variable. If the fact that changes in the intensity of hunger must be detected by introspection before intensity of hunger can acquire the status of a derived magnitude is held to undermine the "scientific" validity of psychophysical measurement, then, for just the same reason, measurement of temperature would have to be suspected as "unscientific."

Selected Readings

Bergmann, G., "The Logic of Measurement," *State University of Iowa Studies in Engineering,* 1956.

—— and W. Spence, "The Logic of Psychophysical Measurement," in H. Feigl and M. Brodbeck (eds.), *Readings in the Philosophy of Science* (New York, 1953).

Brower, D., "Quantification in Psychology," *Psychological Review,* 1949.

Campbell, N. R., *What Is Science?* (New York, 1952), chap. 6.

——, *Physics: The Elements* (Cambridge, 1920). [Reprinted as *The Foundations of Experimental Science* (New York, 1957), part II.]

Churchman, C. W., "A Materialist Theory of Measurement," in R. W. Sellars, V. J. McGill, and M. Farber (eds.), *Philosophy for the Future* (New York, 1949).

—— and P. Ratoosh (eds.), *Measurement: Definitions and Theories* (New York, 1959).

Cohen, M. R., and E. Nagel, *Introduction to Logic and Scientific Method* (New York, 1934), chap. 15.

Comrey, C. J., "Operational Approach to Psychological Measurement," *Psychological Review,* 1950.

Coombs, C. H., "Theory and Methods of Social Measurement," in L. Festinger and D. Katz (eds.), *Research Methods in the Behavioral Sciences* (New York, 1953).

DeBroglie, L., *Physics and Microphysics* (New York, 1955), pp. 78–87.

Gulliksen, H., "Paired Comparisons and the Logic of Measurement," *Psychological Review,* 1946.

Helmholtz, H. von, *On Counting and Measuring* (New York, 1930).

Hempel, C. G., *Fundamentals of Concept Formation in Empirical Science* (International Encyclopedia of Unified Science, II, no. 7, Chicago, 1952), Part III.

Lenzen, V., *Procedures of Empirical Science* (*ibid.*, I, no. 5, Chicago, 1938).

Lundberg, G. A., "Quantitative Methods in Social Psychology," *American Sociological Review*, 1936.

McGregor, D., "Scientific Measurement and Psychology," *Psychological Review*, 1935.

Margenau, H., "Philosophical Problems Concerning the Meaning of Measurement in Physics," *Philosophy of Science*, 1958.

Mehlberg, H., *The Reach of Science* (Toronto, 1958), part 2, chap. 1.

Nagel, E., *On the Logic of Measurement* (New York, 1930).

——, "Measurement," *Erkenntnis*, 1931.

Scott, D., and P. Suppes, "Foundational Aspects of Measurement," *Journal of Symbolic Logic*, 1958.

Stevens, S. S., "On the Theory of Scales of Measurement," *Science*, 1946.

Suppes, P., "A Set of Independent Axioms for Extensive Quantities," *Portugaliae Mathematica*, 1951.

Vining, R., and T. C. Koopmans, "Methodological Issues in Quantitative Economics," *Review of Economics and Statistics*, 1949.

Weyl, H., *Philosophy of Mathematics and Natural Science* (Princeton, 1949), pp. 139–165.

Part Three

INDUCTION
AND
PROBABILITY

CHAPTER 9

Deductive & Inductive Inference

A. INADEQUACY OF THE TRADITIONAL DEFINITION

The difference between formal science, viz. pure mathematics and formal logic, and empirical science is often described as the difference between deductive and inductive science. The reasoning that goes on in pure mathematics and formal logic is purely deductive. That deductive reasoning occurs in the empirical sciences as well is obvious, since the chief practical utility of the formal sciences consists in their providing the empirical scientists with efficient techniques of deduction—for example, the calculus. Further, there is no other way of testing an empirical hypothesis—especially one of highly theoretical character, such as the hypothesis of universal gravitation, or the atomic hypothesis, or the gene theory of biology—than by *deducing* from it directly testable consequences. Whereas there are purely deductive sciences, there are, therefore, no purely inductive sciences. Nevertheless, it *is* characteristic of an empirical science that it also involves inductive reasoning. In particular, inductive generalization, the inference from "some" to "all," enters into the verification of empirical laws but is entirely absent from the process of mathematical or logical proof. Our problem, now, is to work out a general definition of the distinction between deductive and inductive inference (or reasoning).

In traditional terms, deductive inference goes from the general to the particular, inductive inference from the particular to the general. No doubt there are deductive and inductive inferences, in the modern sense of "deductive" and "inductive," that satisfy this definition. In particular, inductive generalization fits the traditional definition of induction because it concludes that all the members of a class K have property P from the evidence that all the observed members of K have P, and the observed members of an unlimited class are only *some* of its members. And certain forms of *syllogistic* inference, the kind of inference whose standards of validity were investigated and formulated by Aristotle, can be argued to proceed from the general to the particular. Certainly "All men are mortal, Socrates is a man, therefore Socrates is mortal" (or equivalently, "No men are immortal, Socrates is a man, therefore Socrates is not immortal") applies a general rule—here the major premise—to a particular case. Ironically, this piece of reasoning, which clearly illustrates reasoning "from the general to the particular," would have been excluded by Aristotle from the domain of scientific knowledge, because he held that only species, not particulars, are subject-matters of science. Consider a syllogistic form that involves, in accordance with Aristotle's conception of science, only species, or classes, not particulars: All M are P, all S are M, therefore all S are P. Here S is asserted, by the minor premise, to be a subclass of M (though, to be quite accurate, it is not asserted to be a "proper" subclass); hence, it is natural to construe the syllogism as the inference that what is true of all the members of M is also true of *some* of the members of M. It is less clear in what sense syllogistic inference proceeds from the general to the particular when one premise is particular, as in "All M are P, some S are M, therefore some S are P" or in "No M are P, some S are M, therefore some S are not P." What is more important is that there are ever so many forms of inference to which the distinction between "general" and "particular" in the traditional sense is not even applicable, so that they would have to be classified as neither deductive nor inductive. Plainly, if the deductive-inductive distinction is intended as exhaustive, it must be entirely redefined.

There are, for example, nonsyllogistic forms of argument represented by means of propositional variables, such as: p or q, not p, therefore q; if p then q, not q, therefore not p; if p then q, if q then r, therefore, if p then r. One of the reasons they are called nonsyllogistic is that the propositional variables range over all kinds of propositions, whereas all the propositions entering into a syllogism in the strict sense have one or the other of the following forms: All A are B, no A are B, some A are B, some A are not B. Again, arguments involving relational predicates are nonsyllogistic: All horses are quadrupeds, therefore all heads of horses are heads of quadrupeds; A is father of B, and B is father of C, therefore A is grandfather of C; some students admire all teachers, therefore all teachers are admired by some student or other; $x = y$, and $x = z$, therefore $y = z$. On the side of inductive reasoning, we note that inference "from particulars to particulars," i.e., from the evidence that an observed sample of a class K has property P without exception to the conclusion that one or more members of K not included in the observed sample also have P, does not fit into the traditional dichotomy at all. There is even a form of inference from the general to the particular that is like inductive generalization in that there is no necessity for the conclusion to be true if the premises are true: x per cent of the members of K have P, and s is a random sample drawn from K, therefore approximately x per cent of the members of s have P.

In contemporary logic and philosophy of science "deductive inference" is used in the sense of *necessary* (demonstrative) inference: the conclusion, in deductive inference, is claimed to follow with logical necessity from the premises. We say "is claimed to follow" rather than simply "follows" in order to allow for invalid deductive inferences, such as: If p then q, q, therefore p; or: All P are M, all S are M, therefore all S are P. (The former is commonly called the "fallacy of affirming the consequent," the latter the "fallacy of undistributed middle.") Saying that C follows with logical necessity from $P_1, P_2, \ldots, P_n$ is equivalent to saying that the conjunction of $P_1, P_2, \ldots, P_n$ with the negation of C is logically inconsistent. But although this intimate connection between the relations of logical consequence and logical inconsistency should be firmly kept in mind, the above equivalence should not be misunderstood as an effective criterion of deductive validity. Indeed, it is not even a definition, for to say that a set of statements is inconsistent is to say that a contradiction is *deducible* from it. Indirect tests of deductive validity are useful, because often it is easier to deduce a contradiction from the set of statements consisting of the premises plus the negation of the conclusion than to deduce the conclusion directly from the premises. But the concept of logical consequence remains logically prior to the concept of logical inconsistency since the latter is, as above, defined in terms of the former.

An inductive inference, again according to contemporary usage, is an inference whose conclusion is not claimed to follow necessarily but only with some degree of probability; hence "inductive inference" is commonly used interchangeably with "probable inference." It will be seen in the following section that inductive inference in this sense, far from being identifiable with inductive generalization, occurs in a large variety of forms.

B. CLASSIFICATION OF INDUCTIVE INFERENCES

The view has been taken (especially by Stanley Jevons, in the nineteenth century) that induction is the converse of deduction. Actually, only one type of inductive inference, in our sense of the term, fits this description, and we might as well baptize it accordingly:

1. *Conversion of Deduction.* When a scientist tests a theory, he deduces from it observation statements; after verification of the latter he pronounces the theory confirmed, which means that it is now more probable than it was before the test. How much more probable, depends on various factors whose study we must defer until we come to the elements of the calculus of probability (cf. Chapter 10, C). But disregarding the question of *degrees* of confirmation, we can say that if q is deducible from p, then q confirms p, in the sense that verification of q increases the antecedent probability of p. In this sense the discovery of the planet Neptune confirmed Newton's theory of gravitation, for the existence of this planet at a specified place in the solar system had been deduced from that theory. Strictly speaking, of course, the observation statement describing the position of Neptune at a specified time was not deducible from that theory alone, but only from its conjunction with the other postulates of Newtonian dynamics and with observation statements describing the deviation of the observed movement of an already known planet from the orbit that was predicated on the assumption that the known planets were all the planets there were.

As this example illustrates, in order to apply the above schema of confirmation to actual cases, we usually have to pack a number of premises into p, some of them theoretical, some observational. What is strictly confirmed through direct verification of observational consequences is the conjunction of all the premises $T, p_1, p_2, \ldots, p_n$. In saying that T in particular has been confirmed, the scientist is tacitly assuming that $p_1, p_2, \ldots, p_n$ are already known to be true. What he should say, in logical accuracy, is that T has been confirmed by the observations that verified q, on the assumption of $p_1, p_2, \ldots, p_n$. And he will become aware of these subsidiary assumptions if q turns out to be false and he is faced with the question whether he is now logically compelled to abandon the theory under test, T. If he finds that by assuming some proposition that is incompatible with one or more of the set $p_1, p_2, \ldots, p_n$ he can consistently retain T while accepting the "facts," he thereby discovers that he had unconsciously assumed $p_1, \ldots, p_n$ all along. A famous illustration is provided by the attempt made by Lorentz and Fitzgerald to reconcile the classical assumption that space is pervaded by an ether relative to which the earth moves with a measurable velocity with the negative outcome of the Michelson-Morley experiment. A light source was fixed on the earth, and light rays were emitted from it simultaneously in mutually perpendicular directions towards reflecting mirrors at equal distances from the light source. One light ray had the same direction as the earth's translational motion, the other was directed perpendicularly to it. Calculation of the times of the two round trips on the basis of the laws of classical kinematics yielded the consequence that there should be a slight difference in the times of return at the light source, but the most accurate observations failed to detect any difference. Now, argued these physicists, our calculation was really based on the assumption that since the paths of the two light rays measured out as equal, therefore they really are equal. But if we assume that all moving bodies, including measuring rods, contract a certain tiny but definite amount in the direction of motion through the ether, we can reconcile the experimental result with the classical assumption that seemed disconfirmed. For the measuring rod whose direction was perpendicular to the direction of the earth's motion was not affected by the latter, whereas the rod used to measure the other distance contracted by $1 : (1 - v^2/c^2)^{1/2}$ of its length when at rest relative to the ether. It is, of course, a legitimate question whether this "contraction hypothesis" is not purely *ad hoc*, in the sense that there can be no independent evidence for it: if all bodies, including measuring rods, suffer the same contraction as they move through the ether, how can this be verified by measurement?[1] But the example serves the purpose of focusing attention on the methodological point that a scientific hypothesis can be confirmed only against a background of assumptions needed as further premises to deduce a testable consequence; and that some of these (in the above example the Newtonian assumption that a measured length is independent of the velocity of the reference frame relative to the measured object) become explicit only when the scientist is faced with the task of reconciling a tested hypothesis with apparently disconfirming observations.

2. *Inductive Generalization.* It may seem that *inductive generalization* is a case of converse deduction, and the belief that it is, is probably responsible for the view that induction in general is simply the converse of deduction. Indeed, the conjunctive statement "a_1 is B, and a_2 is B, . . . , and a_n is B," where $a_1, . . ., a_n$ are observed members of the class A, confirms the generalization "All A are B" and at the same time seems to follow from it. However, such confirming instantial statements are deducible from the corresponding universal statement only if the latter is construed as an indefinite conjunction. And such an interpretation is implausible. In saying "All ravens are black" we are not saying anything about this or that particular raven. In fact, a singular statement of the form "The raven in space-time region R is black" presupposes that there is a raven in R. But "All ravens are black" does not presuppose this, hence the singular statement can hardly be held to express part of the meaning

---

1. That the "contraction hypothesis" is nevertheless testable, not ad hoc, is argued in detail by A. Grünbaum in "The Falsifiability of the Lorentz-Fitzgerald Contraction Hypothesis," *The British Journal for Philosophy of Science*, May, 1959.

of the universal hypothesis. At any rate, modern logicians interpret universal statements as universal *implications*: for any object *x*, if *x* is a raven, then *x* is black. Clearly no conjunction is deducible from an implication, hence "*a* is a raven and *a* is black," which describes a confirming observation, is not a deductive consequence of the hypothesis it confirms. For this reason inductive generalization, the inference from "some" to "all," cannot, in the light of modern logic, be regarded as a case of converse deduction. We must list it as a separate form of inductive inference.

3. *Predictive Inference.* This is the inference, from the fact that the members of an observed sample of a class have a certain property in common, that other members of the same class exhibit the same property. The evidence supporting the prediction that unobserved members of *K* have *P* may be that all the members of the observed sample *s* have *P*, or just that a certain proportion of them have *P*. Clearly the probility of the prediction will vary with that proportion. Confining ourselves to the singular prediction, i.e., prediction referring to a single member of *K* outside of *s*, we may say that according to the usual inductive thinking of scientists the probability of the prediction depends on three factors: the size of *s*, the relative frequency of *P* in *s*, the "fairness" of *s*. Of course, it is meaningless to say simply that *s* is fair: the fairness of a sample is relative to the property about which a prediction is made. Roughly speaking, *s* is fair relative to *P*, if the members of *s* differ in many respects that are relevant to the determinable property of which *P* is a determinate form. For example, let *s* be a sample of voters in a certain voting district that were interviewed, and let *P* be the property of favoring the Democratic candidates for political office. The determinable property in this case is political opinion. Clearly a pollster who made sure that the voters he interviewed differed in height, age, sex, and eye color would not create confidence in his predictions unless he could show that these variables were relevant to political opinion. Indeed one of the most important issues in inductive logic is the question of what relative weights are to be assigned to size and fairness of a sample as factors on which the probability of a prediction depends. In accordance with J. M. Keynes' conception (to be expounded in Chapter 10) of induction as a process of elimination of competing hypotheses, we may say that the larger sample is more likely to be representative *only* if the increase of the sample at the same time increases the *relevant variety* in the sample.

4. *Enthymematic Prediction.* Predictive inference in the explained sense should not be confused with what may be called *enthymematic prediction*. An enthymeme, in the terminology of traditional deductive logic, is a deductive argument with a suppressed premise. For example: He is a member of the Communist party, therefore he is opposed to military aid to Western Europe. The conclusion does not follow deductively from the

stated premise, but the speaker tacitly assumes the major premise "All members of the Communist party are opposed to military aid to Western Europe." Now, since nobody who argues this way really *claims* that his conclusion follows necessarily from the explicitly stated premise alone, enthymemes must be classified as inductive arguments unless we revise our definition of "deductive argument." Every enthymeme, of course, can be transformed into a deductive argument by making the suppressed (tacitly assumed) premise explicit. The confusion of predictive inferences with enthymematic inferences may be responsible for John Stuart Mill's view, still widely held by philosophers who do little or no independent thinking on induction, that every inductive inference is really a deductive, specifically syllogistic, inference with a suppressed major premise. That there is, however, a clear difference between a predictive inference and an enthymeme may be shown as follows: Let x be a member of K that does not belong to s, an observed sample of K (and let x be so described that "x belongs to K" is analytic). Which premise, when added to the premise that all the members of s have P, will enable us to *deduce* that x has P? Obviously, the universal premise that all members of K have P, or the weaker assumption that all members of some subclass of K that includes x have P. But this added premise entails the conclusion all by itself; the evidence about s need not be described by a separate premise. In the case of enthymematic prediction, on the other hand, the suppressed major premise does not entail the conclusion all by itself. You cannot deduce "The heap of dry leaves will shortly stand in flames" from "All heaps of dry leaves stand in flames shortly after they are lit" but only from the latter statement together with the singular statement (the basis of the prediction) "The heap of dry leaves is being lit now."

When we predict an event B from an event A with less than certainty, saying that the occurrence of A makes it probable, though not certain, that B will follow, the presupposed law is statistical, not causal: most occurrences of A are followed by an occurrence of B. It should be noted that, though such probable prediction is sufficiently analogous to prediction based on a causal law to be called "enthymematic" as well, it is not an enthymeme in the traditional sense: for "B will occur" does not necessarily follow from the premises "A occurred" and "Most occurrences of A are followed by an occurrence of B." Enthymematic statistical prediction is similar to a so-called statistical syllogism when the statistical premise is explicitly stated: m/n A's are B's, x is a (randomly selected) member of A, therefore it is probable to the degree m/n that x is B. There is, however, a very important difference: the conclusion of the statistical syllogism is itself a probability statement, whereas the conclusions of inductive inferences, as here conceived, are not themselves probability statements. There corresponds a probability statement to every inductive inference, but the conclusion of the inference is not a probability statement: just as the entailment statement "That p and that (if p then q) entails that q" corresponds to the deductive inference from p and (if p then q) to q, so the *propability implication*, as we shall call it, "q is probable to degree x relative to the evidence (premise) p" (where the nature of the propositions p and q, the evidential and the inferred proposition, depends on what kind of inductive inference is involved) corresponds to the inductive inference "p, therefore q." As we shall see later, it is doubtful whether the statistical syllogism is a form of valid argument at all, because if it were, contradictory probability statements could be validly deduced from true premises.

5. *Statistical Generalization.* The inference that the relative frequency of property P presented by every member of a class is f or close to f based on the evidence that the relative frequency of P in a sample S is f, a fraction greater than 0 and less than 1. If the class is infinite, then the conclusion of a statistical generalization is a statement about a *limit* of relative frequencies (a notion which will occupy us later).

6. *Direct Statistical Inference.* The converse inference, direct statistical inference, does not usually correspond to the actual knowledge situation, since what we know without the aid of inductive inference is the distribution of a property in a sample, not its distribution in an unlimited or unsurveyably large class. Nevertheless, the theory of such direct inference is an important part of inductive logic, which is in a sense prior to the theory of statistical generalization. Note that f was stipulated to be a fraction *between* 0 and 1. The reason for excluding the limiting cases where all or none of the members of the total class have P is that the direct inference, the inference from total class to sample, becomes deductive in that case.

7. *Analogical Inference.* Suppose it to be known that two objects x and y are similar in several respects, and that x has a certain additional property P; by analogy it is inferred that y also has P. Analogical inference could be more generally described as follows: given that a set of objects a, b,..., n have properties P and Q in common, and that a, b,..., m are further known to have R in common; it is inferred that n likewise has R. In this form analogical inference is indistinguishable from predictive inference, or at least the special case of predictive inference where the relative frequency of the inferred property in the sample is one. For such a predictive inference can be reformulated as follows: the members of s have the properties in common that define the class K, they further have P in common, x resembles the members of s in being a member of K (i.e. having the properties that define K), therefore x also resembles the members of s in having P.

Strictly speaking, therefore, analogical inference should not be listed as a separate kind of inductive inference at all. It would be better to speak of the factor of analogy on which the probability of the conclusion of a predictive inference depends. That is, the probability of a prediction depends not only on the factors already listed but also on the degree of similarity of x to the members of s. If the class name K connotes a great many logically independent properties, then the degree of analogy of x to the members of s is high, and such an increase in analogy tends to increase the probability of the prediction. If all the blue things I have observed have a certain further, logically independent, property in common, say, that they weigh more than 10 ounces, that is a poor reason for expecting other blue things to have the same property. But terms denoting natural kinds, such as dog, copper, salt, rose, cow, are much richer in connotation than the simple predicate "blue"; hence the very fact that the predictive inference is concerned with members of a natural kind indicates that there is a strong element of analogy which makes the prediction more probable.

To sum up: Instead of distinguishing within the genus "inductive inference" predictive from analogical inference, one should, more accurately, distinguish the analogical and the enumerative factor in predictive inference. Sometimes we focus attention on the rule "Other things being equal, the larger s, the more probable the prediction that x, which resembles the members of s in some respects, resembles them in a further respect"; the inference then appears as an enumerative induction. Sometimes we focus attention on the rule "Other things being equal, the greater the degree of known analogy of x to the members of s (where s may have just one, or more than one, member), the greater the probability that there is analogy in a further respect"; in that case the inference appears as analogical.[2]

C. THE CONCEPT OF TRUTH-FREQUENCY

We have defined the distinction between deductive and inductive inference in terms of the distinction between *necessary* and *probable* consequences. The latter distinction, however, has been assumed as intuitively intelligible; it has been explicated. An explication attempted by C. S.

2. It is significant that J. S. Mill describes induction in one sentence as analogical inference and in another sentence as generalization, while supposing himself to have given *equivalent* descriptions of the same process of inference: "Induction, then, is that operation of the mind, by which we infer that what we know to be true in a particular case or cases, will be true in all cases which resemble the former in certain assignable respects. In other words, Induction is the process by which we conclude that what is true of certain individuals of a class is true of the whole class, or that what is true at certain times will be true in similar circumstances at all times" (*System of Logic*, Bk. III, Chap. 2).

Peirce, the founder of American pragmatism, goes as follows: If q is a necessary consequence of p, then the form of inference is such that the conclusion of an inference of that form is true *whenever* the premise (or the conjunction of all the premises) is true. To illustrate, consider the syllogism "All animals are mortal, all men are animals, therefore all men are mortal." Its form may be represented by means of the variables S, P, M (subject of conclusion, or minor term, predicate of conclusion, or major term, and middle term), which range over classes, as: All M are P, all S are M, therefore all S are P. Now any three classes M, P, and S that satisfy the premises (i.e. for which the premises are true) also satisfy the conclusion. Defining the truth-frequency of a form of argument as the ratio of the number of ordered sets of values that satisfy both the premises and the conclusion to the number that satisfy the premises alone, it is obvious that the truth-frequency associated with a valid syllogistic form, and generally with any deductively valid argument form, is the maximum, viz. unity. An invalid deductive argument *may* lead to a true conclusion from true premises, but we can easily construct arguments of the same form whose conclusions are false though the premises are true. In this sense the truth-frequency associated with an argument whose conclusion is not a necessary consequence of the premises is less than unity. If, however, the truth-frequency is close to unity, then, according to Peirce's conception, the conclusion is highly probable relative to the premises. For example, suppose that 90 per cent of alcoholics have an unhappy family life,[3] and that x is an alcoholic; relative to this evidence the probability that x has an unhappy family life is 0.9. This means that the truth-frequency associated with the argument form "90 per cent of A are B, x is an A, therefore x is a B" is 0.9.

There is another way in which Peirce's truth-frequency analysis might be understood. The statement "The probability that an alcoholic has an unhappy family life is 0.9" might be interpreted to mean simply that the proportion of alcoholics with an unhappy family life equals 0.9. In terms of truth-frequency associated with a mode of inference this would mean that inferences that illustrate the pattern "x is an alcoholic, therefore x has an unhappy family life" lead to a true conclusion from a true premise in nine out of ten times. Here the statistical generalization "90 per cent of alcoholics have an unhappy family life" is not considered a *premise*. Accordingly, descriptive terms ("alcoholic," "person having an unhappy family life") are employed in specifying the form of inference. But this is not what one usually means by "form of inference"; thus nobody would list "All men are mortal, x is a man, therefore x is mortal" as a

3. Ratios, of course, make sense only with respect to finite classes. In order to extend the truth-frequency analysis to arguments about infinite classes, the concept of the limit must be used.

form of deductive inference. At any rate, we employ the expression "form of inference" to refer to patterns the only constant constituents of which are logical particles, terms such as "all," "are," "not," "and," "if, then." And it is only in this sense of "form of inference" that the analysis of probability in terms of truth-frequency of a form of inference has even a semblance of plausibility. For consider, for example, inferences whose sole premise is a statement of the form "*x* is a man" and whose conclusion is a corresponding statement of the form "*x* is mortal." If all men are mortal, then such an inference will *always* lead you to a true conclusion from a true premise. Yet, the conclusion is not a *necessary* consequence of the premise; there is no contradiction in supposing that there is an immortal man. It follows that on this interpretation of "form of inference," the analysis of *necessary inference* as meaning inference illustrating a form of inference whose truth-frequency is maximal would definitely be incorrect.

The concept of truth-frequency is defined in terms of the concept "*form* of an argument." Let us define the form of an argument as the skeleton that results when all nonlogical constants are replaced with variables, the same variable replacing the same constant if, as is usually the case, the latter occurs more than once in the argument. How the distinction between logical and nonlogical (descriptive) constants is to be explicated is a difficult question, but there is usually no difficulty in identifying the logical constants in a given argument. Now, there is a minor and a major objection to the truth-frequency analysis of probable inference. The minor objection is that it does not fit enthymematic predictions. Consider the prediction that object *x* will dissolve in liquid *y* because *x* is gold and *y* is aqua regia. The form of this inference is: *x* has property *P* and *y* has property *Q*, therefore *x* has relation *R* to *y*. Surely the truth-frequency associated with this form is maximal, since any two objects, are related in some way or other. The truth-frequentist may, however, reply that enthymematic prediction should not be recognized as inductive inference in the first place, and that, secondly, a correspondingly high, but not maximal truth-frequency would emerge once the total evidence on which the prediction is based was made explicit: it is not just the belief that *x* is gold and *y* is aqua regia that warrants the prediction, but further our past experience that pieces of gold usually dissolve in aqua regia. And once this evidence of past uniformity is explicitly listed as a premise, the inference assumes the form of the predictive inference, which fits the truth-frequency analysis. We may accept this reply, but a far more serious question remains.

According to the truth-frequency analysis, inferences of the same form should have the same probability, just as any two deductive inferences of the same form are either both valid or both invalid. And at first glance this does not seem to be the case. An experimental physicist who has established that one or two samples of a certain metal melt at such and such a temperature under standard pressure confidently generalizes that all samples of that metal have the same melting point. But a naturalist will not generalize with nearly the same confidence that all members of a given species of birds have the same color as one or two members that he has observed. Yet, the two inductive inferences have the same form. Those who wish to defend the truth-frequency analysis may use the same strategy as before: the physicist's generalization does not derive its warrant just from the experiment or two he performed on samples of that particular metal, but there is in the background a mass of experimental knowledge to the effect that melting points are constant within any species of metal, in contrast to the known variation of the color of a bird's plumage within one and the same species. And if this total evidence on which the generalization is based is explicitly listed, we obtain a form of argument such that *any* argument of that form is highly probable.

Whether, by invoking the rule to list explicitly all the evidence relative to which the conclusion is assessed as probable, it is possible to defend successfully the view that the soundness of an inductive inference depends only on its form, just as the validity of a deductive inference depends only on the latter's form, is a difficult and controversial question. As we shall see later, there is an approach to inductive logic (Carnap's) that is dominated by the assumption that inductive inference is like deductive inference in this respect. But be this as it may, let us note in conclusion that the truth-frequency analysis can hardly claim to be a correct account of what scientists mean by the probability of a generalization, a law. For they have to rely on probable inference precisely because such propositions of unrestricted generality cannot be known to be *true*. Therefore it is quite impossible to know what the truth-frequency associated with an inductive generalization is. It follows that either scientists never have any grounds for pronouncing a generalization probable, or else they do not mean by probability in this context truth-frequency. Just how the concept "probability of a generalization" is to be analyzed in such a way that it is possible to justify the belief in the probability of a generalization is a question whose discussion we defer for the time being (cf. Chapter 13).

Selected Readings for this chapter are listed at the end of Chapter 13.

CHAPTER 10

Induction by Elimination & Its Postulates

A. MILL'S THEORY OF INDUCTION

In distinguishing different kinds of inductive inference we have already touched on the fundamental question of inductive logic: what are the criteria of sound induction? Following in the footsteps of Francis Bacon, John Stuart Mill felt that no really new knowledge is ever acquired by deductive reasoning, and that logicians who wish to promote scientific discovery should pay more attention to the criteria of a kind of induction that would lead to thoroughly reliable conclusions. Mill's methodology of experimental science, and especially his discussion of "experimental methods" which he recommended to experimental scientists for both the discovery and the test of causal connections, has made its way into most introductory textbooks of logic and scientific method. Accordingly we shall dispense with a detailed exposition and illustration of these methods, and proceed directly to evaluate them as methods of *proof*.

The method of agreement, the method of difference, the joint method of agreement and difference, and the method of concomitant variation are all of them methods of getting at a true causal law by eliminating all but one of the initially possible alternatives. Following G. H. von Wright, an outstanding contemporary philosopher of induction, we shall avoid the ambiguous term "cause" and speak instead of inquiries into sufficient conditions, necessary conditions, or necessary and sufficient conditions for a specified event or for the pressure of a specified property in a thing. A property (of a thing or of an occurrence) P is a sufficient condition for property Q if every occurrence of P is accompanied (simultaneously or a little later) by an occurrence of Q. P is a necessary condition for Q if Q never occurs in the absence of P. Obviously, P is a sufficient condition for Q if and only if Q is a necessary condition for P. Let us see, now, what can be deduced from the empirical data corresponding to ideal applications of Mill's methods as to the necessary or sufficient conditions of an event. An ideal application of the method of agreement consists in a set of occurrences of the effect where the antecedent circumstances differ from case to case so widely that only one circumstance (C) is regularly present when the effect occurs. It follows from the definition of "necessary condition" that those circumstances which are sometimes absent when the effect occurs are not necessary conditions for the effect. From the assumption that one or the other of the antecedent circumstances is a necessary condition for the effect, it follows that C is a necessary condition. An ideal application of the method of difference consists in two sets of circumstances that are entirely similar except for one circumstance (C'); the effect occurs when C' is present and fails to occur when C' is absent. Clearly, it follows from the definition of "sufficient condition" that no circumstance that is present when the effect is absent is a sufficient condition for the latter; hence, if one of the antecedent circumstances is a sufficient condition for the effect, C' must be it.

One might expect that the same sort of eliminative reasoning could lead to a positive conclusion about a necessary and sufficient condition for an effect, i.e., a condition such that the effect is always present when it is present and always absent when it is absent, by combining the methods of agreement and difference. But such a "joint" method of agreement and difference may mean two distinct procedures: having found by the method of agreement that C accompanies E in all observed cases, we institute a set of cases in which C is absent and note that E fails to occur in these cases. Assuming that the negative cases differ in all the other antecedent circumstances, agreeing only in the absence of C, this is simply a double application of the method of agreement. Furthermore, if the method of agreement that was initially applied to positive cases does warrant the conclusion that C is a necessary condition for E, then it is unnecessary to secure further confirmation by observing what happens when C is absent. Nevertheless, since in practice one cannot be sure that the *observed* antecedent circumstances include a necessary condition for E, and the positive conclusion drawn from the empirical data follows only on that assumption, such a double use of the method of agreement has its point: finding that E is absent in several cases in which C is absent certainly confirms the hypothesis suggested by the positive cases.

A combination of the methods of agreement and difference in one and the same causal inquiry is as follows: Let the letters B, D, F, and G represent circumstances that are absent at least once when E occurs; then we must look for, or experimentally produce, a situation in which C is absent while B, D, F, G, are present. If in this situation E is absent, the method of difference seems not only to have confirmed the conclusion that C is a necessary condition but further to have proved that C is also a sufficient condition, since B, D, F, G have been eliminated as possible sufficient conditions. Note, however, that this strong conclusion presupposes that one or the other of the observed antecedent circumstances B, C, D, F, G is a necessary condition, and that one or the other is a sufficient condition for E. What is accomplished by an ideal application of the methods of agreement and of difference to one and the same effect is the demonstration that *if* this strong presupposition is true, then *one and the same* condition is necessary and sufficient for the effect.

Once it is recognized that any positive conclusions that are legitimately derivable from the results of an application of Mill's methods are valid but *relative* to presuppositions of this kind, and that the latter do not admit of a priori proof, one will take a modest view of the probative force of these methods. One will treat the positive conclusions regarding necessary, or sufficient, or necessary and sufficient conditions as confirmed hypotheses that have not been conclusively verified but must be further tested. Viewed in this light, the double method of agreement is by no means pointless; in fact, it is none other than the method of matching a "control group" with an "experimental group," which is widely and successfully used in the biological and social sciences. Suppose, for example, that a physician wishes to test the efficiency of a certain drug as a cure for colds. If people suffering from a cold and who do not take the drug continue to be stricken for a fairly long time, while people who take the drug get immediate relief, he will consider his hypothesis well confirmed. In order to conform his test procedure to Mill's canon, he should make sure that the patients who take the drug as well as the patients who do not take it are in relevant respects as dissimilar as possible, for if there is another relevant property (besides that of taking the drug and that of being cured) that all the cured people have in common and that all the people who continue to suffer fail to have, it would explain the difference as well.

If the scientist who compares an experimental group with a control group aims at the discovery of a necessary condition, then the double method of agreement is appropriate. For if the members of the experimental group agree in no relevant respect except the tested factor, and the members of the control group agree in the absence of the tested factor and in the absence of the effect, then the hypothesis that the tested factor is a necessary condition for the effect has been confirmed. On the other hand, experimental and control group may also be compared in conformity to the requirements of the method of difference, which is appropriate for eliminating possible sufficient conditions. In that case care is taken to make the two groups as similar as possible in relevant respects, so that they differ relevantly only with respect to the tested factor.

In so far as Mill's methods are methods of eliminative induction, methods of discovering true causal laws by eliminating false alternatives, they are based on the logical fact that a generalization cannot be proved by any finite number of confirming instances ("Induction by simple enumeration," said Francis Bacon, "is puerile, for it is always exposed to the danger of contrary instances"), but can be *dis*proved by a single instance. But it can easily be seen that the probative force of eliminative induction cannot exceed that of enumerative induction as much as Mill supposed. Any positive conclusions, the reader will recall, follow only on the assumption that one or the other of the relevant observed antecedent circumstances is causally connected with the effect.[1] Even if one could prove a priori that for every property there is a logically distinct property that is a sufficient, or a necessary, or a necessary and sufficient condition for it, such *specific* assumptions are far from being necessary truths. Therefore any causal hypothesis suggested by even the most critical use of Mill's methods is still subject to disconfirmation. Generalizations face the danger of being overthrown by contrary instances, no matter whether they were reached by eliminative induction or by enumerative induction.

The same must be said about the method of concomitant variation, which is especially relevant to quantitative induction. Suppose a change in variable y is to be accounted for, and suppose that $x_1 x_2, \ldots, x_n$ are other variables, changes in which might be causally responsible for the observed change in y. If we are lucky enough to find a set of cases of the effect where $x_2, x_3, \ldots, x_n$ remain constant, or are able to produce such cases experimentally, we may conclude that a change in these variables is not a necessary condition for a change in y. Therefore x_1 is the variable, according to the canon of concomitant variation, changes in which are causally connected with changes in y. (Mill is careful to point out that the question remains open which is the cause and which the effect, since the changes usually occur at the same time.)

1. In this discussion of Mill's methods we disregard the logical complications that arise when the possiblity of *complex* necessary or sufficient conditions is taken into account. The problem will be dealt with in Part Four, in connection with a close analysis of the meaning of "cause."

In the first place, no conclusions about sufficient conditions are warranted by this method; in this respect it resembles the method of agreement. But, secondly, it is highly implausible to assume either that a change in one variable is a necessary condition or that it is a sufficient condition for a change in another variabe. For what a law of functional dependence usually asserts is: *if* variables $x_2, \ldots, x_n$ are constant, then y varies with x_1 in a determinate manner, expressed by some functional equation $y = f(x_1)$. Obvious illustrations: the gas laws, expressing one of the variables pressure, volume, temperature as a function of a second on the assumption that the third is constant; the law of supply and demand in economics, according to which price varies inversely as the demand provided the supply is constant. Such *conditional* equations, as they may be called, are mathematically concise statements of large families of propositions of the form: if p, then (q if and only if r), where p refers to constancy of relevant variables. For example: If the temperature of a sample of an ideal gas is constant, then the gas pressure is doubled if and only if the gas volume is halved. Absence of certain relevant variables can be conveniently subsumed under the above schema by calling an absent variable one with a constant value of zero. Example: If frictional resistance and buoyancy of the medium are zero, then the velocity of a falling body is directly proportional to the time of fall. The logical point to be grasped is that causal relationships of concomitant variation—expressed by functional equations if the variables are continuous and measurable—cannot be adequately described in the language of simple necessary and sufficient conditions. We need the concept of a change that is *conditionally* necessary and sufficient for another change. Before we can reliably predict a change in y from an observed change in x, or constancy of y from the observed constancy of x, we must ascertain that the other relevant variables remain constant. (cf. Chapter 14.)

B.   THE CHARGE OF CIRCULARITY

John Stuart Mill's theory of induction is at present widely rejected by philosophers of science on the ground that it exemplifies a "quest for certainty" (in John Dewey's phrase) that under close logical analysis has proved wholly utopian. Whether Mill was guilty of the obvious blunder of supposing that a universal empirical hypothesis can be conclusively established in the sense that its future disconfirmation can be ruled out on *logical* grounds is at least debatable. On the other hand,

Mill did recommend his methods of eliminative induction (as we have called them, following the terminology of von Wright) as the only rigorous methods of establishing causal laws. But this position seems to get entangled in a serious logical difficulty. For Mill himself acknowledged that any conclusion drawn from an application of his methods presupposed the *law of universal causation:* that every event regularly follows, and is regularly preceded by, some antecedent event.[2] Unless some antecedent circumstance is a necessary, or a sufficient, or a necessary and sufficient condition for E, no amount of experimental ingenuity can discover *which* it is. But how, asked Mill, can this presupposition be inductively established? There had to be some way, for an empiricist like Mill had to rule out the possibility of an a priori proof. Now, any attempt to establish it by eliminative induction is ruled out too, because that kind of induction just presupposes it. There remains enumerative induction, and Mill did his very best to persuade himself and his readers that the law of universal causation is sufficiently justified by enumerative induction. Enumerative induction, he argued, is valid and can be relied on if the confirmed generalization has very wide scope and is confirmed by a wide variety of experiences. What Mill seems to have had in mind is that an inductive generalization may be considered as well established if the sample of known confirming instances contains a great deal of variety. That all metallic objects whatever conduct electricity is a generalization of considerable scope, but if it has been confirmed by observations of many different metals, it is highly reliable. (Just why variety in the observed sample should enhance the probability of a generalization is a profound question to which we shall attend in the next section.) And since the law of universal causation has been confirmed in widely different areas of human experience, much more extensively than any specific causal law, argued Mill, it may be presupposed in any future use of the methods of eliminative induction as having been established by enumerative induction.

Mill's argument is vulnerable on more than one count. To begin with, if enumerative induction is all right when there is a great deal of confirming material, then it is not at all clear why the law of universal causation but not specific causal laws can be proved by enumerative induction. For the confirming instances of the former *are* specific causal laws. From "C is the cause of E")where C and E are frequently repeated events) it follows that E has a cause, and this proposition confirms the proposition that every event has a cause in the same sense in which the proposition that John has a father confirms the proposition that every human being has a father. And has Mill counted the known

2. For a close discussion of the meaning and logical status of this "law" see Chapter 37.

causal laws and found that there are far more of them than confirming event sequences for any given causal law? Mill might reply that the experiences that confirm the law of universal causation consist of the sum total of experiences that confirm specific causal laws. But in that case any given experience confirms that great law only if it confirms a specific causal law. And if the inductive inference from specific observations to that great law must pass through specific laws, it cannot consistently be maintained that enumerative induction to specific causal laws is invalid yet enumerative induction to the great law of causation valid. At any rate, if it is granted that we have no evidence for universal causation unless we have evidence for specific causal laws, then the proposition that only eliminative induction can justify belief in a specific causal law entails that the belief in universal causation cannot be justified without *presupposing* the validity of eliminative induction. Viewed in this light, Mill's argument for universal causation must be charged with *petitio principii* after all.

The critics of empiricism, who maintain that inductive methods cannot be jusified without presupposing certain a priori principles about the constitution of nature, are only too glad to convict empiricists like Mill of naively circular reasoning. But there is no need for empiricists to concede in resignation just because Mill blundered. In the first place, Mill got himself into unnecessary difficulty by asserting that the methods of eliminative induction presuppose the law of universal causation. Actually, all that is presupposed in a particular causal inquiry is that *the particular event* whose cause one wishes to discover has a cause. There is no need to make at the start the sweeping assumption that *every* event has a cause.[3] To be sure, we are prepared to justify that weaker presupposition by a predictive inference: most other events whose causes were carefully looked for were found to have a cause, or at least the evidence makes it probable that there are laws governing their occurrence (and that they have "causes" in that sense). But no appeal to a law of *universal* causation is really required. Curiously, Mill himself urged substitution of inductive reasoning "from particulars to particulars" for deduction from a major premise: since the only evidence you have for the major premise "All men are mortal," he argued, is that this and that and that man has died, you might as well derive your prediction that you too will die directly from these particulars instead of constructing the impressive syllogism: All men are mortal, I am a man, therefore I am mortal. If so, then Mill was plainly inconsistent

3. That eliminative induction logically presupposes only this weaker form of determinism was recognized by J. Nicod. See his "Logical Problem of Induction," in *The Foundations of Geometry and Induction* (New York: Humanities Press, Inc., 1930), p. 225.

with his own insight when he claimed that all inductions presuppose the law of universal causation as an "ultimate major premise."

Secondly, one of the replies Mill himself made to the anticipated charge of circularity is sound. He distinguished between loose, uncritical enumerative inductions by means of which we first arrive at tentative hypotheses about causal connections, and critical inductions by means of his "methods" that presuppose such tentative hypotheses. Indeed, in order to apply any of Mill's methods reasonably, we must initially separate those antecedent circumstances that might be causally connected with the effect from those that are clearly irrelevant. There are all sorts of things I do before I start a sleepless night: I take off my shoes, I brush my teeth, I remove the bedspread, and so on. But I would not for a moment entertain the hypothesis that any of these "antecedent circumstances" is responsible for insomnia. Why? Because there are innumerable cases where such antecedents are not followed by sleeplessness. On the other hand, I might suspect that drinking coffee late at night has something to do with it, because past experience has shown a high positive correlation between these two events. This illustrates how tentative hypotheses arrived at by plain enumerative induction serve to make that separation of possibly relevant from obviously irrelevant antecedents without which what Mill recommended as "critical" induction could not even start. But there is no circularity in this process, for no "universal law of causation" is logically presupposed at any point.[4]

C. ADDITION AND MULTIPLICATION OF PROBABILITIES

In order to enable the reader to follow J. M. Keynes' theory of induction, to be expounded and evaluated in the following section, we must present first the elements of the calculus of probability. Without going at present into the controversial question of the interpretation of "probability," we can state the *formal* properties of the probability functor by means of a few logically and mathematically simple axioms. We shall write "$P\ (p/q) = x$" for "The probability of p relative to the evidence q equals x, where p and q are propositions and x ranges over fractions between 0 and 1, limits included." The procedure

4. This is explicitly recognized by Mill in a footnote in Sec. 2, Chap. 21, Bk. III, of his *System of Logic*.

for assigning values to x depends on the interpretation of the probability functor. But the calculus of probability is not concerned with the assignment of degrees of probability (except for the limits, 0 and 1). Its problem is that of the deduction of probability statements from probability statements in which x occurs as a variable. We proceed to formulate and explain those axioms which are required for the proof of the theorems of inverse probability; the latter are the theorems we need to know in order to understand Keynes' theory of induction. It is not, of course, claimed that a different axiomatization yielding the same results is impossible.

1. If p is a logical consequence of q, then $P(p/q) = 1$
2. If p is incompatible with r on the evidence q (i.e., if q implies that p implies not-r), then $P[(p$ or $r)/q] = P(p/q) + P(r/q)$
3. $P[(p$ and $r)/q] = P(r/q) \times P(p/r$ and $q)$

Axiom 2 is the addition rule for probabilities, in the special form for incompatible propositions. An obvious illustration: if each side of a symmetrical die is as likely to turn up as any other, then, on the evidence that a symmetrical die is thrown, the probability of a six is $\frac{1}{6}$ and the probability of a five is $\frac{1}{6}$, hence the probability of getting either a six or a five in one throw equals $\frac{1}{3}$. For our purposes we may ignore the general form of the addition rule (which is applicable no matter whether the alternatives are compatible or incompatible on the evidence). Axiom 3 is the general multiplication rule. Suppose that an urn is filled with four blue and six red marbles (this information corresponds to the "evidence" proposition q), and that each marble is as likely to be drawn as any other. The probability of drawing a blue marble on the stated evidence equals $\frac{4}{10}$. What is the probability of obtaining two blue marbles in two successive drawings? If the marble drawn the first time is not put back into the urn before the second drawing, then the probability of drawing a blue marble the second time equals $\frac{3}{9}$; hence the answer is $\frac{2}{5} \times \frac{1}{3} = \frac{2}{15}$. If the outcome of the second drawing is independent of the outcome of the first drawing; i.e., if drawn marbles are put back into the urn before the next drawing, the answer is $\frac{2}{5} \times \frac{2}{5} = \frac{4}{25}$ In general terms: if $P(p/r$ and $q) = P(p/q)$, p is said to be independent of r (or r irrelevant to p). In that case we obtain the special multiplication rule for (inductively)[5] independent propositions:

5. Inductive independence is contrasted with deductive (logical) independence. Two propositions are deductively independent if neither proposition is deducible from the other and they are mutually consistent. Clearly q may not be deducible from p and still q may have a different probability relative to (p and e) than relative to e alone.

$$P(p \text{ and } r/q) = P(p/q) \times P(r/q)$$

Now, by substituting throughout p for r and r for p, we derive from (3):

$$P(r \text{ and } p/q) = P(p/q) \times P(r/p \text{ and } q)$$

Since $P(r \text{ and } p/q)$ is obviously equal to $P(p \text{ and } r/q)$, it follows that

$$P(r/q) \times P(p/r \text{ and } q) = P(p/q) \times P(r/p \text{ and } q)$$

Therefore

$$P(p/r \text{ and } q) = \frac{P(p/q) \times P(r/p \text{ and } q)}{P(r/q)}$$

This is called the *division* theorem. It admits of a significant interpretation in terms of scientific method. Let p be a hypothesis to be tested, q the evidence relative to which p has a certain finite probability before the test,[6] r a description of a new item of relevant evidence disclosed by the test. The four probabilities involved in the theorem then have the following meanings: $P(p/q)$ is the antecedent probability of the hypothesis, $P(r/p \text{ and } q)$ is the likelihood that the present test will have a favorable outcome on the assumption of the hypothesis and the old evidence, $P(r/q)$ is the probability of a favorable outcome of the test relative to the old evidence alone, i.e., without assuming the hypothesis to be true, and $P(p/r \text{ and } q)$ is the probability of the hypothesis relative to the old evidence plus a favorable outcome of the new test. Let us refer to these four probabilities briefly as the *antecedent probability*, the *likelihood*, the *expectedness*, and the *posterior probability*. For the probability of a hypothesis prior to *any* empirical test, i.e., relative to no empirical evidence at all, the name *a priori probability* is appropriate. Following Carnap, we may then speak of probability relative to tautological evidence, writing $P(p/t)$ where t is an arbitrary tautology.

If in particular r is a deductive consequence of p, then, by Axiom 1, the likelihood equals unity, hence we obtain the *special division theorem* for the case where a hypothesis is tested in terms of its deductive consequences:

$$\text{Posterior probability} = \frac{\text{antecedent probability}}{\text{expectedness}}$$

This theorem accords with the intuitive inductive logic of scientists, for it says that, assuming a finite antecedent probability of the tested hypothesis, the latter is confirmed by a favorable test all the more, the less such a confirming observation could have been expected *without*

---

6. At this introductory stage of our discussion of probability we use the notion of "probability of an hypothesis" uncritically. It will be critically examined in Chapter 13.

assuming the hypothesis. Suppose, for example, that the hypothesis has the form "All A are B." That a large sample of A's should be B without exception is maximally probable (i.e., certain) relative to that universal hypothesis, but fairly improbable if the latter is not true. Such evidence raises the posterior probability considerably above the antecedent possibility. Another significant corollary is that a new confirmation of a hypothesis with a finite antecedent probability increases the posterior probability of the hypothesis provided the new confirmation was not certain relative to the old evidence. Let $c_1, \ldots, c_n$ represent the old confirmations of a universal hypothesis h, and c_{n+1} a new confirmation. What is to be proved is that $P(h/c_1, \ldots, c_n \ \& \ c_{n+1})$ is greater than $P(h/c_1, \ldots, c_n)$. According to the special division theorem,

$$P(h/c_1, \ldots, c_n \ \& \ c_{n+1}) = \frac{P(h/c_1, \ldots, c_n)}{P(c_{n+1}/c_1, \ldots, c_n)}$$

And by elementary algebra, a fraction is greater than its numerator if its denominator is a proper fraction less than one. The condition that the expectedness of the new confirmation be less than one is obviously satisfied since c_{n+1} is not entailed by c_n.

Suppose, now, that $h_1\ h_2, \ldots, h_n$ are a set of mutually incompatible and jointly exhaustive hypotheses. Each hypothesis in the set that is compatible with the observed data *might* be the correct explanation. For example, if the data consist in m confirming instances of the universal hypothesis "All A are B," any hypothesis of the form "The proportion of B's within the class A is x/y," where x and y are positive integers and y greater than x, is incompatible with the universal hypothesis and equally compatible with the data. Assuming the class A to be finite, we obtain a finite set of mutually exclusive and jointly exhaustive hypotheses expressing possible proportions of B's in A. Since, by assumption, "h_1 or h_2 or ... or h_n" is a tautology, r is logically equivalent to

$$r \ \& \ h_1 \text{ or } r \ \& \ h_2 \text{ or } \ldots \text{ or } r \ \& \ h_n$$

We now use this logical equivalence to transform the denominator on the right-hand side of the division theorem into

$$P(r \ \& \ h_1 \text{ or } r \ \& \ h_2 \text{ or } \ldots \text{ or } r \ \& \ h_n/q)$$

Applying Axioms 2 and 3 to compute this probability of a disjunction of conjunctions, we obtain *Bayes' theorem* for finite sets of alternative hypotheses:

$$P(h_i/r \cdot q) = \frac{P(h_i/q) \times P(r/h_i \cdot q)}{\sum\limits_{i=1}^{n} P(h_i/q) \times P(r/h_i \cdot q)}$$

If the set h_i has only two members, viz. a hypothesis and its negation, Bayes' theorem assumes the special form[7]

$$P(h/r \cdot q) = \frac{P(h/q) \times P(r/h \cdot q)}{P(h/q) \times P(r/h \cdot q) + P(\overline{h}/q) \times P(r/\overline{h} \cdot q)}$$

D. KEYNES' THEORY OF INDUCTION

In discussing the predictive inference, we said that according to customary ways of inductive thinking the probability of a prediction depends on the size of the sample on which the prediction is based. That is, the larger the number of instances in which two properties have been found conjoined, the greater the probability that they will be found conjoined again. However, a critical scientist is careful to look for confirming instances of a generalization that *differ* in relevant respects. He attaches at least as much weight to the amount of relevant variety as to the mere number of the confirmations. In fact, would he think that the probability of his generalization had at all increased if the new confirming instances[8] were in relevant respects exactly like the old ones? Keynes raised just this fundamental question: under what conditions do additional confirmations of a generalization increase its probability? His answer was: if and only if the relevant variety in the observed sample is increased. His theory of induction is an ingenious attempt to justify this answer, an answer which surely accords with the intuitive convictions of inductive scientists.

Let the generalization to be established by induction have the form: for any x, if x is A, then x is B. And let $a, b, c, \ldots , n$ be observed objects that have both properties, A and B. What is it that inhibits our inference that any other object that resembles $a, b, c, \ldots , n$ in being A also resembles it in being B? According to Keynes it is the suspicion that some property common to $a, b, c, \ldots , n$ other than A may be a necessary condition for B. For if so, then A is not a sufficient condition for B, and hence the generalization is not true. Let C be such a common property of the observed instances which we disregarded in classifying them as A's. If we find a further instance of A that is a B but lacks C, we thereby eliminate the initially possible hypothesis that, not A by itself, but only the conjunction of A and C is sufficient for B. Let $C, D, F, \ldots , N$ be the total set of properties, exclusive of A and

7. The bar above a letter denoting a proposition symbolizes the negation of that proposition.

8. In the present context we define a confirming instance of a generalization "All A are B" as any object or event that is not both A and non-B. This definition leaves the question open whether observation of a confirming instance increases the probability of the generalization.

B, that are common to *a*, *b*, . . . , *n*. Ideally we might by suitable selection of further instances prove that no member of *C*, *D*, *F*, . . . , *N* is a necessary condition for *B*, because none of these properties is common to all the confirming instances of the generalization in question, though all of them are *B*. In Keynes' terminology this is to say that by increasing the variety we have reduced the "positive analogy" in the sample to just the one property *A*, however complex it may be. And Keynes thought that such a reduction of the positive analogy to the bare minimum would be tantamount to a conclusive proof of the generalization.

Keynes was aware that the method of proving a generalization by reducing the positive analogy in the sample of confirming instances is applicable only if every object has but a finite number of logically independent properties.[9] The method assumes that if an object differs from *a*, *b*,..., *n* in many respects while resembling them in being *A* and *B*, this new confirmation greatly increases the probability of the generalization. But if any one object had infinitely many logically independent properties, an infinite number of possible hypotheses to the effect that some property other than *A* is necessary for *B* would always remain no matter how many were eliminated through reduction of the known positive analogy. Keynes therefore postulated, in our language, that every object has a finite number of logically independent properties, in his language, the "limitation of independent variety."

Before discussing this postulate we must call attention to other presuppositions of Keynes' theory of induction which are nowhere made explicit, let alone justified, in Keynes' classical *Treatise on Probability*. He evidently assumed that for every property *Q* there is a logically distinct property *P* which is present in the observed instances of *Q* and which is a sufficient condition for *Q*. Without this assumption—let us call it, following von Wright, the *deterministic postulate*—it would be quite impossible to deduce from negative premises to the effect that such and such properties are not necessary conditions for *B* a positive conclusion to the effect that *A* by itself is a sufficient condition for *B*. The deterministic postulate may be said to guide the scientist in his search for more complex sufficient conditions when what was initially assumed to be a sufficient condition for a given property turned out not to be sufficient. If he encounters a case of *A* that is not a case of *B* he does not abandon in resignation his search for a sufficient condition of *B*;

9. More accurately, the condition is that the number of initially possible universal hypotheses that are compatible with the observed data is finite. This condition is entailed by the condition mentioned in the text without being equivalent to it. But since the essential features of Keynes' theory are the same no matter which of these is postulated, we use the stronger formulation of Keynes' postulate just on grounds of simplicity.

he is confident that though the simple generalization "For any x, if x is A, then x is B" has been refuted, there is a true generalization of the form "For every x, if x is A *and* C, then x is B," and that the exceptions to the simple generalization can be *explained* in terms of the absence of condition C in those contrary instances.

Keynes does mention that the justification of inductive generalization requires an axiom of the *uniformity of nature*. This axiom he interprets, as a "generalized judgment of irrelevance" of mere differences in spatio-temporal position. When we observe further ravens in order to test the generalization "All ravens are black" (let us assume for the sake of the argument that our defining criterion of ravenhood does not include blackness), it surely is not because we suspect that in order for a raven to be black it may have to be in the same space-time region as the ravens so far observed. We are inclined to assume *a priori* that the mere place and time at which an object happens to exist is not a necessary condition for any of its qualitative properties. Suppose that an object a is known to have qualitative properties P, Q, and R and a different object b is known to resemble a in having P and Q. According to the Keynes uniformity axiom the mere fact that b differs from a in spatio-temporal position is no ground at all for doubting that b also resembles a in having R; in other words, knowing that a is a confirming instance for the generalization "Everything that is P and Q is R," and not knowing of any difference between b and a other than spatio-temporal position, one would have no ground for hesitating to predict that b is likewise a confirming instance. On this assumption of inductive irrelevance of spatio-temporal position, Keynes' recommended method of reducing the positive analogy in the sample of confirming instances does indeed approach the true law, if there is one, much faster than it would otherwise. For if spatio-temporal position *as such* is inductively irrelevant, then it is unnecessary to vary spatio-temporal position *as such*. In other words, we can disregard from the start those members of the positive analogy in the set of known confirming instances which are spatio-temporal properties.

Two comments are in order. In the first place, the uniformity axiom as formulated by Keynes is not equivalent to the deterministic postulate. For from the assumption that no spatio-temporal property is a necessary condition for a qualitative property[10] it cannot be deduced that there are laws connecting qualitative properties at all. Even if by virtue of the assumed inductive irrelevance of spatio-temporal position any given qualitative generalization should have a greater antecedent probability,

10. The term "qualitative property" is perhaps misleading in the present context, because we so use it that quantitative properties such as "heavy" or "weighing 10 pounds" are qualitative too: a qualitative property is contrasted with a positional property, such as "occupying place P at time t."

and could therefore be established as highly probable more quickly, it does not follow that there are any true qualitative generalizations (such as "All ravens are black") at all.

Secondly, the meaning of the uniformity axiom is not really clear: by spatio-temporal difference may be meant an empirically observable differ-ence or a difference in *absolute* position which is not empirically ob-servable. If the former, the axiom is not an a priori presupposition at all. We find empirically that some qualitative properties are fairly invariant with respect to spatio-temporal change, others are not. Objects can be moved around without change of color, specific gravity, chemical com-position, and so on, hence we have empirical evidence justifying the judgment that the spatio-temporal difference between *a* and *b* is no ground for doubting that *b* resembles *a with respect to these properties*. But other qualitive properties do not enjoy such invariance: weight varies with relative spatial position, and many characteristics of organisms vary with the organism's age, hence with relative temporal position. The axiom interpreted as an empirically meaningful proposition, therefore, is far from self-evident; we know it to be false. Keynes would of course reply that he meant that *absolute* position in space and time cannot affect the qualitative properties of objects. A body changes its weight as it changes its position relative to an attracting planet, but if it had the same relative position in a different part of absolute space, it would have the same weight. In this formulation the axiom is untestable for obvious reasons. But what is more serious is that it cannot serve the purpose for which it was postulated. It was postulated in order to justify the scientist's restriction of attention to those among the universal hypotheses that are compatible with the data that do not contain spatio-temporal predicates. Now, if the spatio-temporal predicates refer to *relative* positions, then such hypotheses cannot be ignored at all. If, on the other hand, they refer to *absolute* positions, then the universal hypotheses in which they occur are not empirically meaningful, and there would surely be no sense in trying to increase by observations the antecedent probability of an empirically meaningless hypothesis. In other words, no special axiom over and above an empiricist restriction to confirmable hypotheses would be needed on the second alternative.

Although for these reasons the uniformity axiom does not seem to be required by Keynes' theory of induction as a process of elimination of initially possible hypotheses, Keynes made another assumption that is strictly required by his theory but is far from self-evident. Suppose that the hypotheses as to sufficient conditions (s.c.) for B that are compatible with the facts so far disclosed are: A is a s.c. for B, C is a s.c. for B, ..., N is a s.c. for B, $(A \& C)$ is a s.c. for B, ..., $(A \& N)$ is a s.c. for B, $(C \& D)$ is a s.c. for B, ..., $(C \& N)$ is a s.c. for B, and so on for all possible conjunctions that can be formed out of the set $A, C, ..., N$.

Some of the possible sufficient conditions contain A, some do not. But, even granted the deterministic postulate, by what logic can we infer from premises denying that such and such properties are *necessary* for B a conclusion affirming that such and such a property is *sufficient* for B? Keynes must have assumed that if no element of the set $C, D,\ldots, N$ is necessary for B, then no conjunction containing such an element is a smallest sufficient condition for B, i.e., a condition that is sufficient and that is such that no part of it is sufficient. In other words, he must have assumed that if X is a part of a complex smallest s.c. for Y, then it is a necessary condition for Y. But this is to exclude the possibility that a property may have more than one smallest sufficient condition. Thus, all samples of iron conduct electricity and all samples of copper conduct electricity. Here it is plausible to assume that the conjunction of the properties connoted by "metal," which is a common part of the connotations of "iron" and "copper," is already a smallest sufficient condition for electrical conductivity. And in many other cases of plurality of sufficient conditions for one and the same property it can be shown that they are not smallest sufficient conditions, that it is some common part of them that is a smallest sufficient condition. In other words, plurality of sufficient conditions often arises because the sufficient conditions contain elements that are not *necessary* for the occurrence of the conditioned property. Nevertheless, it is not logically demonstrable that every part of a smallest sufficient condition is also a necessary condition. If it were, the following should be a provable theorem: If (p & q) implies r, and p does not imply r and q does not imply r, then r implies p and r implies q. And far from being a provable theorem, it is easily disproved: just put for p and q the premises of a valid syllogism and for r its conclusion.[11]

Keynes evidently believed that, assuming limitation of independent variety, eliminative induction could in principle lead to *certain* knowledge of a generalization in a finite number of steps. But apart from the flaws in his reasoning we have already uncovered, there is a neat argument, due to Jean Nicod, which establishes that if indeed certainty could be attained in the Keynesian way, it would be quite useless. For one could tell in advance that *if* only one generalization survived the process of elimination, it would be the most complex of all the candidates. This follows from the logical fact that in eliminating a conjunction as a possible sufficient condition, one at the same time eliminates all parts of the conjunction, but is still faced with the possibility that some conjunction containing the former as a part is a sufficient condition. Therefore, if only one hypothesis remains possible, it must be the hypothesis that the conjunction of *all* the properties that are common to all the known confirming instances is a sufficient condition for the conditioned property.

11. We shall argue in more detail below (Chapter 14, C) that inductive logic must take the plurality of sufficient conditions for one and the same kind of effect seriously.

But such an enormously complex hypothesis could never be used to make a prediction about an object that lacked even a single property that is common to all the hitherto observed confirming instances. And it is at any rate difficult to reconcile this consequence of Keynes' theory of induction with the belief that the laws of nature are *simple*.

Keynes was careful to point out that in order to prove that by the method of reducing the positive analogy one can increase the probability of a tested generalization, it is not necessary to assume the truth of the limited variety postulate, but only that it itself has a finite antecedent probability. His argument was that (1) it can be demonstrated by means of the calculus of probability that the probability of a generalization g increases with its confirmations and approaches certainty as the limit *provided* g has a finite antecedent probability, (2) the limited variety postulate entails that g has a finite antecedent probability, (3) the same inductive process that increases the probability of g also increases the probability of the limited variety postulate provided the latter has a finite antecedent probability. Let us attend to these three stages of Keynes' argument separately.

1. Referring back to the special form of Bayes' theorem, we see that the posterior probability of a generalization h will approach the maximal value, unity, as h is increasingly confirmed if and only if the quantity $P(\bar{h}/q) \times P(r/\bar{h} \& q)$ approaches 0 as a limit under the same condition, and the antecedent probability of h is greater than 0 (if the latter were equal to 0, the fraction that represents the posterior probability would be indeterminate). Now, replace r by a conjunction of instantial consequences of h, $c_1 \& c_2 \& \ldots \& c_n$. Our question is then reduced to the question whether $P(r/\bar{h} \& q)$ decreases and approaches 0 as a limit as n, the number of confirmations, increases. That this probability decreases as the "size" of the conjunction represented by r increases seems to be an obvious consequence of the multiplication rule. Compare, for example, $P(c_1/\bar{h} \& q)$ with $P(c_1 \& c_2/\bar{h} \& q)$. It follows from the multiplication rule that the latter quantity must be smaller than the former provided the former is neither 0 nor 1 and $P(c_2/c_1 \& \bar{h} \& q)$ is neither 0 nor 1. That neither $P(c_1/\bar{h} \& q)$ nor $P(c_2/c_1 \& \bar{h} \& q)$ is 0, is obvious, since the hypotheses, c_1 and c_2, do not contradict the respective evidence statements.[12] It is also obvious that $P(c_1/\bar{h} \& q)$ is less than 1, for c_1 is not entailed by $\bar{h} \& q$. The

12. It may seem that the above reasoning presupposes an additional axiom: If q contradicts p, then $P(p/q) = 0$. But this is actually deducible from our three axioms, as follows: Since p is a logical consequence of q if and only if not-p contradicts q, Axiom 1 yields: If p *contradicts* q, then $P(\text{not-}p/q) = 1$. By Axiom 2,

$$P(p \text{ or not-}p/q) = P(p/q + P(\text{not-}p/q)$$

But by Axiom 1, $P(p \text{ or not-}p/q) = 1$, since a tautology follows from any proposition. Therefore, $1 = P(p/q) + 1$, on the assumption that p contradicts q. Therefore, if p contradicts q, $P(p/q) = 0$.

only question that remains is whether $P(c_2/c_1 \& \bar{h} \& q)$ is less than 1. But if the instance referred to by c_2 is not exactly similar to the instance referred to by c_1, it surely cannot be predicted with certainty that it will likewise confirm h. At any rate, this last condition is certainly fulfilled if the process of confirmation of h conforms to the Keynesian precept of increasing the (relevant) variety in the sample.

Since this reasoning holds for any two conjunctions of confirming instances for a given generalization, it has been established that the probability of a generalization (whatever "probability" may mean in this context) increases with increasing confirmation, provided the antecedent probability of the generalization is finite. Further, its probability approaches certainty as a limit if $P(c_1 \& \ldots \& c_n/\bar{h} \& q)$ approaches 0 as a limit with increasing n. And this is self-evident since by the time n reaches the value corresponding to the total number of members of the class that is the subject of the tested generalization, the conjunction is logically equivalent to h itself, hence contradicts $\bar{h}$.[13]

2. The limited variety postulate asserts that the number of logically independent properties, present in the observed instances of a given conditioned property, that *might* be a sufficient condition for the latter is finite. How does it follow from this assumption that the antecedent probability of, say, "All A are B" is finite? Actually, all that follows is that *if* B has a logically distinct sufficient condition, then either A or C or D or $\ldots$ is it, where the set of properties $A, C, D, \ldots$ is finite. The deterministic postulate then leads to the conclusion that either A or C or D or $\ldots$ (a finite disjunction, though most of its members are unknown) is *actually* a sufficient condition for the conditioned property. But it still does not follow that the antecedent probability of "All A are B" is

13. In view of what was said about the modern interpretation of universal statements as implications, this logical equivalence holds only if instantial confirmations are expressed in the form "not-(x is A and x is not B)," which is logically weaker than the observed fact that x is both A and B. As a matter of fact, there is a simple consideration that justifies such a weaker formulation. If we took "x is A and x is B" as confirmation, "x is A and x is not B" as disconfirmation, and observations of non-A's as irrelevant—as may seem plausible at first glance—we would be faced with the paradox that the same evidence may confirm a hypothesis but be irrelevant to h' which is logically equivalent to h: "for every x, if x is not B, then x is not A" is logically equivalent to "For every x, if x is A, then x is B," hence a thing that is not B and not A ought to confirm the latter hypothesis. (For a full discussion of this problem, see C. G. Hempel, "Studies in the Logic of Confirmation," *Mind*, 1945.) Another assumption underlying Keynes' proof, however, cannot so easily be accepted: it is the extensional interpretation according to which "All cases of A are cases of B" is logically equivalent to "There are no cases of A that are not cases of B." If, on the other hand, lawlike generalizations are construed as negations of *possibilities,* in the form of subjunctive conditionals (as in Chapter 16), the above step in Keynes' proof collapses.

finite. Those who wish to justify the belief that by induction certainty can be approached indefinitely with the help of probability calculus *plus* synthetic postulates, must further invoke what Keynes called the *principle of indifference:* if no empirical evidence relevant to a set of n mutually exclusive and jointly exhaustive hypotheses is known, and the hypotheses have the same logical form, then they all have the same probability. In particular, each has the a priori probability $1/n$. Or more accurately: the a priori probabilities of a set of mutually exclusive and jointly exhaustive hypotheses of the same logical form are equal. We shall devote a special section (Chapter 12, A) to this famous principle; the meaning of the qualification "same logical form" will there be clarified. In the meantime we just note that Keynes' "justification" of inductive method goes through only if the principle of indifference is assumed along with the limited variety postulate and the deterministic postulate.

Further, whereas such an argument in favor of a finite a priori probability of a tested hypothesis may have some plausibility in the case of qualitative hypotheses such as "All ravens are black," it is not obvious how it could be applied to quantitative hypotheses in the form of conditional functional equations (cf. p. 155). Keynes' theory of induction is really a theory of qualitative induction only. One may be able to argue convincingly that a scientist who guesses at the true law $y = f(x)$ that accounts for the results of measurements of the values of x and y is considering only a finite set of functions (linear, quadratic, logarithmic, and so on), though there are, of course, an infinity of them that are mathematically incompatible and each consistent with the data. Yet, how is one to apply the principle of indifference? Is $y = kx$, for example, a priori equally likely as $y = k/x$?

As regards (3), Keynes' reasoning is none too clear, but we may attempt a sympathetic reconstruction. If, in order to justify induction as the best means for attaining knowledge of laws, one had to assume the *truth* of the limited variety postulate, one would be in a serious predicament. For it is itself a generalization ("*Every* object has a finite number of logically independent properties"); hence its justification would require induction, and so the whole argument would be circular. But, Keynes argued, if only you grant my postulate a finite a priori probability, it can be shown to be itself rendered increasingly probable by experience, by the same argument by which any specific generalization can be shown to become increasingly probable as it continues to be confirmed. For, let p be any proposition that has a finite a priori probability; then it can be proved just by the formal axioms of probability calculus, without presupposing any synthetic postulates, that its probability increases and converges to certainty with increasing confirmation. The argument that experience increases the probability of the limited variety postulate, therefore, does not presuppose the truth of that postulate.

If Keynes were right, he would have established that his postulate is empirically confirmable just like specific generalizations. For the assumption that the postulate has a finite a priori probability is very weak: if it did not have a finite a priori probability, it would be *impossible*, and how could one establish the impossibility of limitation of independent variety? But this is actually just an academic question, since Keynes is demonstrably wrong in his argument. Let us grant him that the inductive method of increasing the antecedent probability of a universal hypothesis is logically justifiable whether or not independent variety be in fact limited. Yet, the inductive method in question consists in increasing the antecedent probability of a generalization by verifying the latter's (varied) instantial consequences. In order, therefore, to strengthen the limited variety postulate by the same method, one would have to verify *its* consequences. The latter are such propositions as "The (logically independent) positive analogy in the set of objects *a, b, c, . . .* is finite." And how could such a proposition be empirically verified? It clearly could not; the plain fact is that such a proposition is assumed solely because it follows from the limited variety postulate! Therefore it remains the case that in order to prove, within the framework of Keynes' theory of induction, that empirical confirmations increase the probability of a hypothesis, we need to assume the *truth*, not just the finite a priori probability, of the limited variety postulate.

E. THE ATTEMPT TO JUSTIFY
INDUCTION BY POSTULATES

Although Keynes' theory of induction is superior to Mill's in its recognition that inductive reasoning is essentially *probabilistic*, the two theories are similar in the following respect: they both assert that inductive inferences are valid only on the assumption of general postulates about the constitution of nature. David Hume had argued that every inductive inference presupposes the "uniformity of nature": why should the fact that the objects before me look like apples and that apples have in the past had the familiar taste that is distinctive of apples be any *reason* for expecting that these objects taste the same way? According to Hume the claim that such observed facts do provide a reason for the expectation entails that there is a reason for believing that nature is uniform, in the sense that if qualities *A, B,* and *C* have been associated with quality *D* in the observed instances, they will also be associated with D in the unobserved instances. Once one goes along with Hume's argument so far, one will have to swallow in the end its bitter, "skeptical" conclusion. For what reason could there be, asked Hume acutely, for believing that general premise of inductive inferences? It is not a necessary proposition, since lack of uniformity in the course of events is conceivable without contradiction; in other words, it is not self-evident, nor is it deducible from self-evident propositions. Could we, then, justify its acceptance by inductive reasoning? But since inductive reasoning is valid only if the general premise in question is true, such a justification would be circular. Mill, as we have seen, is still in the Humean tradition, for he also maintained that inductive reasoning presupposes, in the above sense, the uniformity of nature or universal causation. And we have seen that he was not entirely successful in rebutting the charge of circularity. Keynes did not share Mill's untenable view that inductive arguments are enthymemes with some kind of "uniformity axiom" as suppressed major premise. However, his theory is likewise what A. W. Burks has called a *presupposition theory of induction*[14] in the following sense: according to Keynes the belief that a given generalization is probable relative to empirical evidence as well as the belief that its probability can be increased by induction presupposes a postulate about the constitution of nature. But like Mill he failed in his attempt to show that the belief in the postulate may be justified by induction without circularity.

We shall argue, now, that Mill's and Keynes' failures in the noted respect were inevitable, because any attempt to justify inductive reasoning by postulates about nature is destined to failure for logical reasons. Let us begin by clearing up an ambiguity of the expression "justifying induction by postulates." It may refer to the process of formulating general synthetic propositions that must be true *if* any empirical facts make any inductive conclusions certain or at least probable. Clearly, such a "logical reconstruction" of inductive reasoning[15] cannot establish that the latter's conclusions ever *are* certain or probable. In order to achieve this aim, one would further have to provide reasons for accepting those "postulates" without begging the question at issue, i.e., assuming that some forms of inductive reasoning *are* valid. Only if this could be done would those forms of inductive reasoning have been "justified" in the ordinary sense of the word. To illustrate, consider Mill's claim that the assumption that nature is uniform is the suppressed ultimate major premise

14. A. W. Burks, "The Presupposition Theory of Induction," *Philosophy of Science*, 1953.

15. For a detailed "logical reconstruction" of this kind, see Bertrand Russell, *Human Knowledge, Its Scope and Limits* (New York: Simon and Schuster, Inc., 1948), Part Six.

of all inductive inferences. In order to find out what exactly that major premise is, we need merely solve a simple problem of deductive logic: which premise, added to the empirically known premise "Some A are B," will yield the generalization "All *A* are *B*" as a deductive conclusion? The answer: What is true of the observed members of a class is also true of the unobserved members of the class. But solving this problem does not amount to justifying the method of inductive generalization, unless one can show that nature *is* uniform in this sense. Indeed, we all know that it is not, since our predictions and generalizations have often turned out to be false.

The program of formulating synthetic presuppositions relative to which certain forms of inductive inference are highly probable has a far better chance of success than that of formulating synthetic presuppositions relative to which the particular premises of inductive inferences *entail* their conclusions. For synthetic presuppositions that satisfy the latter condition are not only not known to be true, or probably true; they are simply known to be false. Consider the axiom of the uniformity of nature that the "same" cause is always and everywhere followed by the "same" effect. Without going into the question of the meaning of "cause" for the time being, we detect immediately a crucial ambiguity. It might mean that if a set of conditions *A, B, C* has once been followed by an effect *E*, then *that* same set *A, B, C* will always be followed by *E*. This is the formulation we need in order to convert inductive generalizations into deductive arguments. But in this formulation the axiom is known to be false, since it does not refer to the *total* set of relevant conditions. Whenever I pressed that button, the bell rang, but this time it did not ring (the bell is out of order). If, on the other hand, it means that if *C* is the total set of relevant conditions that was once followed by *E*, then *C* is always followed by *E*, it cannot be used to render a specific inductive argument deductive, for the premise of an inductive argument is an empirically verifiable statement, and one cannot verify that the observed conditions are *all* the determining (relevant) conditions. Therefore, the uniformity axiom is either known to be false or else useless for the purpose of justifying a specific inductive inference in the sense in which "All dry leaves burn when lit" justifies the inference from "These dry leaves are being lit" to "They will burn."

Let us, therefore, concentrate on presupposition theories of induction that recognize the irreducibly probabilistic character of inductive inference. Such theories assert the following: a hypothesis *h* that has been inductively inferred from specific empirical evidence *e* is probable (to whatever degree) relative to *e only* if some general presupposition about the universe, *P*, is true. Alternatively, the contention of such a theory may be that a *complete* statement of inductive probability has the form:

$(h/e \ \& \ P) = x$; and that in order to justify one's acceptance of h one must, first, prove that $(h/e \ \& \ P)$ is greater than 0.5, and secondly that e is the total relevant evidence that is known at the time, and thirdly that P is true. But it is easy to see that such a conception of inductive probability leads inevitably to a Humean skepticism. For either P is a necessary proposition or it is a contingent proposition. If the former, then $e \ \& \ P$ is logically equivalent to e; $e \ \& \ P$ entails e, but e also entails $e \ \& \ P$, for since a necessary proposition is entailed by any proposition, e entails P, and hence $e \ \& \ P$. But in that case "$(h/e) = x$" must be true if "$(h/e \ \& \ P) = x$" is true. Therefore, it could not be maintained that presuppositions are needed to justify statements of inductive probability if those presuppositions were necessary propositions. A necessary proposition holds in every conceivable universe, but the alleged presuppositions of induction are supposed to characterize *this particular* universe with respect to which induction is to be justified. Therefore P would not do the job it is supposed to do if it were a necessary proposition. And, at any rate, few philosophers dare to claim that the alleged synthetic presuppositions of induction are self-evident a priori truths.[16] But if P is a contingent proposition, the question arises how it could be known to be true. Since it is a general, indeed a very general, proposition, it will have to be inductively inferred from empirical evidence. We may safely leave it to the reader to close the circle.

Is there any way of distinguishing valid from invalid inductive inferences, i.e., inductive inferences whose conclusions are, whether true or false, *probable* relative to the evidence, from those whose conclusions are not, without appealing to "presuppositions"? The answer to this fundamental question of the logic of empirical science will have to be deferred until we learn more about the meaning, or meanings, of the word "probability."

Selected Readings for this chapter are listed at the end of Chapter 13.

16. There is one step in the above argument that some may question on the basis of their notion of "entailment": that a necessary proposition is entailed by any proposition.

CHAPTER II

The Frequency Interpretation of Probability

A. EXPOSITION

The frequency interpretation of probability was anticipated, in a vague way, by Aristotle when he wrote, "The probable is that which happens for the most part." But one does not have to be a great philosopher to see that there is a close connection between the probability of an event and the frequency with which it happens under such and such conditions. If the "man in the street" were asked what he meant by saying that a man of eighty will probably die within the next ten years, he would very likely reply that this simply means that most men die before they reach an age of ninety.

We have already discussed the analysis of probability in terms of truth-frequency. The frequency interpretation as elaborated in recent decades especially by Hans Reichenbach and Richard von Mises is similar to but should not be confused with the former, because it construes probability as a relation between events or attributes; on the truth-frequency analysis, it is forms of inference that are assigned degrees of probability. Let A and B be attributes, and consider a statement of the form "On the evidence that x is A, it is probable to degree p that x is B." Symbolically: $(Bx/Ax) = p$. Examples: "On the evidence that x is an attractive woman of twenty-five, it is highly probable that x is married"; "On the evidence that x is a toss of a fair coin, it is probable to degree ½ that x is a toss that yields heads." As the examples show, the same schema

[174]

can be used for probability statements about objects and for probability statements about events. We often talk about the probability that an event of one kind will be followed by an event of another kind; in that case we simply substitute for B—the variable ranging over inferred attributes—the attribute possessed by the antecedent event of *being followed by such and such an event*. Now, the frequency interpretation of "$(Bx/Ax) = p$" is this: the relative frequency of cases of B within the class of cases of A equals p. The class A is called the *reference class*, because the probability of a case of B is "referred" to that class. By changing the reference class, we might of course obtain different relative frequencies for the same attribute B. A convenient geometrical picture of relative frequencies may be obtained by representing the classes B and A by intersecting circles, as shown in Figure 11.1 The common part of

Figure 11.1

the circles represents the class of objects, or occurrences, that have both attributes A and B. The relative frequency of B in A is represented by the ratio of the shaded area to the area representing the reference class A.

The interpretation of a probability fraction as a ratio of the number of a product of classes, $A \& B$, to the number of one of the overlapping classes (the reference class, A), has two virtues to recommend it. First, it accords with the procedure by which statisticians compute their probabilities; second, it satisfies the axioms of the calculus of probability, in the sense that the latter become demonstrable theorems of algebra when probability is interpreted in this way. In particular, our three axioms in Section C of the preceding chapter are easily provable on the basis of this interpretation, as follows:

Axiom 1. If Ax entails Bx, then the class A is included in the class B; hence $A = A \& B$, and thus the ratio of $A \& B$ to A equals unity.

Axiom 2. In the terminology of classes, this axiom asserts that if the product of classes B, C, and A equals 0 (i.e., has no members), then

$$\frac{Bx \text{ or } Cx}{Ax} = \frac{Bx}{Ax} + \frac{Cx}{Ax}$$

Let us now use, for the sake of symbolic convenience, the same letters B, C, and A to represent both the classes and their numbers. Then Axiom

2 asserts in frequency interpretation: If the product of classes B, C, and A equals 0, then

$$\frac{(B \vee C) \cdot A}{A} = \frac{A \cdot B}{A} + \frac{A \cdot C}{A}$$

where "$B \vee C$" denotes the class that is the sum of classes B and C. The class of those objects which belong to A and to either B or C but not to $A \& B \& C$ (which is assumed empty) is obviously equal to the sum of the class products $A \& B \& \overline{C}$ and $A \& C \& \overline{B}$ (which are represented in Figure 11.2 by the sections containing a cross). On the assumption made,

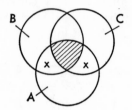

Figure 11.2

$A \& B \& \overline{C}$ and $A \& C \& \overline{B}$ are respectively equal to $A \& B$ and $A \& C$. Hence Axiom 2 is transformed into the algebraic identity

$$\frac{(A \& B) + (A \& C)}{A} = \frac{A \& B}{A} + \frac{A \& C}{A}$$

Axiom 3. This axiom asserts on the frequency interpretation the following equality of ratios (we continue to use A for the reference class):

$$\frac{B \& C \& A}{A} = \frac{B \& A}{A} \cdot \frac{C \& B \& A}{B \& A}$$

That this is an algebraic identity becomes evident when both numerator and denominator of the fraction on the left are multiplied by $B \& A$:

$$\frac{B \& A \& B \& C \& A}{B \& A \& A}$$

which is obviously equal to the product of ratios on the right.

This interpretation, however, does not by itself lead to unique probability values when applied to specified ordered pairs of attributes. The obvious reason is that one does not, in general, know how many objects have a given attribute. Ratio $(B \& A)/A$ must be estimated on the basis of determinations of the frequency of B in samples of the class A, and if the estimate of the relative frequency in the total class is identified with the known relative frequency in a sample, surveys of different samples will lead to different estimates. What is called *the probability Bx/Ax* is a unique number; i.e., only one number represents this probability once *B* and *A* are fixed, just as only one number represents the area of a square once the length of its sides is fixed. But which of the various estimates corresponds to that unique probability?

Reichenbach and von Mises reply that the probability is to be identified with the *limit* approached by the sample frequencies as the samples become larger and larger. Since "limit" is a mathematical concept used in connection with *infinite* sequences of numbers, this interpretation of probability as a limit of relative frequencies involves the idealization of reference classes as being infinite. But it should not be supposed that, therefore, such an interpretation of probability is inapplicable to finite classes, such as the class of actual tosses with a given coin, or the class of actual tosses with some coin or other, or the class of inhabitants of New York, or the class of pigeons. All that is required is that no matter how large a sample has been observed, it always remains conceivable that in the future a still larger sample of the same class, but still a proper part of the latter, be surveyed. And this requirement is obviously fulfilled in all cases where it is not only practically but even theoretically necessary to estimate the probability *Bx/Ax* on the basis of random samples. However, unlike the straightforward identification of probabilities with ratios of numbers of finite classes, the limiting-frequency interpretation entails that probability is a relation between *sequences* rather than classes (Reichenbach accordingly coined the term "probability sequence"). A sequence of empirically derived frequencies of attribute *B* in reference class *A* is obtained as follows: The observed members of *A* we call $a_1\ a_2, \ldots, a_n$ in the order in which they were observed. Then we write down the relative frequency in a small initial segment of the sequence (i.e., a segment beginning with the first element of the sequence), say

$$a_1, a_2, \ldots, a_{10}: f_{10}$$

Next we write down the relative frequency in a larger initial segment, say

$$a_1, a_2, \ldots, a_{100}: f_{100}$$

Thus we obtain a sequence of fractions between 0 and 1 which represent relative frequencies and which, as a matter of contingent fact, tend towards a certain limiting value, f_L. To say that f_L is the limit to which the sequence $f_{10}, f_{100}, \ldots$ converges is to say that for every positive real number ϵ, no matter how small, there is a member of the sequence, call it f_n, such that for any m that exceeds n, f_m is within ϵ of f_L. Note that one's estimate of f_L may well depend on the order in which the members of *A* happen to have been observed. For example, suppose that the true value of Bx/Ax is ⅓, but that a million A's have attribute B and that these A's happen to be observed before the even more numerous A's that are not B's begin to be observed. The initial segment of the sequence of relative frequencies that have been empirically computed may then seem to converge to a much larger value than the true value. But this does not mean that the true value of the probability depends on the contingencies of our samplings, that is, on the order in which we observe members of the reference class. For it follows from the above definition of "limit" that, though even f_{10^6} may be way off, the observed relative frequencies must eventually come close to f_L and stay there provided they converge to a limit at all.[1]

Some writers, notably Richard von Mises, define probability more specifically as a limit approached by a sequence of relative frequencies derived from a *random* sequence of observed events or objects. Roughly speaking, a sequence is random if there is no law that enables prediction of the attribute exhibited by an element of the sequence from a knowledge of the attributes exhibited by its predecessors. If a sequence of penny tosses, for example, were a strictly alternating one, $HTHTHTHT \ldots$, we would not then speak of a *probability* of ½ that a given toss yield heads, for we could predict with certainty the outcome of the nth toss from our knowledge of the outcome of the $(n-1)$st toss. It is this sort of situation that von Mises' requirement of randomness is intended to exclude. The formal definition of randomness is as follows: A sequence of events that may or may not exhibit an attribute B is random if the limiting relative frequency of B in all infinite partial sequences defined by "place-selection" (e.g., the sequence of all even-numbered events, the sequence of all prime-numbered events, the sequence of all square-numbered events) is constant and equal to the limiting frequency in the total sequence.

B. SOME STANDARD OBJECTIONS TO THE "LIMITING-FREQUENCY" INTERPRETATION

1. "The limit concept is applicable only to mathematical sequences of numbers for which there is a generating function."

1. It was on this reflection that Reichenbach based his alleged "justification" of the method of enumerative induction: If our estimate of the limit is wrong, it *must* eventually be corrected as the observed initial segment of the total sequence becomes larger and larger, provided the sequence converges to a limit at all.

Consider the following examples of infinite converging sequences:

$$\tfrac{1}{2}, \tfrac{1}{4}, \tfrac{1}{8}, \cdots; \qquad \tfrac{1}{2}, \tfrac{3}{4}, \tfrac{7}{8} \cdots.$$

Every member of the first sequence is an instance of the function $\tfrac{1}{2}^{n}$, every member of the second sequence illustrates the function $1 - \tfrac{1}{2}^{n}$, where the values of n are the integers representing the position of a term in the sequence. Here the statements "$\lim f(n)\ n \to \infty = a$" are demonstrable; there is no doubt about the existence of a limit nor about its value. If I give you a small number ϵ, say $1/100$, you can easily find an integer n (say 10) such that the difference between 0 and the value of the fraction $\tfrac{1}{2}^{n}$ for that value of n, as well as for all larger values of n, is less than ϵ. A concept, whether mathematical or empirical, is meaningful only if there is a *decision procedure* connected with it, i. e., a way of finding out whether or not the concept applies in a given case (for quantitative concepts, what their values are in given cases). But the convergence of an empirically derived sequence of relative frequencies to a definite limit or even to some limit or other is a postulate that is neither mathematically provable nor empirically verifiable.

Whether statements about limits of frequencies are in some way empirically testable is an intricate question whose discussion we defer to subsection 4. But be this as it may, objection 1 can easily be undermined by pointing out that the extension of the limit concept to sequences without generating functions has a precedent in the application of the calculus to physical magnitudes. An exact rate of change, such as an instantaneous velocity or an instantaneous acceleration, is a limit of difference quotients representing "average" rates of change. Thus, what is meant by saying that an accelerating particle has at a definite instant, t_i, a velocity component along the x-axis equal to vx ft/sec? In order to give meaning to this statement, the physicist considers a time interval containing t_i, subdivides it into smaller and smaller intervals including t_i (or, alternatively, containing t_i as their upper or lower limit), arranges the average velocities corresponding to these diminishing time intervals in a sequence, and, finding that they do not erratically fluctuate but tend towards a certain number, assumes that the sequence converges to a limit. Such is the meaning of the definition

$$\frac{dx_i}{dt_i} = \lim_{\Delta t \to 0} \frac{\Delta x}{\Delta t}$$

And the sequence of average velocities thus imagined to converge to a limit is, like sequences of empirically derived frequencies, not a mathematical sequence generated by a function.

Illustration: Suppose we determine the distances fallen by a freely falling body in definite time intervals. We find according to Galileo's law $s = \frac{1}{2} gt^2$ (where g, the acceleration of gravity, equals 32 ft/sec²):

t (sec)	s (ft)	*average velocities* (ft/sec)
$0 = t_0$	$0 = s_0$	$(s_4 - s_0)(t_4 - t_0) = 64$
$1 = t_1$	$16 = s_1$	$(s_4 - s_1)(t_4 - t_1) = 80$
$2 = t_2$	$64 = s_2$	$(s_4 - s_2)(t_4 - t_2) = 96$
$3 = t_3$	$144 = s_3$	$(s_4 - s_3)(t_4 - t_3) = 112$
$3.5 = t_{3.5}$	$196 = s_{3.5}$	$(s_4 - s_{3.5})(t_4 - t_{3.5}) = 120$
$3.75 = t_{3.75}$	$225 = s_{3.75}$	$(s_4 - s_{3.75})(t_4 - t_{3.75}) = 124$
$4 = t_4$	$256 = s_4$	ds/dt at $t_4 = 128$

From these data we derive the average velocities in the third column corresponding to time intervals whose "lower" limit is t_4, i.e., 4 seconds after the beginning of the fall. The limit approached by these numbers as the time interval with the lower limit t_4 becomes smaller and smaller is 128, according to the equation $ds/dt = gt$, which expresses function of time and which follows from the differential equation expressing fallen distance as a quadratic function of time. A direct empirical verification of this equation requires the determination by measurement of converging sequences of average velocities as illustrated in the table. Of course, since it is a direct consequence of a law relating distance and time, such a direct verification is unnecessary; but the meaning of ds/dt can be explained only in terms of such sequences.

The advocate of objection 1, therefore, must either equally object to the application of the calculus to quantitative empirical sciences or show that those applications of the limit concept differ in some relevant respect from the application made by the proponents of the limiting-frequency interpretation.

2. "The probability that a member of a reference class A have an attribute B should be unique. But since the same infinite set of proper fractions can be arranged into different infinite sequences converging to different limits, the limiting-frequency definition does not satisfy this requirement. According to it the probability may vary with the order in which the members of R are observed."

Though this objection has been advanced by such eminent philosophers of science as Russell and Braithwaite, it does not seem to be valid. What can vary with the order of our observations is our *estimate* of the limit; but different estimates, on the basis of sample frequencies, of the limit of the relative frequencies of B in increasingly larger finite subclasses of A cannot both be true. In order to show that the limit itself, and not just its estimate, depends on the order in which members of A are observed one would have to be able to know the limits of sequences of empirically derived frequencies. But it is just because such knowledge is impossible that we must rely on inductive estimates. Moreover, this objection certainly does not apply to von Mises' definition, since the latter includes the requirement of randomness. If a rearrangement of the elements of a reference sequence results in a different limit of the relative frequencies, then the sequence, by definition, is not random in von Mises' sense.

3. "According to the ordinary meaning of 'probability,' to say that it is maximally probable that a member of A is B is to say that all members of A are B; and to say that it is minimally probable that a member of A is B is to say that no member of A is B. But these equivalences do not hold on the limiting-frequency definition."

Indeed, the statement that the limiting frequency of B in A is unity is compatible with the existence of many, even infinitely many, members of A that lack B; and the statement that the limiting frequency of B in A is zero is compatible with the existence of many, even infinitely many, members of A that are B. Just imagine that the sequences were sequences such as

$$\tfrac{1}{2}, \tfrac{3}{4}, \tfrac{7}{8}, \ldots \quad \text{or} \quad \tfrac{1}{2}, \tfrac{1}{4}, \tfrac{1}{8}, \ldots .$$

The definition of statistical probability under criticism, accordingly, makes it impossible to regard *universal* generalization, i.e., those of the forms "All A are B" and "No A are B," as extreme cases of *statistical* generalizations. In other words, it does not allow us to translate "The probability of a member of A's being B is one" into "All A are B" and "The probability of a member of A's being a B is zero" into "No A are B," since universal generalization are refutable by contrary instances whereas limit statements are not.

Whether this objection, which has been advanced by such eminent inductive logicians as Kneale and von Wright, is fatal depends on how similar we expect our precise *explicatum* to be to the intuitively employed but somewhat inexact *explicandum*. If, like Reichenbach, we want to think of the universal implications with which both Aristotelian deductive logic and classical inductive logic were predominantly concerned as extreme cases of probability implications, then we certainly must give up the limiting-frequency definition.[2] On the other hand, one might take the position that although "All A are B" is usually intended as a proposition that is contradicted by propositions of the form "x is A but not B," as a critical scientist one should never assert such a proposition. One should be content with the safer assertion, "Our best estimate of the limiting relative frequency of B in A is one." Such assertions are not, of course, strictly refutable. And if there are demonstrable ad-

2. Reichenbach was strangely inconsistent on this point.

vantages in this kind of reinterpretation of universal generalizations, objection 3 is not fatal.

4. "Statistical probability statements—statistical generalizations—are completely untestable according to the limiting-frequency interpretation. For any possible frequency between 0 and 1 (limits included!) is logically compatible with any possible hypothesis about the value of the limit."

Indeed, statistical generalizations about infinite classes are not just incapable of *conclusive* verification and refutation. They are not even *confirmable* and *disconfirmable* in the straightforward sense in which a mixed general statement (i.e., a statement containing both universal and existential quantifiers) such as "Every human has a father" (H) is confirmable and disconfirmable. The singular statement "b is human and a is father of b" confirms H in the sense that it entails a substitution instance of H, viz., "b has a father." H cannot be refuted with theoretical certainty, since to establish its negation, "There is a human that has no father," would require establishing that no human whatever is father of a given human. But suppose that no likely candidate to the title "father of b" had been discovered in an extensive survey. Then "b has no father" would have been confirmed to some degree; and the entailed existential statement "Some human has no father" would have been confirmed to at least an equal degree, and to that same degree H would have been disconfirmed. But this relatively clear and simple notion of confirmation is not applicable to statistical generalizations. What is to count as a sample of coin tosses that confirms the statement "The probability of throwing heads with this coin is ½"? Ten tosses with five heads; or 100 tosses with 50 heads; or 100 tosses with a number of heads between 45 and 55; or what? Evidently the definition of confirmation here requires specification of two variables, (1) the length of the confirming sequence and (2) the interval within which the relative frequency must lie. Similar considerations apply to disconfirmation. What is the minimal length an observed sequence must have in order that a considerable deviation of the relative frequency from the probability should disconfirm the probability statement? And what amount of deviation is sufficient to disconfirm it?

Nevertheless, statisticians have developed a workable theory of testing statistical hypotheses about infinite classes. The theory derives rules of rejection and acceptance of statistical hypotheses from theorems of the calculus of probability concerning the probabilities of sample frequencies' approximating closely to the probability of the event in question. The basic theorem by which such rules are justified is the *theorem of Bernoulli*. A good way of approaching an understanding of this useful (but often misinterpreted) theorem is by considering the following question: Which of the possible frequencies of occurrence of an event of probability p in a finite sequence of independent occasions is the most probable? The provable answer is: that frequency which equals p. Thus, the most probable number of heads in four independent tosses of a coin is two, if the probability of throwing heads in any given toss is $\frac{1}{2}$. (Check: There are six possible ways of getting two heads in four tosses; four possible ways of getting one head; four possible ways of getting three heads, and, of course, only one way of getting nothing but head or no heads at all.) Sometimes the probability could not possibly be equal to the relative frequency in a sample of n members, because no possible fraction with n as denominator is equal to the probability (thus, for example, the relative frequency of heads in five tosses cannot be equal to $\frac{1}{2}$). But in those cases the possible relative frequency that is closest to the probability is the most probable. Now, to expect that "in the long run" the probability be *exactly* realized as a frequency would be unreasonable, since it can be demonstrated that such an exact equality becomes increasingly improbable as n increases, and impossible in the limit. For example, getting 50 heads in 100 tosses is considerably less likely than getting 5 heads in 10 tosses. In fact, any possible frequency becomes less and less likely as n increases, because the larger n, the larger the total number of possible frequencies. But what the Bernoulli theorem asserts is that a *close approximation* of the relative frequency to the probability becomes more and more probable as n increases, and that this (second-order) probability approaches one as a limit. Thus, if the probability of heads is $\frac{1}{2}$, then a relative frequency between 0.4 and 0.6 is more probable for $n = 100$ than for $n = 10$, and still more probable for $n = 1,000$, and so on.

The following is an exact symbolic formulation of the theorem. Let p be the probability that a member of a reference class A have attribute B, and assume that A is sequentially ordered, the position of its members being indicated by integers. Then, for any arbitrarily small positive real numbers ϵ and δ, there is a position N in the sequence such that for any position n beyond N, the probability that the absolute difference between p and the relative frequency of B in the initial segment of n elements be less than ϵ differs from one by no more than δ. This theorem obviously provides a justification for *rules of rejection* of statistical hypotheses if the following principle is accepted: If the observed data (such as relative frequencies of an attribute in random samples drawn from a large class) would be highly improbable if hypothesis H were true, then they make it highly probable that H is false. In the terminology of the theory of inverse probability this means that, assuming a constant a priori probability of the alternative hypotheses $h_1, h_2, \ldots, h_n$, the posterior probability of h_i relative to the observed data is directly proportional to the likelihood of those data relative to h_i. And as this follows immediately from Bayes' theorem, the principle in question is acceptable as implied by the very formal meaning of "probability" expressed by the axioms of probability calculus.[3]

To illustrate this sort of test of a statistical generalization, consider the hypothesis that the relative frequencies of heads in a random series of tosses with a specified coin converge to ½ as the limit. And suppose that in 1,000 consecutive trials the relative frequency was about $\frac{3}{10}$. Now, mathematical statisticians have worked out formulae for calculating the probability that a random sample of size n will exhibit an attribute B in a proportion differing from the (constant) probability of occurrence of B in an element of the reference class by no more than some small number ϵ. So, if we fix n as 1,000, the probability of B in A as ½, and ϵ as, say, 0.01, we can calculate the probability that the relative frequency of B in a sample of 1,000 elements lies within the interval whose limits are 490/1,000 and 510/1,000. Assume that probability to be x. Then calculate the probability of the same proposition, about the interval containing the relative frequency of B in a sample of 1,000 elements, relative to a different statistical hypothesis about the same coin, say, the probability of throwing heads with it is $\frac{2}{5}$. Assume this probability to be y. Then a Bernoullian rejection rule (as we might call it) will demand that given a sample frequency within the specified interval, we prefer the latter hypothesis if y exceeds x. Our rejection of the former hypothesis, however, is only provisional. For in a still larger sequence of trials the relative frequency may be found to lie within the interval of relative frequencies that are more likely on the former hypothesis than on the latter.

It may be thought that this procedure of justifying a preference for one statistical hypothesis as against another leads to a vicious infinite regress if the probability statements of second order, viz. those about the probabilities of sample frequencies' being "close" to probabilities, are in turn given a frequency interpretation. But this is not the case, because these probability statements of second order are purely analytic, whether or not the frequency interpretation be adopted. Hence, they do not need to be tested empirically.

In order to gain an intuitive understanding of such statements, consider the following simple illustration. Imagine a large box containing 100 balls, and suppose it to be known that exactly 50 of the balls are black. Now form all possible subsets of 10 balls from that set of 100 balls; the

---

3. Many statisticians use the method called, after Fisher, "the method of maximum likelihood": Accept that one of the initially posssible statistical hypotheses which confers the greatest likelihood on the observed data. They would not justify this directive, however, in terms of the theorems of inverse probability because they distrust the concept of "a priori probability" of an hypothesis. For a discussion of the method of maximum likelihood, see Chapter 13.

number of such subsets can be calculated by the formula for the number of combinations of n things taken m at a time:

$$\frac{n!}{m!(n-m)!}$$

These possible subsets will contain black balls in proportions ranging from 0 to 1; the proportion will be either 0 or $\frac{1}{10}$ or $\frac{2}{10}$ or ... or 1. Question which of these possible proportions occurs more frequently, those close to $\frac{5}{10}$ or those close to the limits of the interval of possible proportions of black balls to white balls? The obvious answer is: those close to $\frac{5}{10}$. For they can be realized in more ways than the "non-representative" proportions. It should be clear, therefore, that to say that a random sample of 10 balls is fairly likely to contain black balls in approximately the same proportion as the box is not to make a prediction of a high frequency of selections of representative samples, but rather a purely logical assertion about the proportion of representative subsets in the class of all possible subsets of indicated size.[4]

Bernoulli's analytical theorem is, as we have seen, of central importance for the testing of statistical hypotheses. It should be carefully distinguished from what J. Neyman[5] has aptly called the *empirical law of large numbers*. The latter, not the former, describes a contingent feature of the world that renders empirical applications of probability calculus possible. Let f be the relative frequency of an event M in Nn trials, where n is some small fraction of a large number N (e.g., $N = 1000$, $n = 10$). Let m_k be the number of sets of n similar occurrences (for short, "n-sets") in which M occurred k times; m_k/N, then, is the relative frequency of n-sets containing k occurrences of M in a hyperset (i.e., set of sets) of N n-sets. The empirical law of large numbers asserts that we may expect m_k/N to be approximately equal to the following, "binomial" function of n, k, and f:

$$\frac{n!}{(n-k)!\,k!}(1-f)^{n-k}f^k$$

To gain an intuitive understanding of this law, consider a simple special case of it. Suppose that the relative frequency of sixes in $2N$ throws of a

4. We shall return in Chapter 13 to the question of the relevance of the "likelihood" theorems of the calculus of probability—the theorems of "direct" probability in the terminology of Carnap—to the philosophical problem of the justification of induction.

5. Cf. *Lectures and Conferences on Mathematical Statistics*, delivered by J. Neyman at the Graduate School of the U.S. Department of Agriculture, April, 1937, pp. 24–27 (Washington, D.C.: The Graduate School of the U.S. Department of Agriculture, 1952).

die is approximately equal to ⅙. By substituting in the above formula 2 for n, 2 for k, and ⅙ for f, we derive the prediction that the relative frequency of double sixes in a sequence of N pairs of throws (N being a large number) will be approximately $(⅙)^2$. To the extent that this empirical law of large numbers is satisfied by long sequences of events, the concept of probability used in the formal calculus may be *interpreted* as relative frequency in long random sequences of events, and the theorems of the calculus are then useful tools for predicting certain frequencies of derived attributes in hypersets from given frequencies of simple attributes in sets of elementary events. To be sure, as Neyman points out, "Whenever the law fails, we explain the failure by suspecting a 'lack of randomness' in the first-order trials." Indeed, the concept of a random sequence of events could be defined as a sequence that satisfies the law in question. The latter would then be analytic, and the condition of applicability of the calculus of probability would have to be formulated as the *existence* of random sequences, just as Boyle's law for ideal gases could be treated as a definition of "ideal gas," the question of fact then being whether there are any gases that are approximately "ideal" under specified conditions of temperature and pressure.

5. *The difficulty of applying the frequency interpretation to singular predictions.* "The frequency interpretation gives a meaning to *general* probability statements, such statements as 'The probability that a human birth is a birth of a boy equals approximately ½.' But a probability statement such as 'It is highly probable that *this* patient will improve after undergoing *this* treatment at *this* time' has no meaning at all according to it. Yet such statements have great practical importance and are far from meaningless."

This objection can easily be answered by the advocate of the frequency interpretation by construing singular probability statements as incomplete. If a doctor judges an improvement of his patient's condition as probable, it is because he believes that the relative frequency with which this *kind* of treatment of this *kind* of illness is followed by improvement of the treated patient's condition is high. He inductively estimates—to abstract the general pattern of such reasoning—that the relative frequency (or the limiting relative frequency) with which an event of kind A is followed by an event of kind B is high. He knows that *this* event is an event of kind A, and hence has a high degree of confidence in his prediction that this event will be followed by an event of kind B. Or suppose I see a man with the kind of bluish-red nose that is characteristic of drunkards. I may with perfect justification say, "Probably he is a drunkard," but this statement must be construed as elliptical for "His nose is bluish-red and most men with this kind of a nose are drunkards."

Yet, we must beware of contradictions. It is tempting to suppose that a singular probability statement "It is probable, to the degree p, that object a has property Q" follows from the premises "The probability that x is Q on the evidence that x is P equals p" and "a is P"; similarly that "It is probable, to the degree p, that an event of kind B will occur" follows from the premises "The probability that an event of kind A is followed by an event of kind B equals p" and "An event of kind A has just occurred." Such deductions are, of course, valid if their conclusions are elliptical statements that, when fully explained, are restatements of the premises. But in that case nothing has been inferred from the premises. If, on the other hand, their conclusions are taken at their face value, as categorical probability statements that are inferred by a principle of *modus ponens* from a statistical generalization together with a singular minor premise, contradictions are easily generated. For it may also be true that the probability that x is Q on the evidence that x is R (a different reference class) equals some different fraction q, and the particular object a may also be a member of R. In such a case the same method of reasoning would lead to the conclusion that the probability that a is Q equals q, not p. And then the question arises: Which probability value, q or p, should guide us in our actions? For example, a physician who must decide whether or not to administer penicillin to a patient may consider the patient as a member of the class of patients of his who suffered from a similar virus infection and were treated with penicillin. If a large majority of these patients were helped by penicillin, the rule to act on a highly probable hypothesis would lead him to administer the penicillin in the given case. But suppose that a minority of the patients thus treated in the past turned out to be "allergic" to penicillin, and that the present patient is in some relevant physiological respects similar to them. Clearly, it will then be reasonable for the doctor to abstain from this treatment. This means that the probability of the singular prediction that serves as a rational basis for his decision is its probability *relative to a narrower reference class*.

Generalizing, we might say that, though the same singular prediction has different degrees of statistical probability relative to different reference classes, the degree of statistical probability that ought to be taken as a basis for action is the degree computed without omitting relevant information. In the above example, the reference class was narrowed when more relevant information (similarity to patients who turned out to be harmed by penicillin) was taken into account. But it would be unreasonable to prefer reference class R_1 to reference class R_2 as a basis for determining the probability of occurrence of an attribute A just because R_1 is a proper subclass of R_2 still containing the particular case of interest. Thus, suppose I wish to determine from statistical data the probability that the baby my wife is now pregnant with is male. Should I consult a statistic of the proportion of male births produced by wives of men of the same profession as mine, or of the proportion of male births produced by American wives, or of the proportion of male births produced by slim wives, or by women born in the same state as my wife, or by women born in the same city as my wife, or what? Provided the event whose outcome is in question has all the attributes by which these possible reference classes are defined, i.e., is a birth of a child whose father is, say, a university professor, is a birth of a child whose mother is American, and so on, all of these reference classes are offhand eligible. The rule to select the narrowest reference class is obviously absurd; it would presumably lead to the prediction that it is certainly going to be a boy on the ground that our first, and so far only, child was a boy! The rule to take all and only known relevant information into account in selecting the reference class is much more reasonable. Thus the information that the baby's mother is married to a university professor and that she was born in New York is irrelevant to the question whether the baby to be born is male or female; hence it would be unreasonable to restrict the reference class to births by wives of university professors or to births by women born in New York. The sense of "irrelevant" here is the sense in which applicability of the *special* multiplication theorem to the problem "What is the probability that a member of reference class R have *both* attributes A and B?" requires that A and B be (inductively) "independent" attributes relative to R:

$$\text{prob}\,\frac{Ax}{Rx \cdot Bx} = \text{prob}\,\frac{Ax}{Rx}$$

If R is the class of human births, B the class of births by wives of university professors, and A the class of male births, this equation asserts, in frequency interpretation, that the relative frequency of male births within the class of births by wives of university professors is equal to the relative frequency of male births within the class of human births. It is in this sense that the information that a particular pregnant woman is married to a university professor is *irrelevant* to the question how probable it is that her child is going to be a boy.

But must we, then, investigate how frequently wives of university professors who bear children give birth to a male before being justified in asserting such irrelevance? No, it is sufficient to have observed that the relative frequency of the attribute in question does not significantly vary with the profession of the childbearing woman's husband: the proportion of male births is about the same whether the father be a musician, a carpenter, a policeman, a banker, or whatever. Hence we generalize and conclude that information specifying the *determinable* attribute "father's profession" is irrelevant to the question at issue. Similarly, if we find that the proportion of male births is about the same over a long period of time no matter *where* the birth occurs, we can infer that the information that the expectant mother lives in New York is irrelevant to the question at issue without first consulting a statistic of the proportion of male births by residents of New York. It is important to keep clear, however, that any assumption of irrelevance is a generalization from past experience, not an a priori certainty. We unhesitatingly estimate the probability of throwing six with a symmetrical, uniformly dense die as equal to the probability of throwing six with a symmetrical, uniformly dense *and blue* die. But the reason is that a great mass of experience in the past has indicated that there is no significant correlation between the color of a solid object and its mechanical behavior. There is no *internal* contradiction in supposing that the relative frequency of sixes varies with the color of the dice thrown; such an assumption of relevance only contradicts our past experience of the mechanical behavior of solids.

C. THE PROBLEM OF THE "INFINITY" OF THE REFERENCE CLASS

In concluding this critical survey of standard objections to the frequency interpretation—most of which we found to be invalid—it may be suggested that there is really *no* need for defining statistical probabilities as limits rather than as ratios of finite numbers of finite nonordered classes. The only reason, it will be recalled, why von Mises and Reichenbach felt it necessary to define probabilities as limits was that they postulated that the reference classes (or "collectives") be infinite, and noted that it is meaningless to speak of ratios with an infinite denominator. But what exactly is meant by saying that such *empirical* classes as the class of tosses of a particular coin, or the class of tosses of some coin or other, or the class of human births, or the class of swans, or the class of penicillin injections, are infinite? Does the statement, "The probability that a penicillin injection is shortly followed by the patient's improvement (provided the patient has such and such characteristics) is high," presuppose that the number of actual penicillin injections—past, present, and future—exceeds every assignable finite number? Of course, nobody really means to make such a fantastic claim. What seems to be meant by "infinite" in such contexts is just that though the number of actual members of R may be finite, and even relatively small, it always remains conceivable that R have still more members than those actually observed.

The practical function of probability statements is to guide our actions; hence they are essentially predictive. This predictive function might be expressed by the formulation "The probability that an unobserved member of R have attribute A equals p." Clearly, if R is the sort of class that is the subject of a genuine statistical generalization, it always remains significant to suppose that it have unobserved members, presently existing or to exist in the future. Suppose that a divine statistician looked at his complete statistical protocol after the last coin toss in the history of the universe and found that the relative frequency of heads was 0.51. Would there be any reason for him to say "The probability of a coin toss yielding heads is 0.51" instead of "The relative frequency of heads in the class of actual coin tosses is 0.51"? If he used the word "probability" as it is actually used in human life, then he would make the former—the probability statement—in order to convey what relative frequency of heads is to be expected in any sufficiently long future run of coin tosses if such should occur. We might say that probability statements are about *open* classes in the sense that no matter how many *observed* members the class has at any given time, it is always logically possible that it have still other—so far unobserved—members. This is logically possible in the sense that it is not excluded by the *meaning* of the predicate by which the class is determined. Clearly, openness in this sense is compatible with finitude. Even if a given biological species, for example, should become totally extinct after a certain finite number n of members of it had existed and never again come into existence in some conceivable process of cyclical evolution, it will remain true to say that n *may be* greater than the number of members actually observed, even if we postulate a divine observer. For at no time could the divine observer be *logically* certain that there would not be further members in the future.

Why not define, then, the probability that a member of R have attribute A as the ratio of two finite, though in principle unknowable, numbers, viz., the number of members of R with A divided by the number of members of R? Since no contradiction is derivable from the assumption of finitude of an empirical class—in the way a contradiction is derivable from the proposition that the class of prime numbers is finite—and since there is no *conceivable* empirical evidence for its infinity, we are pragmatically justified in making whatever assumption simplifies probability theory. The problem of devising reasonable test methods for statistical generalizations remains, since the number of an open class is in principle unknowable. But the objections against the frequency interpretation from the mathematical meaning of "limit" (objections 1, 2, and 3) cannot then arise.

Selected Readings for this chapter are listed at the end of Chapter 13.

CHAPTER 12

The Range Interpretation of Probability

A. THE LAPLACIAN DEFINITION AND THE PRINCIPLE OF INDIFFERENCE

Suppose you were asked the probability of getting a black ball in a random selection from a box containing four black and six white balls. Very likely you would answer "⅖" even if you did not know anything about the relative frequency of random selections of black balls from boxes of the described content. You would support your answer by the argument that there are ten possible outcomes of the random selection, corresponding to the ten balls in the box, and that four of them are "favorable" to the event in question, i.e., four of them would constitute realizations of the event of selecting a black ball. This illustrates Laplace's definition of the probability of an event as the ratio of the number of ways in which it may be realized to the total number of possible events. The Laplacian probability of throwing six with a die equals ⅙ because there are six possible outcomes of the throw, corresponding to the six faces of the die, and the event of throwing six can happen in only one way.

But it is easy to show that, as it stands, this definition can justify incompatible evaluations of probability. What is the probability of getting heads twice in two successive tosses of a coin? One can argue that it is ¼ because the "possible" events are four: two heads, two tails, first head and then tail, first tail and then head. One can also argue that it is ⅓ because the "possible" events are three: two heads, two tails, exactly one head. Further, when conjoined with the special addition theorem, the Laplacian definition in its provisional form may even lead to plain nonsense. Thus one might argue that the probability of throwing six equals $\frac{1}{2}$ since there are two possible alternatives: throwing six and throwing some number other than six. The same kind of argument, however, would justify the statement that the probability of throwing five equals $\frac{1}{2}$. If so, the probability of throwing either six or five equals unity, which means that it is impossible to get some number other than six or five!

Such difficulties, however, arise from the fact that alternatives of unequal range have been treated as "equals." Obviously the possibility of throwing a non-six can be disjunctively divided into "throwing five or four or three or two or one." Similarly the possibility of getting exactly one head in two successive coin tosses can be divided into "getting first heads and then tail or getting first tail and then heads." The classical theory accordingly required that the alternatives that jointly exhaust the field of possibility be *equiprobable*. Superficially it looks as though this amendment rendered the definition circular: is this not defining probability in terms of probability? But if equiprobability can be defined without reference to probability, then this is an innocuous verbal circularity, logically harmless (analogy: Russell defined "a number" as "a class of all classes that have the same number," but he supplied a definition of "having the same number" that did not refer to the concept of "a number"). Thus, if it were sufficiently clear what was meant by *equally specific* alternatives, we might substitute "equally specific" for "equiprobable" and obtain a definition of probability in terms of possibility. A definition reached this way, whatever its defects may be, is not circular. At first sight, it is even consistent and useful for computing probabilities independently of statistical data, at least when applied to the sort of gambling problems that provided the practical stimulus for the development of the classical theory of probability. Thus the amended Laplacian definition clearly yields the value $\frac{1}{4}$, not $\frac{1}{3}$, for the probability of two successive heads, since the possibility of getting exactly one head can be subdivided, unlike the other two possibilities, and therefore cannot be regarded as equally specific.

Unfortunately even the requirement of equal specificity does not guarantee that the Laplacian definition will always yield a unique probability. Suppose there are two boxes, A and B, A containing two black and three white balls, B containing one white and one black ball. A box is to be selected at random and then a ball at random from that box. What is the probability that the ball will be white? Now, there are two ways in which the Laplacian definition can be applied to this problem:

1. We first consider selections of box A and of box B as two equally specific, mutually exclusive, and jointly exhaustive alternatives. Each of them, accordingly, has a probability of ½. If A is selected, there are five equally specific realizations of the event of drawing a ball, three of which are favorable to the event of drawing a white ball. If B is selected, there are two such possibilities, one of them favorable. The proposition "A white ball will be drawn," therefore, is equivalent to the proposition "Box A is selected and a white ball drawn from it," and an obvious application of the multiplication and addition axioms of the calculus of probability yields

$$\frac{1}{2} \times \frac{3}{5} + \frac{1}{2} \times \frac{1}{2} = \frac{11}{20}$$

2. We consider all possible pairs of random selections the first member of which is a selection of one of the two boxes and the second member a selection of a ball from the box. Clearly, these seven alternatives are equally specific, and four of them are realizations of the event "drawing a white ball from one or the other of the two boxes"; hence this calculation yields ⁴⁄₇. And it is not clear how one could justify acceptance of one rather than the other of these fractions as the measure of the "true" probability of the event in question without any reference to the relative frequencies of white-ball drawings in a long series of pairs of random selections.

The requirement of equal specificity of alternatives is intimately connected with the classical principle of insufficient reason, or the principle of "indifference," as it was called by J. M. Keynes: If there is no reason for expecting that one rather than any other of a set of mutually exclusive and jointly exhaustive alternatives will be realized, then they are all equally probable. For if one alternative can be disjunctively divided into two or more subalternatives, in a way in which a second alternative cannot be divided,[1] this is surely a reason for expecting a realization of the former to a higher degree than a realization of the latter. (The former "can happen in more ways" than the latter.) Thus, suppose you are about to meet a man about whose characteristics you know absolutely nothing and you are forced to choose between a bet of X dollars on the prediction that he has dark hair and a bet of the same amount on the prediction that he either has dark hair or has a bank balance of at least $100. Clearly, it would be rational to choose

1. Note that by importing irrelevant predicates one can always subdivide a proposition still further, in accordance with the principle that for any propositions p and q, p is logically equivalent to $(p \cdot q) \lor (p \cdot q)$. But if two propositions p and r can be disjunctively divided *only* in this way, by means of a proposition q which is logically independent of both p and r, then they may be said to be equally specific.

11/20 = .55, 4/7 = .57 ... the ratios are close to each other. Dm both formulations, the weight is Towards the 4/5 (box A)

to bet on the latter, the weaker prediction. The latter is a priori more probable; for, denoting "He has dark hair" by p and "He has a bank balance of at least \$100" by q, the prediction "p or q" would be true in the cases "p and not q," "not p and q," "p and q," whereas the prediction p would be true only in the cases "p and not q" and "p and q."

But such purely logical considerations do not always suffice for a reasonable and consistent application of the principle of indifference. The six sides of a die constitute alternatives that are, in the logical sense, equally specific, yet we would not consider them equiprobable if we discovered that the die was not physically homogeneous, that is, its center of gravity did not coincide with its geometrical center. On the other hand, differences of color between the six sides would not be regarded as differences entailing a difference in the probabilities. Clearly, it is on the basis of experience that we expect more strongly that the side furthest from the center of gravity will turn up, and it is likewise on the basis of experience that our expectation that a blue side will turn up does not exceed our expectation that a red side will turn up. The conditional statement "*If* there is no evidence favoring one rather than another of a set of alternative outcomes of an experiment, *then* these outcomes are equally probable" is analytically true but does not help us to determine equal probabilities unless we know whether or not the evidence does discriminate between alternatives. The latter knowledge is in some cases purely logical, but in others it is empirical.

Further, to the already discussed example of inconsistency yielded by the principle that equally specific alternatives are equally probable, another striking example may be added. Suppose that we had no information whatever relevant to the question of what is the specific gravity of a certain substance. A priori we might then say that it is as likely to lie within the interval of possible values (1–2) as within the interval (2–3). Of course, there are infinitely many real numbers within any such interval, so in a sense even unequal intervals contain equal numbers of possible values. But let us admit only measurable fractions and, hence, a finite number of values within each interval. It is then plausible to say that there are equal numbers of possible specific gravities in equal intervals and that hence, the principle of the equal probability of equally specific alternatives entails that the specific gravity of the substance is as likely to be contained in the one as in the other interval. Now, that the specific gravity of X has the value n can be equivalently expressed by saying that the specific volume of X is $1/n$. Hence, the proposition that the specific volume of our substance lies between 1 and ½ should be exactly as probable as the proposition that it lies between

½ and ⅓, though the interval (1–½) is clearly larger than the interval (½–⅓).

It is understandable that empiricists would reject the Laplacian definition as a rule that, backed by the principle of indifference, enables a priori calculations of numerical probabilities. This does not mean, however, that an empiricist who embraces some form of frequency definition of probability cannot avail himself of the analytic theorems of the calculus of probability for computing probabilities of events. The Laplacian "definition" itself is properly regarded, not as an *interpretation* of probability that competes with the frequency or any other interpretation, but as an easily derivable theorem in the calculus of probability that, like all the other theorems, is neutral with respect to the question of the interpretation of probability. The derivation is as follows:

Suppose that $A_1, A_2, \ldots, A_n$, are all the possible outcomes of an experiment and that each given two of them are incompatible. Since, by hypothesis, the evidence e entails the disjunction of all these alternatives, and since the alternatives are pairwise incompatible relative to e, we have

$$A_1 \vee A_2 \vee \cdots \vee \frac{A_n}{e} = 1 = \frac{A_1}{e} + \frac{A_2}{e} + \cdots + \frac{A_n}{e}$$

Suppose that $(A_1/e) = (A_2/e) = \cdots = (A_n/e)$. Then

$$1 = nx\frac{A_i}{e} \quad \text{hence} \quad \frac{A_i}{e} = \frac{1}{n}$$

Let p be a subdisjunction $A_1 \vee A_2 \vee \cdots \vee A_r$. Then by the addition axiom

$$\frac{p}{e} = \frac{r}{n}$$

Note that what has been formally derived from the axioms of the calculus is the *conditional* proposition "If $A_1, A_2, \ldots, A_n$ are equally probable on e, then $p/e = r/n$." What the empiricist denies is that the antecedent of this conditional proposition can ever be justifiably asserted on a priori grounds; according to him such an assertion must be backed up by direct or indirect statistical evidence.

B. LOGICAL AND STATISTICAL PROBABILITY

We have seen that the classical, Laplacian "definition" of probability cannot be regarded as an interpretation of the axiomatically defined probability functor of the formal calculus that enables consistent a priori calculations of numerical probabilities. Nevertheless it suggests a method of measuring probabilities without recourse to empirical data. This does not mean that there are two radically different methods—one a priori and the other empirical—for determining the values of one and the same magnitude called "probability." Rather there are, corresponding to these different methods, two different concepts of probability. It is only in recent times, however, that an *ambiguity* in the word "probability" has been recognized as the source of the heated controversies between apriorists and empiricists about the true meaning of "probability." What makes it easy to overlook the difference between the concepts, here distinguished by the names "logical" and "statistical" probability, is that there is sometimes a close agreement between their values. (Analogously, it required some effort in the history of physics to distinguish conceptually mass and weight, and even greater effort to distinguish gravitational and inertial mass.) Thus, a statement of the form "The probability that a member of A is a member of B equals m/n" (e.g., "The probability that a dealer in used cars will try to cheat you is $9/10$") is properly interpreted as a statistical statement requiring empirical support. Now, the probability that Jolly Dick will try to cheat you *on the evidence* that Jolly Dick is a dealer in used cars and that 90 per cent of used car dealers try to cheat their customers is likewise $9/10$. But the latter statement is logical, not empirical.

That there is a meaning of "probability" other than relative frequency is obvious on reflection on our earlier example of a comparison of predictions of the forms p and $(p$ or $q)$. If p and q are logically independent predictions, then $(p$ or $q)$ is more probable than p in the sense that the former prediction can come true in more ways than the latter. So far, however, we have only *comparative* statements of logical probability. Moreover such comparisons are restricted to propositions standing in entailment relations: we can only say that for any propositions A and B, if A entails B but B does not entail A, then the logical probability of B exceeds that of A. In order to obtain a method of measuring logical probability that can be applied to any pair of propositions, whether deductively independent or not, we must first introduce the concept of *state description*. It is a formalization of the intuitive notion of a specific "way" in which a relatively indeterminate state of affairs may be realized. Thus we speak of six different ways in which the event "throwing exactly two heads in four trials" may happen, or the n different ways in which the event "selecting a black ball from a box containing n black and m white balls" may happen (corresponding to the n different black balls that may be picked). Suppose that in a given investigation we talk about two individual objects, a and b, and that we characterize them exclusively in terms of two primitive predicates P and Q. Then a possible state description in this miniature language (viz., the language containing the names a and b and the primitive predicates P and Q and no other primitive descriptive terms) is: $Pa \cdot -Qa \cdot Pb \cdot Qb$. Other possible state descriptions are obtained by replacing one or more of the atomic statements with their negations. In general, a state description in a language L is a conjunction that contains, for every atomic statement in L, either it or its negation but not both, and no other statements. A state description, then, is a complete description of all the individual objects the language has names for.

The primitive predicates must, of course, be logically independent; otherwise some state descriptions would be inconsistent. Thus, if we talk about uniformly colored things we cannot use both "red" and "blue" as primitive predicates, for we cannot allow the possibility that a uniformly colored thing be both red and blue. If we can assume that all the things our predictions are concerned with are either red or blue, we can, say, choose "red" as primitive and introduce "blue" by the definition "blue = not-red." What should we do if such an assumption cannot be made—as when, for example, we want to compute the probability that in two successive drawings from an urn containing four white, three blue, and three red marbles we get one white and one blue marble? Let us spread the contents of the urn out in time, so to speak; i.e., let us construct all possible sequences of ten drawings. Each sequence will be completely and uniquely characterized if we assign a particular color to each element. One such possible sequence is

white (x_1), blue (x_2), blue (x_3), red (x_4), white (x_5),
white (x_6), red (x_7), red (x_8), blue (x_9), white (x_{10}).

This is a state description, but it does not contain any negative statements; it contains a positive characterization of each object. Generalizing, we define state descriptions for languages containing several primitive predicates from the same family of predicates (as, for example, the family of color predicates) as follows: a conjunction of atomic statements that ascribes to each individual object exactly one primitive predicate from each family of primitive predicates.

We can now proceed to explain what is meant by the logical probability of an hypothesis h relative to evidence e: namely, a measure of the overlap of the ranges of h and e. The range of a proposition is the class of all the state descriptions that constitute alternative realizations of the proposition. Thus the following class of state descriptions is the range of the proposition "Exactly two heads occur in four tosses with this coin":

HHTT, HTHT, HTTH, THTH, TTHH, THHT

Intuitively, the greater the range of a proposition, the smaller the risk that it will be falsified by the facts; or, a measure of the range of a proposition may be considered a measure of the a priori probability of the proposition, i.e., its probability relative to no empirical evidence (sometimes this is also called "absolute" probability). If e entails h, then the range of e is wholly included in the range of h, and if e contradicts h, then the range of e is wholly excluded from the range of h. If, on the other hand, e and h are deductively independent, then their ranges overlap, and the greater the ratio of their intersection to the range of e, the greater the logical probability of h relative to e. Using $c(h, e)$ (Carnap's notation, suggesting "the degree to which e *confirms* h") for the logical probability of h relative to e, we get the definition:

$c(h, e)$ is a measure of the range of $(h \cdot e)$ divided by the corresponding measure of the range of e; that is,

$$c(h, e) = \frac{m(h \cdot e)}{m(e)}$$

The next question is how to measure these ranges. It may seem natural to take as the measure of a range simply the number of state descriptions it comprises. This stipulation would amount to assigning equal a priori probabilities to all state descriptions. Surprisingly, however, it can be shown that the theorems of logical probability that result from such a method of measurement of ranges are wholly counterintuitive. Specifically, it can be shown that the probability of a prediction is wholly independent of past experience (e.g., the probability of the prediction that the next swan we meet is white on the evidence that 100 observed swans were white would not exceed the probability of the same prediction on the evidence that just one observed swan was white).[2] Any explication of a concept already in use in science or everyday talk must be guided by some nonarbitrary adequacy criteria. Some, if not all, such adequacy criteria are propositions involving the "explicandum" (i.e., the concept to be explicated) that are self-evident in terms of the intuitive meaning of the explicandum. That the probability, whether logical or statistical, of h relative to e should be maximal if e entails h is an example of such an adequacy criterion. The all-important adequacy criterion, which is violated by an explication of logical probability that is based on the assignment of equal a priori probabilities to all state descriptions, is what Carnap has called "the principle of learning from experience." This principle states that the

2. See R. Carnap, *Logical Foundations of Probability* (Chicago: University of Chicago Press, 1950), p. 565.

larger the number of observed members of a class K that have a property P, the greater the probability—relative to this evidence—that an as yet unobserved member of K likewise has P; and, further, the greater the relative frequency of objects with P in a sample s contained in K, the greater the probability that a member of K outside s has P.

In order to obtain a method of measuring logical probabilities that satisfies this all-important adequacy condition, Carnap has proposed that equal measures (a priori probabilities) be assigned to the *structure* descriptions, not the *state* descriptions. A structure description specifies *what number* of individuals have the various properties; it does not tell us *which* individuals have them. Thus "two heads in four tosses" is a structure description; *HHTT*, *HTHT*, and so on are state descriptions corresponding to that structure description. Obviously, a structure description is the disjunction of all the state descriptions that correspond to it. State descriptions that correspond to (i.e., entail) the same structure description are isomorphic in the sense that one can be transformed into the other by a unique interchange of individual constants. More specifically, Carnap's preferred method of measuring logical probabilities is based on the assignment of equal measures to all structure descriptions in terms of the *Q-predicates* of the given languages. A *Q*-predicate characterizes an individual as completely as the stock of primitive predicates in the language allows. Thus, if we have not only "red" but also "round" as primitive predicates in L, then the Q-predicates in L are: red and round, red and not round, not red and round, not red and not round. By elementary deductive logic, any predicate is equivalent to a disjunction of Q-predicates, e.g., "red" to "red and round or red and not round." We proceed to illustrate the method in terms of a simple example.

Suppose a language L with four individual constants (i.e., names of individual objects) a, b, c, d and just one primitive predicate P. In such a simple language P is itself a Q-predicate (Q_1) and its negation is the other Q-predicate (Q_2). Now let us compute the logical probability of the prediction that d has P relative to the evidence that a and b have P and c lacks P. The table lists all the state descriptions of L and their measures, computed as follows: The structure descriptions have equal measures adding up to unity (since it is logically necessary that one or the other structure description be true). All isomorphic state descriptions have the same measure, according to the principle that the logical probability of a statement p does not depend on *which* individuals are mentioned by p as long as the individuals are mentioned only by numerically differentiating names (e.g., the a priori probability of $Pa \cdot Pb$ can hardly differ from the a priori probability of $Pc \cdot Pd$ if a, b, c, d are just identification tags that do not connote any qualities). Since a structure description is the disjunction of all corresponding, isomorphic state descriptions, and any two state descriptions are incompatible, its measure must, by the addition axiom, be equal to the sum of the measure of the corresponding state descriptions; hence the measure of a state description is derived by dividing the measure of the corresponding structure description into the number of isomorphic state descriptions. We then determine $m(h \cdot e)$ as $\frac{1}{20}$, since there is just one state description in which $(h \cdot e)$, viz. $Pa \cdot Pb \cdot - Pc \cdot Pd$, is true, and its measure is $\frac{1}{20}$. On the other hand, e is equivalent to the disjunction of two state descriptions with measures $\frac{1}{20}$ and $\frac{1}{30}$, hence

$$c(h, e,) = \frac{m(h \cdot e)}{m(e)} = \frac{\frac{1}{20}}{\frac{1}{20} + \frac{1}{30}} = \frac{3}{5}$$

$$\left. Pa \cdot Pb \cdot Pc \cdot Pd \right\} \frac{1}{5} \qquad \left. \begin{array}{l} Pa \cdot Pb \cdot - Pc \cdot - Pd \\ Pa \cdot - Pb \cdot Pc \cdot - Pd \\ Pa \cdot - Pb \cdot - Pc \cdot Pd \\ - Pa \cdot - Pb \cdot Pc \cdot Pd \\ - Pa \cdot Pb \cdot - Pc \cdot Pd \\ - Pa \cdot Pb \cdot Pc \cdot - Pd \end{array} \right\} \frac{1}{30}$$

$$\left. \begin{array}{l} Pa \cdot Pb \cdot Pc \cdot - Pd \\ Pa \cdot Pb \cdot - Pc \cdot Pd \\ Pa \cdot - Pb \cdot Pc \cdot Pd \\ - Pa \cdot Pb \cdot Pc \cdot Pd \end{array} \right\} \frac{1}{20}$$

$$\left. \begin{array}{l} Pa \cdot - Pb \cdot - Pc \cdot - Pd \\ - Pa \cdot Pb \cdot - Pc \cdot - Pd \\ - Pa \cdot - Pb \cdot Pc \cdot - Pd \\ - Pa \cdot - Pb \cdot - Pc \cdot Pd \end{array} \right\} \frac{1}{20}$$

$$\left. - Pa \cdot - Pb \cdot - Pc \cdot - Pd \right\} \frac{1}{5}$$

The computation is more complicated if we shift to a language L' that contains two, logically independent, primitive predicates, say P and R. We now have four Q-predicates:

$$\begin{array}{ll} Q_1 & P \cdot R \\ Q_2 & P \cdot - R \\ Q_3 & - P \cdot R \\ Q_4 & - P \cdot - R \end{array}$$

We transform a state description in terms of the primitive predicates into one in terms of the Q-predicates. For example,

$$Pa \cdot Ra \cdot - Pb \cdot Rb \cdot - Pc \cdot Rc \cdot Pd \cdot Rd$$

is equivalent to

$$Q_1 a \cdot Q_3 b \cdot Q_3 c \cdot Q_1 d$$

The structure descriptions can be given simply by specifying the numbers of individuals with the various Q-properties, thus:

$$Q_1 = 4, \quad Q_2 = 0, \quad Q_3 = 0, \quad Q_4 = 0$$
$$Q_1 = 3, \quad Q_2 = 1, \quad Q_3 = 0, \quad Q_4 = 0$$
$$Q_1 = 3, \quad Q_2 = 0, \quad Q_3 = 1, \quad Q_4 = 0$$

and so on. In order to determine by deductive logic which state descriptions entail $(h \cdot e)$ and which entail e, it is advisable to express these statements in terms of Q-predicates. Thus $Pa \cdot Pb \cdot - Pc$ is equivalent to

$$(Q_1a \lor Q_2a) \cdot (Q_1b \lor Q_2b) \cdot (Q_3c \lor Q_4c)$$

The computation of $c(h \cdot e)$ in L'—which we will leave to the patient reader—yields $\frac{4}{7}$. The question whether this discrepancy of the logical probabilities of the same hypothesis relative to the same evidence as one shifts from L to L' is a serious objection to the whole method will be taken up later.

Actually, a description of the evidence relative to which a certain probability is assigned to a prediction in the form $Pa \cdot Pb \cdot - Pc$ contains a redundancy, since all that matters is how many individuals have been found to have P and how many have been found to lack P; *which* of them had P and which lacked P is irrelevant. If the relative frequency of heads in, say, ten tosses with a given coin is reported, the logical probability of the prediction that the eleventh toss will yield heads can be computed without the irrelevant knowledge of which tosses yielded heads and which tail. Accordingly we should expect that if for e the *statistical* information "Two out of three observed objects had P" were substituted, the logical probability should be the same, since no relevant information would have been omitted. This is indeed the case, as the reader can verify for himself by substituting in our example for $Pa \cdot Pb \cdot - Pc$ the disjunction

$$Pa \cdot Pb \cdot - Pc \lor - Pa \cdot Pb \cdot Pc \lor Pa \cdot - Pb \cdot Pc$$

A famous theorem in the classical, Laplacian theory of probability is the *rule of succession*: If an event has occurred m times in n occasions, then, relative to this evidence, the probability that it will occur again on the next occasion is $(m + 1)/(n + 2)$. This formula was derived by Laplace from Bayes' theorem. An essential step in the proof was the assumption that all possible relative frequencies of a given property in a large (though finite) class comprising the n observed elements are a priori equally likely. Since this assumption corresponds to Carnap's stipulation of equal measures for all structure descriptions (if the property is primitive and the only one designated by a primitive predicate of the language), one would expect a similar "rule of succession" in Carnap's theory. Indeed, it provides us with a theorem of "singular predicate inference" which is a generalization of Laplace's rule for predictions formulated in terms of primitive or compound predicates, in a language with an arbitrary finite number of primitive predicates. Let $k =$ the number of Q-predicates in the language and $w =$ the *logical width* of the predicate occurring in e and h, i.e., the number of Q-predicates into which it can be disjunctively resolved. Then

$$c(h, e) = \frac{m + w}{n + k}$$

If the predicate occurring in e and h is primitive and moreover the only primitive predicate in the language, then $w = 1$ and $k = 2$, giving Laplace's rule as a limiting case.

Two major criticisms have been advanced against Laplace's rule.

1. In case there is no relevant empirical evidence at all, $m = 0$ and $n = 0$. Hence Columbus, had he known Laplace's theory of probability, might have said that there was an even chance that America's first inhabitant he would encounter would have red skin. But surely we cannot derive probabilities from complete ignorance.

2. Laplace's rule leads to contradiction. Suppose that we make drawings from a box, getting first a white marble, next a red marble, and next a blue marble. Now we apply Laplace's rule to calculate the probability, on this evidence, that the fourth marble we draw is white: the result is $(1 + 1)/(3 + 2) = 2/5$. Clearly 2/5 is, by the same reasoning, the probability that the fourth drawing will bring forth a red marble, and also the probability that it will yield a blue marble. Applying now the addition axiom, we find that the probability of getting either a white or a red or a blue marble the fourth time is 6/5!

Criticism (1) is, of course, valid if by "probability" is meant the relative frequency of occurrence of an event. One cannot deduce statistical predictions from a priori assumptions. Wherever this seems to be possible an equivocation on the term "probability" has surely been committed, or else a synthetic premise connecting logical and statistical probability must have been smuggled in. For example, suppose that a disk is divided into ten equal sectors, each being marked with one of the ten integers from 1 to 10. A pointer is set rotating and the question is asked what the probability is that it will come to rest in a sector marked with a prime number between 1 and 10. Since there are five such sectors, one may be tempted to answer "½" before making any experiments. But in claiming that the probability can thus be derived a priori, one is probably confusing the proposition "Five out of ten sectors are marked with a prime number" with the entirely different proposition "The pointer comes to rest in a sector marked with a prime number five out of ten times." If, to be sure, there is *before* this particular experiment ample evidence that rotating pointers generally come to rest with equal frequency in a given sector and another sector of the same size, then the purely mathematical proposition about the proportion of prime numbers will warrant the prediction of the corresponding relative frequency. But a statistical prediction has then really been deduced from a statistical, not an a priori, assumption. The point of this cautionary remark is that criticism (1) is irrelevant to the extent that the classical theory distinguishes logical from statistical probability and does not claim that by means of the rule of succession relative frequencies can be deduced from zero empirical information. Further, the value ½ as measure of rational belief or expectation in situations of zero empirical information is quite plausible if the predicate in question is compared only with one alternative of equal range. For example, if I were confronted with a box which I knew to contain colored marbles, and I knew that each marble was either red or blue, then the question could be put in the form of a dichotomy: Is the marble I am going to pick at random blue or not blue? Consequently, if I were forced to bet but given a choice of odds, it would certainly be rational for me to choose even odds.

Laplace's rule cannot, however, be applied to problems involving more than two alternatives. If I did not know how many different colors were represented by the marbles in the box, I should certainly hesitate to bet on the same prediction, that the marble I pick first is red, at even odds, for its negation has a larger range. This consideration brings us to (2), the charge of inconsistency. Carnap's theorem is invulnerable by this charge because, unlike Laplace's rule, it explicitly takes differences of logical width into account. In order to deal with the problem in (2), we need to use a language containing "white," "red," and "blue" as primitive predicates. Since the problem refers only to color, not to any other determinable attribute of the objects, these are the only relevant primitive predicates, hence they are at the same time the Q-predicates. Substituting, we have $w = 1$ and $k = 3$ for each of the three successive computations, hence 2/6 as the probability of each of the three simple predictions. With the addition axiom, this yields 1 as the probability that the next marble is either white or red or blue. Is this value unreasonable? Not if we consider that to choose a set of primitive predicates $P_1, P_2, \ldots, P_n$ belonging to the same family is to assume that every object about which the language is used to make predictions is characterized by one or the other member of the set. If we were to reckon with the possibility that the box also contained, say, green marbles (but were quite sure that none of them had colors other than white, red, blue, and green), then we would apply a language system containing these four primitive predicates. Each simple prediction would then have the probability 2/7, the disjunctive prediction 6/7, leaving a little room for the possibility that next time a green marble will show up though no green marble showed up in the first three selections.

Certainly Carnap's theorem has definite advantage over Laplace's in that it is not restricted to dichotomies of simple equispecific alternatives, such as "red or blue," and can never give rise to absurd values, such as 6/5. Carnap also claims that Laplace's rule, when applied to properties of different logical width, can come into contradiction with the calculus of probability. Thus, assuming the same empirical data as above, let us ask for the probability of getting next a marble that is either white or red. Laplace's rule, when applied directly to the property "white or red," yields 3/5, but if we first apply it to the simple properties "white" and "red" and then use the addition axiom we obtain 4/5. As can easily be checked, no such contradictions arise in Carnap's theory. It should be noted, however, that the classical theory is guilty of this charge only if the word "property" there is used as broadly as in contemporary deductive logic. And this is doubtful. Outside of formal logic one does not say "x has the property of being either red or white" but rather "Either x has the property of being red or x has the property of being white." Clearly, if the intended *direct* applications of Laplace's rule are restricted to predictions involving simple properties, no such contradiction with the calculus arises.

There is a close relationship between logical probability, as explicated by Carnap, and statistical probability. Consider the previous example of a singular prediction based on a relative frequency of 2/3 in an observed sample of three objects. If the predicate P is the only predicate that appears in e and h, it is plausible to apply, for the computation of $c(h, e)$, the language with just P as the only primitive predicate; hence we accept 3/5 as the value of $c(h, e)$. What does this value represent? Carnap demonstrates that it is equal to the *estimate*, relative to e, of the relative frequency of P in the population including the sample described in e. For example, if the sample consists of three New Yorkers we encountered, two of whom we found to be unfriendly, then ascribing to the prediction that the next New Yorker we will meet is unfriendly the logical probability 3/5 is equivalent to estimating the relative frequency of unfriendly people in the class of New Yorkers as 3/5. Strictly speaking, the estimate refers to another, nonoverlapping sample of the same class, but since it can be shown that its value does not depend on the size of that sample, it is a good approximation to the relative frequency in the whole class if the latter is very large in comparison to the sample described in e. The estimate of the relative frequency of P (in K) relative to *e* is defined as the sum of all the products of the possible values of the relative frequency and their logical probabilities relative to *e*. Thus, if $f_1, f_2, \ldots, f_n$ are the possible values, and $c_1, c_2, \ldots, c_n$ their logical probabilities relative to *e*, the estimate equals [3]

$$f_1c_1 + f_2c_2 + \cdots + f_nc_n$$

It follows from the equality of an estimate of relative frequency to the logical probability of the corresponding singular prediction, together with the theorem of singular prediction cited above, that the estimate of relative frequency is very close to the relative frequency in the observed sample if the latter is large. Hence an empirically ascertained statistical probability is a fairly close measure of a logically ascertained logical probability of a prediction. Nevertheless, a confusion of the two *concepts* of probability would be philosophically disastrous.

This concept of the "estimate" (more commonly called "mathematical expectation") of relative frequency—or, in the case of infinite classes, of the limit of a relative frequency—is very important for the clarification of Hume's problem of the justification of inductive inference. How, asked Hume, can we justify the belief that an unsurveyably large, perhaps infinite class resembles, in specifiable respects, a small observed sample from it? If we attempt an inductive justification, by pointing out that inductive generalization has usually led to successful predictions in the past, we are (according to Hume) guilty of circular reasoning since this very argument is an instance of inductive generalization.[4] But if we interpret inductive probability statements, such as "On the evidence that all observed offspring of humans are, in biological respects, themselves human—and not, for example, dogs—it is highly probable that humans will also in future have human offspring," as estimations of relative frequency, Hume's dilemma is, as it were, undercut. For only empirical statements call for inductive justification, and statements of an *estimate* of relative frequency are, if correct, analytic. To be sure, an inductive logician like Carnap cannot entirely avoid Hume's problem. If we are told that it is reasonable to expect unobserved samples of a certain class to resemble statistically the observed sample—provided the latter is

---

3. If *K* is infinite, the estimate of the relative frequency of *P* in *K* must be replaced by the estimate of the *limit* of that relative frequency. The latter is defined as the limit approached by the estimates of *P* in increasing samples (nonoverlapping with the evidential sample) of *K*. Since these estimates all have the same value (equal to the logical probability of a singular prediction), the estimate of a limiting relative frequency is—unlike the limiting relative frequency—a limit that demonstrably exists, and is likewise equal to the logical probability of the corresponding singular predictions (see Carnap's *Logical Foundations of Probability*, pp. 553–554).

4. As to whether this charge of circularity can be rebutted, see the concluding section of Chapter 13.

sufficiently large and variegated—because the corresponding predictions have a high logical probability in a certain system of inductive logic, we shall naturally ask why we should accept that system as a guide to rational predictions. In particular, since choices of different measure functions will result in different logical probabilities for the same hypotheses on the same bodies of evidence, we must be provided with a *rationale* for choosing this rather than that measure function. Many contemporary scientists and philosophers of science are, for good or for bad reasons, skeptical about the prospects and even the importance for science of an inductive logic based on Carnapian measure functions. At any rate, statisticians have developed methods of acceptance and rejection of hypotheses that do not depend on the choice of a measure function. We shall consider these methods in the next chapter.

In the meantime, let us attend to a peculiar feature of Carnap's c^* function which was briefly mentioned above: that the value of $c^*(h, e)$ depends, for any given pair of sentences h and e, on the number of Q-predicates, and therewith on the number of primitive predicates in the language used. This becomes evident if we look at the theorem of predictive inference for the c^* function in which k, the number of Q-predicates, occurs as a variable. This dependence raises two questions—one philosophical, the other practical. The philosophical question is whether logical probability can be regarded, like logical entailment and logical compatibility, as a logical relation between *propositions*, i.e. states of affairs that may or may not be expressed by sentences. Consider a logical entailment, such as that from p to (p or q). If for p and q we substitute synonymous sentences p' and q', and the logical constant "or" keeps a constant meaning (fixed by the rules of inference governing disjunction), then p' must likewise entail (p' or q') however the language may have been changed in other respects. This is what is conveyed by saying that a logical entailment is a relation between proposititions, meanings that may be alternatively expressed by different sentences. But a statement of logical probability "$c^*(h, e) = p$" may hold in a language L and fail to hold in a language L' which differs from L just in the occurrence of an additional primitive predicate although the latter does not occur in h and e at all. Consequently the value of c^* is not uniquely determined by the meanings of its arguments, the sentences h and e. And it is seen that a conventional element enters into the determination of the values of the c-function even after a measure-function, such as m^*, has been chosen: the choice of a set of primitive predicates, and therewith of a language system. In this respect conventionalism with respect to quantitative inductive logic Carnapian style seems to contain more truth than conventionalism with respect to deductive logic. For whereas deductive relations between two sentences are fixed once the meanings of the sentences, especially of the logical constants in them, are fixed, the analogous assertion about inductive relations does not hold for an inductive logic based on the c^* function.

The practical question is simple: If $c^*(h, e) = p$ in language L, and $c^*(h, e) = q$ in language L', which language should be used to compute that logical probability of h relative to e which may be used as a basis for action? The question is highly pertinent because Carnap holds that knowledge of logical-probability values is relevant to action; specifically, he suggests that a logical probability may be interpreted as a *fair betting quotient*. Thus, consider our example of the prediction Pd on the evidence $Pa \cdot Pb \cdot -Pc$, or on the statistical evidence that in a sample of three objects two have the property P (we assume that this is the total evidence on which the prediction is based). Suppose that you were to bet on the prediction that the next member of the population in question, here artificially named d, has P, agreeing to pay your betting partner, who predicts that d will not have P, \$3 if his prediction is true. What amount should he pay you if your prediction comes true? Since it is, intuitively, more probable that you will be right, fairness requires that the amount he should pay you be smaller than \$3. Now, if we accept 3/5 as the fair betting quotient for the prediction Pd (i.e., the ratio of the stake on this prediction to the sum of the two stakes) then the answer is that he should pay you \$2. Is there any way of justifying the value 3/5 as against the value 4/7, which represents the logical probability of the same prediction relative to the same evidence as computed in a language containing an additional primitive predicate? It can certainly be justified in terms of the plausible principle that the language system to be applied for the computation of a logical probability is that language system which contains *only* primitive predicates occurring in the pairs of sentences whose logical probability relations are to be ascertained.

For this reason the dependence of c^* on k is not, from the point of view of the application of quantitative inductive logic, a serious disadvantage. On the other hand, if one is impressed with the above philosophical argument against this dependence, one may look around for a c-function whose values do not depend on k but only on w/k, the *relative* logical widths of the predicates. The ratio w/k remains constant as k changes. For example, for any k, the logical width of a primitive predicate is always $k/2$, hence w/k is always $\frac{1}{2}$ for any primitive predicate. Readers who are interested in such language-independent c-functions will be able to locate them in Carnap's *The Continuum of Inductive Methods*.

Before leaving the subject, let us try to make clearer the difference between logical and statistical probability, and especially the relevance of logical probability to expectations of future events, by considering again the simple problem of the probability of throwing heads twice in two consecutive throws. Actually, the temporal order of the events is immaterial; "What is the probability of getting two heads if two coins are tossed simultaneously?" is obviously exactly the same problem (the difference between "heads first and tail second" and "tail first and heads second" is translated, in this formulation, into spatial terms: you might get heads with the coin in your left hand and tail with the coin in your right hand, or the other way around). If the probability we are asking for is statistical, there are two ways of finding the answer: we may observe a long sequence of pairs of tosses and note the relative frequency of double heads; or we may assume, on the evidence that coins are fair, that the statistical probability of throwing heads with either coin is ½, and then use the special multiplication axiom to compute the statistical probability of double heads. The use of the special multiplication axiom would have to be empirically justified by producing evidence of the statistical independence of consecutive or simultaneous coin tosses. That is, simple multiplication of the probabilities of the two events is justified only if the relative frequency of heads following a tail is about equal to the relative frequency of heads following heads (and similarly for the spatial representation). If, on the other hand, we are asking for the logical probability, statistical data are irrelevant. Denoting the two events by a and b, and a priori probability by c_0, we get the following equation from the general multiplication axiom:

$$c_0(Ha \cdot Hb) = c_0(Ha) \times c(Hb, Ha)$$

Since it is plausible to use for the problem at hand a language in which H is the only primitive predicate ("tail" being defined as "not heads"), $c_0(Ha)$ is ½. Remembering the general definition of the c-function, we set

$$c(Hb, Ha) = \frac{m(Hb \cdot Ha)}{m(Ha)}$$

If the confirmation function we use is the c^* function, we must assign equal measures to the three structure descriptions in this language, hence we obtain

$$\frac{m^*(Hb \cdot Ha)}{m^*(Ha)} = \frac{\frac{1}{3}}{\frac{1}{2}} = \frac{2}{3}$$

$c_0(Ha \cdot Hb)$, therefore, turns out to be ⅓ not ¼. Indeed this result could have been obtained directly by considering that $Ha \cdot Hb$ is one out of the three possible structure descriptions (not to be confused with the four possible *state* descriptions). But the advantage of the calculation based on the multiplication axiom is that it brings out that in the realm of logical probability we cannot assume independence in problems of this sort. That is, having chosen our measure function, we find that $c^*(Hb, Ha)$ is not equal to $c_0(Hb)$. This is evident also from the theorem of predictive inference, for substituting in Carnap's formula of predictive inference $m = 1$ and $n = 1$ and $w = 1$ and $k = 2$, we get

$$c^*(Hb, Ha) = \tfrac{2}{3}$$

But, the reader may exclaim, does not this result show that the theory of logical probability cannot serve as a guide to rational expectations? If a betting partner were to stake \$1 on the prediction of double heads (h), my stake on the contradictory prediction should be \$3 if the bet is to be fair, most experts on betting would say. This yields ¼ as the fair betting quotient on h (the stake on h divided by the sum of the stakes); but according to Carnap, logical probability may be interpreted as a fair betting quotient. What is wrong? The fallacy, it may be suggested, is that a problem of a priori probability has been confused with a problem of predictive inference. The bettor who judges the probability of double heads to be ¼ does so on the empirical evidence that heads and tails occur with about equal frequency and that coin tosses are independent with respect to the two attributes in question—which entails a relative frequency of ¼ for double heads. But then he really ought to apply the theorem of predictive inference. Suppose, for example, that in 24 pairs of tosses double heads occurred 6 times; then the logical probability of double heads occurring the next time, on this statistical evidence, equals 7/27, since there are three Q-predicates that may apply to such an event pair: HH, TT, TH (the last Q-predicate means "containing one head and one tail"). This is very close to ¼, and the larger the sample the closer the approximation to ¼.

We must repeat that, in Carnap's conception, the choice of a measure function is to be judged mainly in terms of the adequacy of the theorem of predictive inference to which it leads. Thus, the assignment of equal measures to all state descriptions was rejected because it demonstrably violates the "principle of learning from experience." Such being the case, it is difficult to justify the acceptance of one rather than another value for a given a priori probability (such as the a priori probability of double heads) in isolation from the question what theorem of predictive inference is entailed by the choice of the corresponding measure function. Still, if anyone feels that ¼ is not only the statistical but also the a priori probability of double heads because there are four, not three, a priori equiprobable alternatives, he can without formal inconsistency assign equal measures to all state descriptions in problems of a priori probability provided he computes a priori probability directly, not via the multiplication theorem, and shift to the c^* function (or some other function satisfying the principle of learning from experience) in problems of inductive probability. The fact that the theorem of predictive inference would then have to be restricted to positive values of n (i.e., the a priori case, $n = 0$, excluded) in problems like the one just discussed, would be a minor inelegance as compared with the resulting gain of intuitive satisfaction.

But further, the assignment of equal a priori probabilities to the structure descriptions does not accord with certain fruitful applications of the theory of probability to physics. In statistical mechanics certain assumptions of equiprobability are made in order to derive thermodynamic laws of the behavior of gases from the conception of a gas as an aggregate of molecules in random motion. One such assumption is that all possible velocities with which a given molecule might move are equally probable, so that the actual velocity of a molecule may be represented by a simple average over all possible velocities:

$$\bar{v} = \frac{(v_1^2 + v_2^2 + \cdots + v_n^2)^{1/2}}{n}$$

where n is the number of molecules that, on the assumption that each molecule moves with constant velocity, is equal to the number of possible velocities. This is one of the statistical assumptions on which Clausius based the classical deduction of the general gas law, $PV = RT$ for all ideal gases. In contradistinction to the general gas law, the famous law of entropy (second law of thermodynamics) refers to evolving systems, not to systems in a state of equilibrium. Now, in qualitative interpretation the law of entropy asserts that a gas to which no energy is added and from which no energy is subtracted (an "isolated" system) will approach a state of uniform density and uniform temperature. If, for example, a mass of gas is enclosed in a container divided into two compartments, one of them hotter than the other, then, after the wall separating the compartments is removed, diffusion will take place in such a way that the hotter part of the gas is cooled and the colder part becomes warmer, until finally the temperature is uniformly distributed over the entire mass of gas. According to the kinetic theory of heat, an addition of heat energy to a physical system means, microscopically, an addition of kinetic energy to the constituent molecules, and a loss of heat energy means a loss of kinetic energy of the constituent molecules. This theory naturally suggests that a transition to a state of uniform temperature distribution is a transition to a state where the average molecular velocities in different parts of the space filled by the gas are equal. Now, in Boltzmann's statistical interpretation the law of entropy reads as follows: An isolated physical system, conceived as an aggregate of molecules in random motion, evolves almost always from less probable to more probable states, the most probable state being the state of maximum disorder. Boltzmann assumes that the statistical probability of a macroscopic state is proportional to the number of possible microscopic states that correspond to it, or are possible realizations of it. This is similar to the assumption that the statistical probability of a certain number r of successes in n independent trials is proportional to the number of ways in which r successes in n independent trials can come about. Thus it is self-evident that two successes in four independent experiments, a favorable outcome of each of which has a probability of $\frac{1}{2}$, is the most probable number of successes because this event can happen in more ways than any of the other possible events (viz. in six) *and* because probability means in this context the relative number of possible realizations.

The following simple model may clarify the statistical meaning of the law of entropy. Suppose we consider possible distributions of slow and fast molecules over two volume cells, assuming uniform density, i.e., equal numbers of molecules in equal volume cells. To simplify the picture, let us assume that just four molecules, two of them fast, two of them slow, are to be considered. The fast ones we name v_1 and v_2, the slow ones u_1 and u_2. We consider two macroscopic states, one of maximum order and the other of maximum disorder. The former corresponds to two possible microstates (Figure 12.1a), viz. v_1 and v_2 in the left

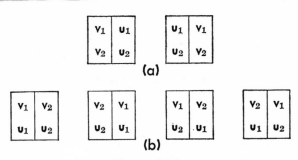

(a)

(b)

Figure 12.1

cell and u_1 and u_2 in the right cell, or u_1 and u_2 in the left cell and v_1 and v_2 in the right cell. The state of maximum disorder is the state where each cell contains one slow and one fast molecule; the slow and the fast molecules are mixed, not segregated. But, as shown in Figure 12.1b, this macroscopic state can be realized in four different microstates. And it is clear that the greater the number of molecules, the greater the number of ways in which a "mixed" distribution of the molecules over the two cells may occur, while the macrostate of all the fast molecules being in one cell and all the slow ones in the other can occur in only two ways.

A macroscopic state of a physical system is obviously a statistical distribution, described by what Carnap calls a "structure description." Thus the orderly macrostate in our model may be described as "The relative frequency of fast molecules is unity in one cell and zero in the other cell," and the disorderly macrostate as "The relative frequency of fast molecules in each cell is $\frac{1}{2}$." In Carnap's theory the uniform structures, i.e., those in which one Q-property occurs with maximal frequency and all the others with minimal frequency, are just as likely as the disorderly structures. But the basic assumption of the statistical deduction of the entropy law is just that disorderly structures are vastly more probable than orderly structures. And since disorderly structures have a greater Laplacian a priori probability than orderly structures—as illustrated by the maximal Laplacian probability of an equal number of heads and tails in four, or any even number of trials—Laplacian a priori probability is a better indication of relative frequency than Carnapian a priori probability.

The moral of this is that assumption of a priori probabilities can be justified only in terms of the consequences to which they lead. That an assignment of equal a priori probabilities to all state descriptions entails a violation of the "principle of learning from experience" is a strong argument against such an assignment in the context of a theory of inductive probability (i.e., probability of inductive inference) but not in a different context such as that of statistical mechanics or that of betting on strictly a priori grounds—if one ever should—on certain relative frequencies of success.

Selected Readings for this chapter are listed at the end of Chapter 13.

CHAPTER 13

The Probability of Universal & Statistical Hypotheses

The task of inductive logic consists in the formulation of criteria of sound inductive reasoning. This enterprise is inseparable from the clarification of the concepts "probability," "degree of confirmation," "rational prediction," "confirming evidence," and so on. The preceding two chapters have been devoted to a clarification of two different concepts of probability, distinguished as "statistical" and "logical" probability. The question we face now is: In terms of which of these two kinds of probability should inductive reasoning be evaluated? In particular, what is meant by the probability of an *inductive generalization?* What could be meant by a statement such as, "On the evidence that in all observed cases wood has been found to float on water, it is probable that all wooden objects float on water"?

A. THE FREQUENCY INTERPRETATION

That the frequency interpretation does not fit this use of the word "probable" was indicated when we examined Peirce's definition of the probability of an inference in terms of "truth-frequency" (Chapter 9). Consider an inference of the form "All members of S are members of K, all members of S have P, the members of S exhibit relevant variety, therefore all members of K have P." If saying that such an inference is probable meant that it leads us to a true conclusion from true premises in a large proportion of cases, then we just could not know that it is probable; for a universal hypothesis must be supported by inductive reasoning precisely because there is no way of knowing with certainty that it is true. Some staunch frequentists attempted to measure the probability of a universal hypothesis by the proportion of true instantial consequences, or the limit approached by such proportions in case the hypothesis applies to infinitely many cases. But this proposal is based on a confusion of the *reliability* of a universal hypothesis as an instrument of prediction with its *probability*. As we have seen, in either of the two distinguished senses probability is a relation. For this reason it is represented by a two-place functor in the formal calculus of probability. The latter was used by Keynes to clarify the problem of the probability of universal hypotheses, and he was careful to emphasize that the probability of a proposition is always relative to "data" or "evidence" (including, as a degenerate case (in the mathematicians' idiom) a priori probability as probability relative to zero empirical evidence, or purely logical evidence). But if so, then we are not allowed to speak of the probability of a universal hypothesis simply, but only relative to specified evidence; the statement that the probability of the generalization "All wood floats on water" is high must be construed as elliptical for the statement that its probability relative to the sum total of relevant evidence is high.

Now, it is apparent at once that the proposed measure of probability of a universal hypothesis is absurd, since the probability that it is proposed to measure must be understood as relative to the conjunction of all the tested instantial consequences at a given time. For, if even a single one of those consequences turned out to be false, then the total evidence would contradict the hypothesis, hence the latter's probability relative to the total evidence ought to be zero, whereas it could be very close to one according to the suggested measure. On the other hand, a universal hypothesis that is strictly refuted by contrary instances may, of course, have a high degree of reliability in the sense that there is a high probability that an instance that satisfies its antecedent also satisfies its consequent.

It seems, therefore, that the controversy between the frequentists and their critics about the tenability of a frequency measure of the probability of universal hypotheses is, like many philosophic controversies, rooted in an ambiguity. The frequentist confuses "There is a high probability that *an A* is a *B*" with "There is a high probability that *all A* are *B*." The former means that Bx/Ax equals a fraction close to one. This is, of course, compatible with the existence of A's that are not B's, but the latter statement is incompatible with such contrary instances. I can consistently say, "On the evidence that x is a corporation president and that the majority of corporation presidents whose political party is known are Republicans, it is probable that x is a Republican." But I cannot consistently say "On the evidence that the majority of corporation presidents whose political party is known are Republicans it is probable that all corporation presidents are Republicans."

A further difficulty with the frequency interpretation of the probability of universal hypotheses is that universal hypotheses of *theoretical* character are not testable in terms of their instantial consequences. The law of universal gravitation, for example, cannot be tested by independent measurements of the masses, the spatial separation, and the gravitational attraction of two bodies. To determine in this "direct" way whether, for example, the interacting pair consisting of the sun and the earth satisfies the gravitational formula, would even be a circular procedure since the mass of the sun is usually computed *by means* of the law of gravitation from the centripetal acceleration of the earth. As was explained in an earlier context, directly testable observation statements are deducible from a theoretical hypothesis only when the latter is supplemented, not only with singular statements of initial conditions (e.g., positions and velocities of the planets at some initial moment) and singular statements of boundary conditions (e.g., the solar system is dynamically closed; gravitational attractions exerted by bodies outside it, such as the "fixed" stars, are negligible), but also with other theoretical hypotheses. It follows that in any case the proposed measure would be acceptable at best as a measure of the probability of the conjunction of several theoretical hypotheses, not of a given theoretical hypothesis. A theoretical hypothesis, unlike a qualitative generalization of the "All ravens are black" variety, can be empirically tested only in the context of a system of theoretical hypotheses. And this is the case even if it does not mention postulated entities that are not directly observable, such as electrons, just as long as its instantial consequences are not observation statements. A simple illustration is the law of the lever, in the special form "If bodies of equal weights are suspended at equal distances from the fulcrum of a perfect lever, then the lever is in equilibrium." That two designated bodies, A and B, have the same weight is not an observation statement because it is not usually established by observations of pointer coincidences without presupposing a universal hypothesis. When we find that A and B stretch a spring the same amount, we conclude that they have the same weight *on the assumption* of Hooke's law. The usual method of confirmation of the law of the lever, therefore, involves the deduction of observation statements from a set of premises including at least one other universal hypothesis besides the one under test.

Another frequency interpretation rests on the construction of a reference class of similar universal hypotheses. The reader will recall that Bayes' theorem can be used to justify the assignment of a comparatively high (comparatively, that is, to competing hypotheses) posterior probability to a hypothesis provided the latter's antecedent probability is not too small. Some frequentists think that such a use of Bayes' theorem is justifiable without any commitment to a priori probabilities derived from the principle of indifference, because they think that a frequency interpretation of antecedent probabilities of universal hypotheses is feasible. The antecedent probability of H is, on this view, the relative frequency of well-confirmed hypotheses in a reference class consisting of hypotheses that resemble H in specified respects. These respects may be logical, like the *form* of a functional equation in the case of numerical laws of physics, or sociological, like the competence of the scientist who proposes H as an explanation of the data. But even if plausible rules for constructing such reference classes could be laid down, it is obvious that this frequency interpretation rests on the one already criticized, and so collapses with it. If a nonstatistical meaning of the expression "Evidence E *confirms* H to a high degree" is accepted, then the proposed frequency interpretation is otiose from the start. And if that expression is interpreted in terms of large proportions of true instantial consequences, then the same objections apply again.

B.   CARNAP'S "QUALIFIED-INSTANCE CONFIRMATION"

Let us see, now, whether the range interpretation of probability offers any help in this matter. Unfortunately, any universal hypothesis has, in Carnap's theory, a zero degree of confirmation relative to any finite amount of confirming evidence if it is formulated in a language with variables ranging over infinitely many individuals. This result was, of course, to be expected on the *extensional* interpretation[1] of universal statements as infinite conjuctions of singular statements about different individuals: "*All A* are *B*" means, on this interpretation, "It is not the case that x_1 is A and not B, and it is not the case that x_2 is A and not B ... and it is not the case that x_n is A and not B," where $x_1, x_2, \ldots, x_n$ are all the individuals in the universe. But this result did not break Carnap's optimism about the relevance of quantitative inductive logic to science. Without being entirely explicit about his change of strategy, he drops

1. On a contrasting intensional interpretation of such statements, as subjective conditionals, see Chapters 15 and 16.

the initial explicandum "The probability of universal hypothesis *H* on the total observational evidence *E* is high" and offers instead an explication of the different explicandum "The reliability of *H*, as an instrument of prediction, is high." His explicatum for the latter concept is called "qualified-instance confirmation": what for practical purposes of prediction and action based on prediction requires a high value is not the degree of confirmation of "All *A* are *B*" relative to *E* but rather the degree of confirmation of a singular prediction "x_i is *B*" relative to "*E* and x_i is *A*." Why should a farmer, for example, care whether the unrestricted generalization "All hens of this type, past, present, and future, lay good eggs" has a high degree of probability or not? What is of practical concern to him is whether it is rational to expect that *this* hen will lay good eggs on the evidence that all observed hens of type *A* (say, a sample of one hundred such animals) have laid good eggs and that this hen is of the same type *A*. And Carnap's theory does provide reasonably high degrees of confirmation for such singular predictions.

This view of the probability of universal hypothesis is reminiscent of John Stuart Mills' theory that all genuine inductive inference goes "from particulars to particulars," for according to it one never really infers a proposition of the form "All *A* are *B*" from particular data; rather one infers from the fact that the already observed instances conformed to the universal proposition that as yet unobserved instances likewise conform to it. Mill held (cf. Chapter 10) that from the point of view of scientific advancement, a syllogism of the form "All *A* are *B*, *x* is *A*, therefore *x* is *B*" should be replaced by an inductive argument of the form "All observed *A* are *B*, *x* is an as yet unobserved *A*, therefore *x* will turn out to be *B*." If we interpret Mill's advocacy of inference "from particulars to particulars" as equivalent to the view that there is no conceivable warrant for asserting a contingent universal proposition and therefore no conceivable warrant for believing a singular prediction because it follows from the two premises of a syllogism, Carnap's endorsement of "qualified-instance confirmation" appears unmistakably as a return to Mill. For if one is warranted in asserting "All *A* are *B*," then one either knows the proposition to be true or knows that it is highly probable on the known evidence. But neither condition is fulfilled according to Carnap. On his view, the expression "In the light of evidence *E*, *H* is highly probable" should be replaced by the expression "On evidence *E*, an inference from '*x* is *A*' to '*x* is *B*' is highly reliable—i.e., may be rationally expected to yield true predictions in the large majority of the cases."

The question that is immediately provoked by this analysis is whether universal hypotheses can, in principle, be dispensed with for the purpose of reliable prediction. What if in certain cases a prediction has a sufficiently high probability, not relative to evidence consisting only of individual observations, but only relative to such evidence in conjunction with certain universal hypotheses? The simple law of the lever may again serve as illustration. Suppose we wish to predict reliably that two objects A and B will balance each other when placed in the opposite pans of a beam balance X. This prediction will be supported by the premise that A and B have the same weight together with the report that in the past objects of equal weight have been observed to balance each other at equal distances from the fulcrum of a lever. Now, as already noted, the premise describing equality of weight is not an observation statement; rather it is inferred from observation statements (equal stretchings of a spring) *with the aid of a law* (Hooke's law of the proportionality of stress to strain). The full statement of the degree to which the prediction of equilibrium is supported by the evidence, therefore, takes the form $c(h, e \cdot L) = x$, where h and e are observation statements and L a universal hypothesis. But if we are never warranted in asserting a universal hypothesis, then we cannot be warranted in predicting h even if x should be very high. The advocate of inductive inference from particulars to particulars, then, must be able to show that wherever a universal hypothesis is included in the premises from which a prediction is derived, it may be replaced by the observation statements describing the evidence by which it is supported.

Now, it seems that such an elimination of universal hypotheses is, indeed, feasible in the simple example we have considered. For what, after all, does it mean to infer from the fact that A and B stretched a given spring by equal amounts that they have the same weight? Is it not to predict, among other things, that they would balance each other if placed in the opposite pans of a beam balance? If so, then we might have replaced the two moves from "A and B stretched the spring by equal amounts" to "A and B have the same weight," and from "A and B have the same weight" to "A and B will balance each other on a beam balance," by the single move from "A and B stretched the spring by equal amounts" to "A and B will balance each other on a beam balance." The latter procedure dispenses with the mediating construct "weight," and therewith Hooke's law becomes dispensable as well: we have found repeatedly that bodies that stretch a spring an equal amount will balance each other on a beam balance; now A and B have been observed to stretch a spring by equal amounts; hence we predict *inductively*, without reliance on universal hypotheses, that A and B will balance each other on a particular beam balance. The problem raised by Carnap's proposal of replacing confirmation of universal hypotheses by qualified-instance confirmation is thus none other than the problem whether *theoretical constructs* are merely economizing devices that could in principle be done without. The issue may be clarified by considering a set of reduction sentences (cf. Chapter 2, F):

$$Q_1 \supset (Q_2 \equiv Q_3), \qquad Q_4 \supset (Q_5 \equiv Q_3), \qquad Q_6 \supset (Q_7 \equiv Q_3)$$

Q_3 represents a "construct," Q_1, Q_4 and Q_6 alternative test operations, and Q_2, Q_5, and Q_7 the corresponding test results. Q_3 might be a state of magnetism that manifests itself in different ways, or a state of temperature that can be operationally determined by alternative methods. Now, from these three reduction sentences, which anchor, so to speak, the construct Q_3 in the plane of observables, we can formally deduce no less than twelve correlational statements referring exclusively to the observables; in Carnap's terminology, they express the *factual content* of the set of reduction sentences.

$$Q_1 \cdot Q_2 \supset (Q_4 \supset Q_5) \qquad Q_1 \cdot - Q_2 \supset (Q_6 \supset - Q_7)$$
$$Q_1 \cdot - Q_2 \supset (Q_4 \supset - Q_5) \qquad Q_4 \cdot Q_5 \supset (Q_1 \supset Q_2)$$
$$Q_1 \cdot Q_2 \supset (Q_6 \supset Q_7) \qquad Q_4 \cdot Q_5 \supset (Q_1 \supset - Q_2)$$

$$Q_4 \cdot Q_5 \supset (Q_6 \supset Q_7) \qquad Q_6 \cdot - Q_7 \supset (Q_1 \supset - Q_2)$$
$$Q_4 \cdot - Q_5 \supset (Q_6 \supset - Q_7) \qquad Q_6 \cdot Q_7 \supset (Q_4 \supset Q_5)$$
$$Q_6 \cdot Q_7 \supset (Q_1 \supset Q_2) \qquad Q_6 \cdot - Q_7 \supset (Q_4 \supset - Q_5)$$

The only purpose served by the construct Q_3, it seems, is to allow a more economic formulation of the correlations on the basis of which we predict observable results from observable antecedents.

We have seen, however, that operationism has its limitations (cf. Chapter 3). In particular, the thesis of the conditional definability (reducibility) of all theoretical concepts in terms of observables was found to be untenable. And to the extent that there are reasons for doubting its validity, there must be reasons for doubting that all scientific predictions that are actually made with the help of universal hypotheses could be made in a purely inductive way. Consider, for example, an astronomer's prediction of the position at some future time of a planet, or of a man-made satellite. He uses a law of motion in the form of a differential equation expressing the gravitational attraction keeping the body in its orbit as a function of its distance from the central body. Since the gravitational attraction is proportional to the product of the masses of the revolving body and the central body divided by the square of their distance (law of gravitation), and by Newton's second law of motion is equal to the product of the mass of the revolving body times its centripetal acceleration, it can be deduced that the centripetal acceleration at any given time is proportional to the ratio of the mass of the central body to the square of the distance of the two bodies at that time. Since the mass of the central body is a constant, the resulting equation expresses the acceleration as a function of the distance. By integration the astronomer then derives an equation expressing the position at some future time as a function of some initial position and simultaneous velocity of the revolving body and of the time separating the two positions. Now, it is true that force and acceleration are auxiliary constructs that disappear in the process of integration; and since instantaneous velocity is definable, by a limiting process, in terms of position and time, the equations that are finally used to make the predictions may be said to refer only to the observables position and time. But it is hard to believe that the precise predictions that astronomers make with the help of the universal hypotheses of dynamics might have been made without them just by inductive correlation of measurements of position and time—not to mention the staggering difficulty of making position measurements in astronomy without assuming universal hypotheses of optics and physical geometry.

C. IS BAYES' THEOREM
OF ANY USE?

But even if it were *in principle* possible to do science in a purely inductive way, without the use of universal hypotheses formulated in terms of constructs, it would certainly be utopian to attempt a measurement of the degree of probability of such prediction as the astronomers', or the physicists' prediction of the destructive effect of the explosion of an atom bomb, or a hydrogen bomb, by applying Carnap's concept of qualified-instance confirmation. In all fairness, it should be recorded that Carnap explicitly restricts his explication of "degree of confirmation" to qualitative languages in which we can formulate such biological laws as "All ravens are black," "All vertebrates reproduce by sexual intercourse," but not such quantitative laws as the differential equations of motion. Still, as we have seen, qualitative-instance confirmation is not really a measure of the probability of a universal hypothesis if the word "probability" is taken to have the same formal meaning in this context as in the calculus of probability. Perhaps we will have to conclude eventually that the probability of a universal hypothesis is not a magnitude that can be handled by the calculus of probability, but let us first see how Bayes' theorem might be relevant to the desired measurement. The reader will recall Keynes' proof that induction can be "justified" in the sense that the probability of a generalization increases with its confirmations and approaches certainty as the limit, provided the generalization has a nonvanishing antecedent probability. If our pragmatic justification of the assumption of finitude of the natural kinds that are the subjects of inductively confirmed generalizations is sound, then we actually do not need Keynes' postulate of limitation of independent variety to guarantee such a non-vanishing antecedent probability, for, if the class A is finite (though open), then there are finitely many alternative hypotheses as to the proportion of A's that are B's. If that (unknowable) number is n, we get the disjunction: either n A's are B's, or $n - 1$ A's are B's, or . . . or 0 A's are B's. Carnap's principle of equal a priori probability of all structure descriptions then yields $1/(n + 1)$ as a finite a priori probability of "All A are B."

Whereas Keynes' theorem is purely topological, Bayes' theorem applied to hypotheses describing statistical distributions of properties in finite classes may seem to allow numerical computations. For if, following Carnap and some classical writers on probability, we feel justified in assigning equal a priori probabilities to all possible statistical distributions of a given property in a class A, then the a priori probability for any given hypothesis h_i cancels out in Bayes' fraction for the posterior probability of h_i, and we are left with

$$P\left(\frac{h_i}{r \cdot q}\right) = \frac{P\left(\frac{r}{h_i \cdot q}\right)}{\sum_{i=1}^{\omega} P\left(\frac{r}{h_i \cdot q}\right)}$$

We can simplify this equation still further by substituting for q a tautology and taking r as representing the sum-total of all empirical evidence that is relevant to h_i:

$$P\frac{h_i}{r} = \frac{P\dfrac{r}{h_i}}{P\sum_{i=1}^{\omega}\dfrac{r}{h_i}}$$

This maneuver of eliminating the a priori probabilities from the Bayes' equation is further justified by the consideration that the posterior probability is very little affected by the a priori probabilities if the evidence r describes a large sample. In other words, the simplified Bayes' theorem states that the probability conferred on h_i by the empirical data r is equal to the likelihood of r on h_i divided by the sum of the likelihood of the same empirical data on the assumptions of any of the alternative hypotheses. Now, these likelihoods are easily computable by means of the *binomial law*, which is easily derivable from the addition and multiplication axioms:[2] Let p be the constant probability of occurrence of an attribute P in a class A. Then the probability that P occur m times in a random sample of A which contains n members is given by the following product:

$$\binom{m}{n} \times p^m \times (1 - p)^{n-m}$$

If p is the relative frequency of P in A described by hypothesis h_i, and r is the statement that m members of a random sample of n members drawn from A have P, then the likelihood r/h_i is obtained by substituting the values of n, m, and p in the binomial formula.

But even if this maneuver of eliminating the antecedent probabilities from Bayes' formula can be justified without invoking a problematic principle of indifference, the question would remain how the posterior probability of a hypothesis that has been computed from the likelihoods alone is to be interpreted. What, after all, is it that has been measured? The great strength of the theorems of the calculus of probability, including the theorems of inverse probability, is just that they are formally provable independently of any commitment to a particular *interpretation* of numerical probability. One does not, therefore, answer the question about the *meaning* of numerical probabilities ascribed to universal or statistical hypotheses by showing how they can be computed by means of Bayes' formula. The models commonly resorted to in order to illustrate the computation of posterior probabilities[3] involve antecedent probabilities of hypotheses a frequency interpretation of which is not implausible. Thus, suppose that a random drawing is made from a box filled with dice whose probabilities of showing six are unknown, and that the latter are to be inferred by means of Bayes' formula from the outcomes of 100 throws of each die. In this case an antecedent probability p of the hypothesis that the limiting frequency of sixes in a long random sequence of trials with die x equals, say, 1/5, can be interpreted as the relative frequency with which dice similar to x in relevant respects have been found to behave statistically in such a way that 1/5 seemed the most plausible hypothesis about the limiting frequency. But we have already seen that the frequency interpretation of the probability of universal hypotheses is untenable; and the same criticisms apply, *mutatis mutandis*, to

2. The binomial law is a good approximation if the class A is very large in relation to the sample of n members. The reason for this restriction is that it is derived on the assumption that p remains constant as more and more elements are "drawn" from A and this is approximately the case if n is very small in relation to the unknown number of A. If A is infinite, the binomial law holds exactly.

3. See, for instance, R. von Mises, *Probability, Statistics, and Truth* (2nd rev. ed.; New York: The Macmillan Company, 1957), pp. 117–120.

the frequency interpretation of statistical hypotheses. And the range interpretation, as reported, does not yield a finite probability for a generalization about an infinite class.

Are the prospects for the latter interpretation any better in the case of universal hypotheses about finite open classes? No, for a finite degree of confirmation in the sense of a measure of overlap of ranges can be obtained for a statement of the form "All A are B" only if the latter is translatable into a finite conjunction:

not-$(x_1$ is A and not-$B)$ and not-$(x_2$ is A and not-$B)$ and . . .
$$\text{and not-}(x_n \text{ is } A \text{ and not-}B)$$

But as a generalization about an open class A it cannot be so interpreted. It means that *if* there is an object x, at any time and at any place, that is A *then* x is B; and the question how many members class A has—which would have to be answered before one could undertake to translate the statement into an n-fold conjunction—is meaningless in the sense that there is no conceivable method of finding the answer. But even if it be held meaningful and even necessarily true to assert that, say, the class of human beings, past, present, and future, has a definite finite number n, it will be admitted to be impossible to discover that number. A fortiori, it is impossible to discover the number of objects to which the predicate "human" is significantly applicable. Therefore the number of conjuncts in the conjunction

not-$(x_1$ is human and survives his two-hundredth birthday)
and not-$(x_2$ is human and survives his two-hundredth birthday)
and . . .
and not-$(x_n$ is human and survives his two-hundredth birthday)

is unknowable. It follows that even the assumption of finitude would not render the Carnapian degree of confirmation of such a generalization measurable. Obviously this result can be extended to the degrees of confirmation one might want to ascribe to statistical hypotheses about open classes.

D. MAXIMUM LIKELIHOOD

Many statisticians, following R. A. Fisher, reject any attempt to justify the acceptance of a statistical hypothesis by an assignment of a high probability to the hypothesis. Although their arguments against "inverse probability" arguments are not always cogent, their refusal to ascribe numerical probabilities to statistical hypotheses is commendable. As an alternative to the rejected Bayes' method they practice the method of "maximum likelihood": accept that h_i which confers the greatest likelihood on the observed sample composition. Such maximum likelihood problems are easily solved as follows: Substitute constant values for n and m in the binomial formula. Then find that value of p for which the resulting function of p has the largest value, and assume the hypothesis ascribing this value of p to the relative frequency of P in A until new sample data force you to replace it by an alternative hypothesis.[4] Since this method employs differential calculus (the maximum is found by equating the derivative of the binomial function with respect to p to zero), it assumes that p is a continuous variable ranging over all rational numbers between 0 and 1 (limits included). But no assumption need be made about the number of objects in class A since the likelihoods of the sample frequencies relative to the alternative hypotheses need not be computed individually—in fact, for constant r the sum

$$\sum_{i=1}^{\omega} \frac{r}{h_i}$$

has a constant value no matter whether the set of mutually exclusive and jointly exhaustive hypotheses h_i contain 10 or 750 or 10^6 or any number of members.

The maximum likelihood method is relevant only to the choice between alternative hypotheses of the form "m/n A's are B's." For the limiting cases where m/n equals one or zero it leads, of course, to the rule to assume that all A are B if all observed A's are B's and if it is desirable to make any general assumption at all. It is impossible to lay down an exact rule as to the conditions under which it is desirable to make a general assumption that will account for the observed data. In particular, it would be foolish to specify the exact minimal size of the observed sample that is required for a reasonable adoption of a universal hypothesis. For one thing, inductions of a higher order that are already well established sometimes warrant a primary induction from a very small sample. The often

4. The method of maximum likelihood has been combined with the range interpretation of degrees of confirmation ascribed to hypotheses by Hempel and Oppenheim, in an article which appeared at approximately the same time as Carnap's first outline of his approach to quantitative inductive logic. The main difference from Carnap's approach is that the measures assigned to the statements depend not only on the forms of the statements and the language but also on empirical evidence. The authors claim that in this respect their explication of degree of confirmation is more in the spirit of empiricism than Carnap's. Nevertheless, as regards the probability of universal hypotheses, this approach is no more successful, for it turns out that the degree of confirmation of a universal hypothesis relative to any confirming evidence, whether scant or extensive, is always one!

cited example of this procedure is induction to a proposition of the form "metal M has, under standard pressure, melting point X" from just one or two measurements of the temperature at which a sample of M melted: here the generalization that all metals have a constant melting point (i.e., that any two samples of the same metal melt, under the same pressure conditions, at the same temperature) is obviously presupposed. Secondly, even if such a minimal sample size were specified, the universal hypothesis would still not be uniquely determined since the same sample of objects may be described with varying degrees of specificity. A sample of observed cats may be described just as a sample of cats, or more specifically as a sample of gray cats, or still more specifically as a sample of gray cats regularly fed twice a day, and so on. Suppose we have observed a sample of fifty cats and found that they keep themselves clean by licking their fur; are we then warranted in assuming that all cats have this disposition, or only that all gray cats have it, or only that all gray cats who are regularly fed twice a day have it? Clearly it would be utopian to look for any general rules of inductive inference that would yield the answer to these questions. Induction is a "concatenated" process, to borrow a phrase of Reichenbach's, in the sense that the results of inductions that have already proved successful become the criteria of soundness of inductions as yet untested. In our example, we already know that domestic animals of different colors display the same esthetic sense whether they are fed once, twice, or thrice a day, hence we have reason to believe that such properties as these, distinguishing the observed sample of cats from other cats, are not connected with the inferred property.

Although the reasonableness of an inductive generalization depends not only on the size but also on the relevant variety of the sample, it is certainly a rule of inductive reasoning that, other things being equal, a universal hypothesis is better supported by a large than by a small sample of confirming instances. Can this belief be justified in the absence of a method of measuring degrees of confirmation of universal hypotheses? Yes, it can be justified by means of the motion of likelihood: the likelihood that there should exist a small number of A's that are B's on the assumption that not all A are B is greater than the likelihood that there should exist a large number of A's that are B's on the assumption that not all A are B. Suppose a large population, say a million, only 90 per cent of which are B. Now, let the number of 100-fold samples of this population that contain only B's be x, and the total number of 100-fold samples from the population be y. Then compute the number of 10-fold samples that contain only B's and the total number of 10-fold samples, representing the former by u and the latter by z. It will be found that the ratio x/y is considerably smaller than the ratio u/z. In this sense it is more likely that there are very few exceptions, if any, to the generalization "All A

are B" on the evidence that a large sample of A's are B's than on the evidence that a small sample of A's are B's. In general, it can be proved that the larger a random sample drawn from a population A, the greater the chance that it resemble A in statistical composition (i.e., in the relative frequencies of specified attributes), in the sense that the proportion among possible samples of the same size of those that are statistically similar to A is larger, the larger the sample. That is, the proportion of representative random samples increases with the size of the samples. If the observed sample is large but atypical, then, by definition of "atypical," a continued process of random sampling on the same scale stands a better chance of revealing that it was atypical, and hence of disproving the adopted hypothesis, because the proportion of atypical large samples is relatively small.[5]

Considerations of likelihood are of no avail, however, where a choice between numerical laws connecting continuous variables must be made. What is to guide a scientist in his choice of a particular functional equation $y = f(x)$ to account for a set of corresponding values of the connected variables y and x, obtained by measurement? The measured values must obviously "fit" the equation, but infinitely many functional equations will satisfy this requirement of consistency, and the likelihood of the data is the same on all of them, viz. a maximum, for the observed data must be strictly deducible from the equation.[6] The scientist, of course, adopts the mathematically *simplest* hypothesis that is consistent with the data. For example, he will assume a linear equation rather than a quadratic equation if both fit the data and if there is no indirect evidence indicating that it is quadratic. To be sure, the justification for this policy cannot be exclusively pragmatic, for it is surely conceivable that nature is such as to frustrate all attempts to predict her course by means of mathematically simple equations. It is true that mathematically simple equations represent to some extent an idealization of the actual results of measurement; for, if the scientist accepted the arithmetic means of repeated measurements of the same quantity as the "true" values, without allowing for "errors," he could not, in most cases, derive simple equations that are satisfied by the "true" values. Still, it is a fact that by refining measurements and improving their control of relevant variables the scientists bring about ever closer approximations to simple equations, and to this extent the policy of assuming simple equations reflects a convenient simplicity of that part of the universe which is open to man's

5. D. Williams builds a purely logical justification of induction on this simple reflection, in his spirited book *The Ground of Induction* (Cambridge, Mass.: Harvard University Press, 1947).

6. This statement deliberately ignores the difference between "true" values and measured values.

experimental investigation. On the other hand, if one were to insist that if only we were to test the assumed equations for a sufficient number of values of their variables, by ever repeated inter- and extrapolations, we would encounter exceptions to every manageable simple equation, he would be making a claim immune against refutation. Since, from the very

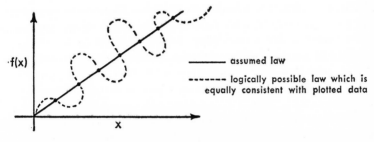

Figure 13.1

nature of measurement, we can only obtain finite and discrete sets of data (graphically represented by discrete sets of points), we might always arbitrarily assume that between the measured values the function makes queer jumps (see Figure 13.1). And this reflection brings out that the policy of assuming the simplest equation is *partly* dictated by the desire for easy calculation.

E. UTILITARIAN JUSTIFICATIONS

The statisticians who, following Fisher, justify acceptance of a statistical hypothesis by "maximum likelihood" calculations, do so mainly because they reject the concept of (numerical) probability of a hypothesis, and they reject the latter because it is tied up with assumptions of a priori probabilities of the competing hypotheses. But this is a purely negative motivation for the use of Fisher's method. Why, so it may be asked, should one act as though the hypothesis that confers the maximum likelihood upon the observed data were true? The advocates of maximum likelihood cannot reply "Because the hypothesis relative to which the data have the highest probability is, relative to those data, the most probable," for this is just an argument in "inverse" probability whose validity depends on an application of Bayes' theorem to the probability of hypotheses.

Now, for one who rejects numerical a priori probabilities, and therewith numerical posterior probabilities of hypotheses, utilitarian considerations must inevitably enter into scientific methodology, specifically into the justification of his acceptance of one hypothesis as against competing ones that, like the accepted hypothesis, are logically compatible with the data. The basic idea underlying utilitarian justifications is the *pragmatist* idea that acceptance of an hypothesis is instrumental to action and hence justified to the extent that it leads to successful action. Of course, it is obvious that hypotheses, whether in universal or in statistical form, are used to make predictions and hence must be evaluated in terms of their predictive success. But a utilitarian justification refers not just to the truth-values of the predictions made by means of the hypothesis; it considers the *gains and losses* connected with such predictions. The first method of utilitarian justification to be expounded is the *minimax method* of A. Wald.

Let us assume that we want to make a justifiable choice of one out of several methods of estimation of a parameter characterizing an unsurveyably large population. In particular, let us restrict attention to methods of estimation of relative frequencies. If one has a system of quantitative inductive logic, such as the system based on the c^*-function, there is no problem of choosing a method of estimation; for an estimate function is then defined on the basis of the chosen c-function. But the statisticians who reject a priori probability, at least numerical a priori probability, have no use for Carnapian c-functions, hence they are faced with the problem of utilitarian justification of a method of estimation. One such method of estimation is what Carnap has aptly named the *straight rule:* the relative frequency of a property P in a large population K is to be estimated as equal to the relative frequency of P in the observed sample, provided the latter is sufficiently large. This simple method was justified by Reichenbach by the following argument: If the relative frequencies of P in increasing (temporally ordered) random samples "drawn" from an infinite population K converge to a limit at all, then that limit will eventually be discovered by this method. For, by definition of "limit," if the successively ascertained relative frequencies in larger and larger samples converge to a limit, then there must exist a finite subclass of K such that the relative frequencies of P in still larger subclasses remain arbitrarily close to the limit. Consequently, the method of successively modifying our estimates by always "positing" the relative frequency in the largest observed sample as the limit must eventually lead to an estimate that is very nearly right provided a limit exists at all.

But there are two reasons why this justification of the straight rule is not compelling. First, *any* estimation method of the following form satisfies the requirement of "asymptotic convergence to the limit": Take the limit as equal to $m/n + c_n$, where m/n is the relative frequency in the largest observed sample and c_n is some function of n that approaches 0 as a limit as n increases without limit (e.g., k/n^2, where k is an unspecified constant). Perhaps the preference for the straight rule as against methods involving c_n can be justified by some requirement of simplicity, but the second objection to Reichenbach's justification is at any rate more serious: Reichenbach identifies the goal of enumerative induction with the discovery of a limit and then justifies the straight rule by the consideration that by means of it the goal will be attained if it is attainable at all. But it follows from what has already been said in Chapter 11 that it is impossible to know whether this goal has been attained or even whether it has been approached. It is small comfort to be told that if a treasure is buried under a certain rock, then one is bound to discover it by removing the rock and digging and digging—though there is no criterion for determining whether an object that is uncovered after prolonged digging is or is not the treasure one was after. Why should anyone go through the trouble of digging under such conditions?

At any rate, Wald's method of justifying a particular method of inductive estimation is much more sophisticated. Consider an estimation method E, employed to make estimates r' of the relative frequency of P in K. Assume that the actual value of this relative frequency is r. The absolute difference between r and r' is called the error associated with the estimate. (Wald assumes that some kind of loss, whether monetary or not, is connected with the errors and measures losses in terms of squared errors.) Let us imagine E to be applied to all possible samples of a fixed size s in which the relative frequency of P runs through all possible values, that is all fractions x/s where x ranges over the integers from 0 to s. The class of the $s + 1$ possible samples is called the "hyperclass" for the sample size s. The estimate r' obtained by applying E to a member of the hyperclass depends, of course, on x/s; hence the probability of a particular loss resulting from an application of E depends on the probability that the estimate be made on the basis of a sample exhibiting a particular relative frequency x/s. These probabilities can be computed by means of the binomial law and then used as weights of the losses that *would* result if r were estimated on the basis of such a sample. The thus weighted mean of all possible losses is called the *risk* associated with E when E is used to estimate r, on the assumption that the unknown actual value of r in K is some particular value.[7] So far s and r have been treated as constants, s known, r unknown, x (the number of objects in the sample that have P) as independent variable, and the binomial probability associated with x/s as a function of x. Next r is also varied; i.e., all possible values of r are considered. We are, that is, to compute the risks associated with E for all possible states of K (with respect to P), and then

7. Often the "mean-square error" is taken as the risk function, i.e., the (binomial) probability-weighted mean of the squared errors.

find *the maximum risk* associated with E. Finally this procedure is to be repeated to find the maximum risks associated with all the other methods of estimation that have some initial plausibility. The minimax policy is the policy of choosing that method of estimation for which the maximum risk is minimal.

The minimax policy does not guarantee that the maximal loss incurred by the use of the estimation method it recommends will actually be smaller *in a particular investigation,* based on a particular sample, than that resulting from the use of an estimation method it advises against. For the calculation of the "minimax solution" of the problem of choosing an estimation method refers to the average result of estimations on the basis of all possible samples of a fixed size (the average being a mean weighted with the probabilities of encountering the various possible samples). And it might happen that the random sample on which a particular investigation is based is so constituted that the "minimax" estimate based on it is far from the actual value, whereas the estimate entailed by a rejected method of estimation would have been closer to the truth. But the justification of this policy is a Peircean "long-run" argument: we know that the maximal risk associated with the estimation method it recommends is minimal when that method is repeatedly applied to all possible samples. When an insurance company fixes a premium on the basis of calculations of the probability of the type of accident it covers, it runs the risk of losing out to any particular policyholder, but if the premium it charges for the insurance and the number of policy-holders are sufficiently large there is a high probability that it will not lose in the balance. Even so, it *might* make a deficit, and similarly the minimax policy cannot guarantee a minimum of loss even "in the long run," for there is no guarantee that all possible samples of a given size from a given population will actually be confronted by estimating scientists with frequencies proportional to their binomial probabilities. But if this were an argument against the type of utilitarian justification under discussion, it would be an argument against any possible justification of a method of inductive estimation. For any such justification must be based on considerations of binomial probabilities, and to assume that samples with a high binomial probability will be encountered with high frequency in the long run is to assume that all possible samples, i.e., all members of the hyperclass (their number depending on both the sample size and the population size), will in the long run be encountered with equal frequency—an assumption which just may not be true.

The assumption that all members of a hyperclass of possible samples of a given size will in the long run be encountered with equal frequency by the estimating statistician seems to underlie also the *prudential* (*"maximin"*) *policy* recommended by R. B. Braithwaite, for there likewise the binomial probabilities play an essential role in the justification of a particular method of estimation. Braithwaite speaks of "strategies," where other inductive logicians speak of methods of estimation. A strategy is a rule prescribing the choice of a particular statistical hypothesis, out of a set of competing hypotheses, for each possible sample composition. Again assuming that all inductive inferences are based on a fixed sample size, a strategy is expressed by a conjunction of hypothetical imperatives of the following form: If x_1 members of the sample have P, accept hypothesis H_1, and if x_2 members have P, accept hypothesis H_2, ... and if x_n members have P, accept hypothesis H_n (where the hypotheses recommended for different sample compositions may or may not be different). Obviously a large number of such strategies are formally possible, their number increasing with both the size of the sample and the number of initially plausible competing hypotheses. The prudential policy, now, recommends as the optimal strategy the strategy that satisfies a certain maximum condition formulated in terms of possible gains and losses.

Braithwaite explains the prudential policy in terms of a very simple example. Assume a two-membered sample from a class A, and assume that on the basis of the composition of this sample we want to choose rationally between two hypotheses, say, "$3/5$ of the A's are B's" (H_1) and "$2/5$ of the A's are B's" (H_2). There are eight possible strategies in this case: if both A's are B's, choose H_1, otherwise choose H_2; if one or both A's are B's, choose H_1, otherwise choose H_2; if no A's are B's, choose H_1, otherwise choose H_2; and so on. Now compute the probability of a correct choice of hypothesis on the assumption that H_1 is true for each strategy. For example, the probability of correct choice yielded by the first strategy on the assumption that H_1 is true is the probability that in a random sample of two members of A both A's are B's given that the proportion of B's in the total population A equals $3/5$; and this can be calculated by the binomial law as equal to $9/25$. Next assume that a gain of a units will result from a correct choice of hypothesis if H_1 is true and a loss of b units from an incorrect choice if H_1 is false (i.e., if H_2 is true, for the prudential policy applies only on the assumption that one or the other of the hypotheses between which the scientist chooses is true) and that a gain of c units will result from a correct choice if H_2 is true and a loss of d units from an incorrect choice if H_2 is false (i.e., if H_1 is true). We are to suppose, of course, that the preferred hypothesis will be used as a basis of some kind of action that will bring gains or losses. For example, by means of Bernoulli's theorem one might deduce that if H_1 is true there is a high probability that the number of B's in a large random sample of fixed size from the class A will lie within specified limits; and one might adopt the rule to predict sample frequencies whose probability relative to the accepted hypothesis is at least, say, 0.9 (more accurately to predict a sample frequency within an interval $f \pm E$ if there is a probability of at least 0.9 that the sample frequency lies within $f \pm E$). Then we are to imagine some sort of gain to be connected with true predictions of this sort, as though we invested some sort of stake, perhaps monetary, perhaps just prestige, in the predictions.

The next step is to compute the expectation of gain (in the general sense in which a loss is a negative gain) for each strategy S_i on the assumption that H_1 is true. The expectation (expected value) of a random variable R, i.e., a variable each possible value of which has a definite probability of occurrence, is defined as the sum of the products of the possible values of R times these probabilities. Denoting the expectation of gain by X_1 and the probability of correct choice on the assumption that H_1 is true by x_i, we obtain from the definition of "expectation" the equation

$$X_i = ax_i - d(1 - x_i)$$

By perfectly similar reasoning, we find the expectation of gain for each strategy S_i on the assumption that H_2 is true:

$$Y_i = cy_i - b(1 - y_i)$$

where y_i is the probability of correct choice on the assumption that H_2 is true. Thus eight pairs of numbers will be obtained, one pair for each strategy. Then from each of the eight pairs of numbers select the smaller numbers, which represent the minimal expectations of gain for the alternative strategies. The prudential policy is the directive: select that strategy for which the minimal expectation of gain is maximal.

Here again we should clearly understand that there is no guarantee that selections of strategies in accordance with the prudential policy will lead to success in the balance, or in the long run. For, as in the case of Wald's risk functions, the (binomial) probabilities of the various samples enter essentially into the mathematical expectations of gain, and the assumption is made that if a sample of size n containing members with the attribute in question has a probability p relative to H_i, then such samples will be encountered with a relative frequency equal to p. One may reply that this assumption must necessarily be true if the process of selecting samples is truly *random*. But what does "random" mean? If it means selecting samples in complete ignorance of the relevant attributes of their members except the attribute defining membership in the sampled population, then it is clearly not analytic to say that the relative frequency with which a specified kind of sample is "drawn" in a long process of random selection is equal, or approximately equal, to the (binomial) probability of that kind of sample. There is, for example, no contradiction in supposing that in a billion sets of four tosses with a fair coin sets containing two heads occur far less frequently than sets containing just one head, though the (binomial) probability of such a set of four (independent) tosses containing two heads exceeds the (binomial) probability of such a set containing just one head. On the other hand, it may be used as the defining criterion of randomness that the relative frequencies of sets of specified statistical composition correspond to the binomial probabilities; in that case the assumption in question is, of course, analytic and trivial, but the synthetic assumption that must replace it is simply that our sampling processes are really random!

Braithwaite, like Wald, considers it an important advantage of his recommended method of choosing a statistical hypothesis, or of choosing a strategy for choosing a statistical hypothesis, that it does not depend on assumptions about "prior" probabilities. But it is not clear that the utilitarian justifications we have reviewed really steer clear of such assumptions. How, in the case of inductions about open classes, is one to justify restriction to a finite, sometimes small, subset of an infinite set of formally possible hypotheses, if not by the argument that the initially selected candidates are the only ones that have a sufficiently high prior probability? It is true that in avoiding inverse-probability arguments statisticians avoid arbitrary assignments of numerical values to the prior probabilities, but if they did not allow themselves to make at least *comparative* statements about prior probabilities, it is difficult to see how minimax or maximin policies could have any application at all. For example, suppose that previous experience with the quality of chicken eggs has shown that the percentage of good eggs supplied by farms in Pennsylvania within any one year has varied between 80 and 95 per cent. And suppose that we want to decide, on the basis of examination of a random sample of eggs from a given Pennsylvania farm, what percentage of good eggs may be expected from that farm during the next year. It will then accord with established inductive method to apply the maximin policy to statistical hypotheses asserting a percentage of good eggs between 85 and 95 per cent, because these are the only ones with a sufficiently high prior probability in the light of past experience. Such prior probabilities are not, of course, a priori probabilities in the epistemological sense (though, confusingly, the terms "a priori probability" and "a priori distribution of probabilities" are often used by statisticians in the sense of the *antecedent* probabilities in Bayes' theorem). In fact, unless one indulges in the fantasy that a long time ago rigorous statistical inference made a start before *any* rough inductive knowledge bearing on the tested hypotheses had been acquired, it is hard to think of a situation where an estimate of comparative prior probabilities of logically independent[8] hypotheses must be made on no empirical evidence at all.

F. THE NEYMAN-PEARSON THEORY OF TESTING STATISTICAL HYPOTHESES

A difficulty confronting the prudential policy is that the mathematical expectations that determine the optimal strategy depend on the gains and losses[9] a, b, c, d; hence two scientists who both have adopted the prudential policy may nevertheless select different strategies because they assign different values to one or the other of these four coefficients. It is true that a utilitarian justification of a method of accepting and rejecting hypotheses is, characteristically, entangled with value judgments. Nevertheless the widely practiced Neyman-Pearson theory has the advantage that estimates of gains and losses do not *directly* enter into the method for deciding to accept or reject a statistical hypothesis. It prescribes a method of testing that guarantees a high probability of rejecting a false hypothesis and a high probability of accepting a true hypothesis, on the basis of sample findings—without, however, employing the concept of probability *of* a tested hypothesis. We shall expound the theory in terms of an illustration borrowed from J. Neyman's *First Course in Probability and Statistics*.[10]

A patient is to be tested for tuberculosis by means of several X-ray examinations of his chest. Since there is an appreciable chance of mistaken diagnosis if the verdict is based on a single examination, it is decided to make five independent examinations of the same patient and to make acceptance or rejection of the hypothesis (H) "The patient is to some degree affected by tuberculosis" depend on the number of

8. This qualification excludes such cases as the a priori probability of "All A are B or C" exceeding that of "All A are B," and the a priori probability of "All things that are A and B are C" exceeding that of "All A are C," where A, B, C are logically independent properties.

9. Strictly speaking, these coefficients represent utilities and disutilities connected with correct and incorrect choices of hypotheses. The intuitive meaning of "utility" is the satisfaction produced by a gain, as distinct from the gain itself. For example, one and the same increase of tangible fortune may have different utilities depending upon the initial fortune. But these distinctions may be ignored in the present context.

10. Jerzy Neyman, *First Course in Probability and Statistics* (New York: Holt, Rinehart, & Winston, 1950), vol. I, pp. 268–271.

examinations that indicate a trace of the disease (for short, on the number of "positive" examinations). We can, of course, make the rough statement that the greater the number of positive examinations, the more reasonable it is to accept H, without mastering the subtleties of mathematical statistics. But a more precise and reliable decision procedure requires knowledge of two important probabilities: (1) the probability that a single examination of a patient who does not have the disease will be erroneous, i.e., positive; (2) the probability that a single examination of a patient who has the disease will detect it.[11] Call these two probabilities p_1 and p_2. They are, of course, statistical probabilities, and the statisticians who practice the Neyman-Pearson method usually arrive at such probabilities by means of the straight rule; i.e., without philosophical scruples, these statisticians identify such probabilities tentatively with the relative frequencies so far found in large random samples. Denoting the number of positive examinations by X (with values 0, 1, 2, 3, 4, 5), we can say that X is a *random variable*, i.e., a variable each possible value of which has a definite statistical probability of occurrence though it cannot be predicted with certainty. That is, even if we knew whether the examined patient had tuberculosis or not, we could not predict how many of the five independent examinations would be positive. What we can determine on the basis of p_1 and p_2 are the probabilities of the various values of X relative to H and relative to non-H. More exactly, given the statistical assumptions (1) and (2), which refer, respectively, to X-ray examinations of patients who do not have tuberculosis and to X-ray examinations of patients who do have tuberculosis, we can derive by substitution the more specialized statistical propositions (A) "The probability that a single X-ray examination of *this* patient will be positive *if* he does not have tuberculosis is p_1" and (B) "The probability that a single X-ray examination of *this* patient will be positive *if* he has tuberculosis is p_2." But if (A) and (B) are granted, then the *singular* hypothesis H implies (h) "The probability that a single X-ray examination of this patient will be positive is p_2" and the contradictory of H implies (h') "The probability that a single X-ray examination of this patient will be positive is p_1." It is h and h', which are statistical hypotheses referring to a single patient, that are being tested directly, though the final action that is taken, depending on whether h or h' is the accepted hypothesis, is based on the assumption of H or non-H; i.e., in the end one must decide whether to treat the patient as though he had tuberculosis or to treat him as though he did not have that disease.

11. These assumptions are perhaps quasi-analytic, since a construct such as "tubercular" must be defined by probabilistic reduction sentences of the form "If x is tubercular, then there is a probability p that x will show symptom S when examined by test T."

Now, if h is true, then the probability that the random variable X will assume the value k equals, according to the all-important binomial law,

$$\binom{5}{k} \times p_2{}^k \times (1 - p_2)^{5-k}$$

And if h' is true, then the probability that X will assume the value k equals

$$\binom{5}{k} \times p_1{}^k \times (1 - p_1)^{5-k}$$

Suppose that the actual value of X is k_i and that the binomial probability that is a function of p_1 $[F(p_1)]$ is very high for that value k_i whereas the binomial probability that is a function of p_2 $[F(p_2)]$ is very low for that same value. This is to suppose, in other words, that the observed number of positive examinations is highly probable on the assumption non-H and highly improbable on the assumption H. Then, of course, it is reasonable to reject H. More specifically, suppose we decide to reject H (i.e., to accept non-H) if the value of $F(p_1)$ for the observed value k_1 is at least 0.9. For example, let $k_1 = 0$, and $p_1 = 0.02$, and let us see whether $\binom{5}{0} \times (0.98)^5$ is at least 0.9. If it is, then we are committed to reject H. As a matter of fact, this binomial probability exceeds 0.9; hence we must assume h' and therewith non-H. Next we calculate the probability of a mistaken rejection of H (i.e., of rejecting H though H is true) relative to our decision to reject H if $F(p_1)$ is at least 0.9 for the observed value of the random variable—which general decision entails, as we have just seen, the more specific decision to reject H if $k_i = 0$. This probability equals the value of $F(p_2)$ for $k = 0$. Assume $p_2 = 0.6$. We then have to calculate $\binom{5}{0} \times (0.4)^5 = 0.010$ (roughly). This result means that the rejection method decided upon would, on the assumption of complete randomness, lead us to mistaken rejection of H (dismissing a patient as free from the disease though he has it) in about 1 per cent of the cases. It is a very small error percentage, and since error of this kind is very undesirable, the rejection method decided upon is very reasonable.

Now, let us turn to the question of the probability of the mistaken acceptance of H, i.e., pronouncing the patient as affected by the disease though he does not have it. If 0 is the only value of our random variable whose binomial probability $F(p_1)$ is at least 0.9, then we must, in accordance with our general decision, accept H whenever the number of positive examinations lies between 1 and 5. The probability of a mistaken acceptance of H, then, equals the probability that k_i is greater that 0 relative to the assumption that non-H is true. This probability equals

$$1 - \left[\binom{5}{0} \times P_1^0 \times (1 - P_1)^5 \right]$$

(or more simply, $1 - (1 - P_1)^5$). It is the probability of mistaken acceptance of H, and is close to 0.05. On the same assumption of complete randomness, our general decision procedure would therefore lead to about 5 per cent errors consisting in pronouncing patients who do not have the disease as affected by it. If error of this type is judged less serious than error of the former type, then a decision procedure that entails a greater probability of committing it than of committing the error of "mistaken rejection" of H is reasonable.

Let us abstract from this illustration the general pattern of testing. The statistical hypothesis to be tested asserts that a specified kind of event E has a statistical probability p of occurrence. Let X be a random variable whose possible values have probabilities of occurrence that are binomial functions of p. The possible values of X are possible numbers of occurrences of E in a sample of fixed size; they are usually called the "sample points." The experimenting scientist will reject or accept the hypothesis depending on the binomial probability of the observed sample point. He runs, in this enterprise, two risks of committing errors: he may reject a true hypothesis (mistaken rejection) or he may accept a false hypothesis (mistaken acceptance). If he considers error of the former type more serious in its practical consequences, he will have to select a decision procedure that minimizes the chance of a mistaken acceptance.

To select a decision procedure, now, is to fix a *critical region* in the sample space, i.e., to decide which sample points, if observed, entail a rejection of the hypothesis. Suppose, for example, that we do not want the chance of a mistaken rejection to exceed 0.05 but allow as much as a 0.1 chance of a mistaken acceptance. And suppose that we fix the critical region as the set of sample points X such that $X < k$. If these decisions are mutually consistent, then the binomial probability of a sample point's being less than k given that the hypothesis is true must be less than 0.05, and the probability of a sample point's being equal to or greater than k given that the hypothesis is false must be less than 0.1. Whether the choice of critical region is thus consistent with the choice of "significance level" (maximal errors of both kinds) depends, of course, on the size of the sample. Suppose, for example, that we wanted to test the hypothesis that the probability of heads with a given coin is ½, using as random variable the number of heads in a set of ten independent tosses. It would then be plainly inconsistent to take as the critical region all possible numbers of heads that are less than four or greater than six *and* allow no greater chance of mistaken rejection than 0.05, for the probability of the number of heads falling within this critical region given the truth of the tested hypothesis exceeds 0.05 considerably. In fact, with such a small sample it is impossible to choose a critical region that guarantees a small percentage of errors.

In concluding our exposition of the Neyman-Pearson methodology of statistical inference we repeat that the decisions it dictates guarantee a small percentage of errors in the long run *only* on the assumption of randomness. The binomial probabilities are derived on the assumption of the special multiplication theorem, which applies only if the probability of occurrence of the event or attribute in question on a given occasion is entirely independent of its occurrence or nonoccurrence on previous occasions. If this assumption of independence is false, the binomial probabilities may not agree with the long-run frequencies. But the assumption of such independence is itself a *general* hypothesis concerning the equality of certain statistical probabilities; hence, induction will enter into its justification. It follows that, though the Neyman-Pearson method of justifying decisions to accept or reject a statistical hypothesis can rely on the solid theorems of the calculus of probability once the assumption of independence is made, we must fall back on induction if we wish to justify the latter. However the precision of mathematical statistics may fascinate us, as philosophers of science we cannot ignore Hume's old problem of the justification of inductive inference simply on the ground that it does not worry mathematical statisticians.

G. CONCLUDING REFLECTIONS
ON THE "JUSTIFICATION
OF INDUCTION"

Our critical survey of attempts to measure the probability of universal hypotheses and of actually practiced methods of justifying acceptance or rejection of a statistical hypothesis without ever using the expression "probability *of* the tested hypothesis" points to the conclusion that, whatever may be meant by the "high probability" or "high degree of confirmation" of a universally quantified proposition, it cannot be a magnitude amenable to calculation by the laws of probability. If so, it will be impossible to justify a cetrain method of inductive generalization by showing that a hypothesis *h* that is made in order to account for data *e* and in order to guide further predictions has a high numerical probability relative to *e*. It does not follow, however, that we are never justified in saying that *h* is *well confirmed* by *e* in a nonquantitative sense, or that *h* is, again in a nonquantitative sense, better confirmed by *e* than by *e'*, or that *h* is better confirmed by *e* than *h'* by *e'*. In fact, to "justify" one's belief that all *A*, or nearly all *A*, are *B* means to produce evidence to the effect that all or almost all members of a large and varied sample of the class *A* were found to be *B* (of course, no relevant evidence must be suppressed). Sometimes, especially in advanced sciences, such an inductive justification can be postponed by deducing the generalization in question from more comprehensive generalizations that are already well confirmed, but to postpone it is not to dispense with it.

But how may we justify the *rule* of inductive inference which we presuppose when we justify our acceptance of an inductive conclusion in this manner? Can we say that we are justified in using the rule because it has "worked" in the past? Or is this, as charged by Hume, a circular argument? Let us formulate this rule, the rule of critical enumerative induction, as follows: If you have reason to believe, i.e., have either yourself observed or else been reliably informed that other competent observers have observed, that a large and varied sample of *A*'s are *B*'s infer that probably all or almost all *A*'s are *B*'s (rule *R*). By the "working" of *R* is, of course, meant that predictions in accordance with *R* are by and large successful. And it may be objected that it is quite impossible to tell without induction, and so without presupposing *R*, whether *R* has in fact worked, since one cannot determine the truth of a generalization by observation. In order to meet this objection, let us define "*R* has worked in the past" to mean "In the past generalizations inferred from already made observations in accordance with *R* have usually been confirmed by subsequent observations." Our problem is whether our present use of *R* can be justified *without circularity* by the argument that *R* has worked in the past.

It cannot be denied that such an inductive justification of *R*, the fundamental rule of all inductive inference, is almost a natural impulse which it is hard to inhibit. If I lay down a specific rule of behavior, it is surely appropriate to justify it by reference to its past successes provided the relevant conditions have not changed. "If you want your eyes to be reliably examined, go to oculist *X*, not to oculist *Y!*" Why? "Because most patients who went to *X* were satisfied with the results, and most patients who went to *Y* were dissatisfied with the results." This is a perfectly respectable justification, provided the examination methods employed by *X* and *Y* have remained the same, their optical equipment is unchanged, their knowledge of the subject is still the same, and so forth. But it does not follow that *R* can be justified by the same kind of argument; for *R* is not a specific rule of behavior; *R* is rather a rule prescribing a general method for justifying specific rules of inference.

According to R, the specific rule of inference "When you see a white object with an eggish shape, expect that it will have an eggish taste" is justified by the evidence that most white objects with an eggish shape turned out to have an eggish taste; *according to R*, the specific rule of inference "When you see a tea cup, or any other object made of thin china, dropping onto a rock, expect it to break" is justified by the evidence that almost all objects that were made of thin china and that were observed to drop onto a rock (or any other hard surface) broke; and so on. Since R thus enters, as it were, into the very definition of "inductive justification," and this concept of inductive justification applies to specific rules of inference, which R is not, it is surely a mistake to give in to the natural impulse of justifying R inductively, by reference to its "working" in the past.

To be sure, a *formal* circularity in such an inductive justification of R can be avoided just because R is a rule of higher type than the specific rules of inductive inference that are justified in accordance with R. R directs us to expect that specific generalizations that have been confirmed will continue to be confirmed (provided the relevant conditions, to be specified in detail, remain unchanged); in this sense it is a rule that refers to specific generalizations. But then it cannot be said that the argument "R has worked in the past, so it will (probably) work in the future" is itself an instance of the application of R. An inductive justification of R is formally circular only if the variables A and B which we employed in our formulation of R are allowed to range not only over classes of natural objects and events, such as are mentioned in specific generalizations, but also over the class of past uses of R and the class of past successful uses of R. We would then obtain the argument "All, or almost all, past applications of R have been successful, therefore (probably) all or almost all future applications of R will be successful." This argument will be formally circular in the sense that its premise does not establish its conclusion unless the rule it exemplifies is accepted, which acceptance presupposes acceptance of the conclusion—*provided* we identify the exemplified rule with R, the very rule mentioned in the premise and in the conclusion. Artificially, however, one might restrict R to generalizations that do not mention R, and invoke a similar but typically different rule R', which is illustrated by the above justification of the reliance on R in terms of R's successful performances in the past.

Still, it remains undeniable that an inductive justification of R is *epistemologically* circular. For what reason for accepting R'—a rule just like R except that it refers explicitly to past uses of R, whereas R does not refer to itself—could be offered to him who wants a justification of R? What led us to formulate R' was just the desire to justify the use of R inductively without formal circularity; but then consistency requires that we justify R' inductively in just the same way; hence, to avoid formal circularity at this higher level, we must invoke R''—and so on, without end. Thus an inductive justification of R can escape formal circularity only by incurring an infinite regress. The situation is strikingly similar to the one confronting us in the realm of deductive inference if we insist on a deductive proof of the very principle that defines "deductive proof": whatever proposition is implied by a true proposition (or by a set of true propositions) is itself true. This is itself a proposition (call it P); hence one may be tempted to ask for a proof of it. But to prove P *means* to show that P is implied by some true proposition, say Q; and one who doubts P may surely be expected to doubt the proposition "If Q is true, and Q implies P, then P is true" on the same grounds, whatever they may be. *Formally* the argument "Q; if Q, then P; therefore P" is not circular if we segregate propositions, as well as principles of deductive inference, into types. If the propositions referred to by P are of the first type, P is of the second type, and since P refers only to propositions of the first type, P does not refer to itself. The argument "Q; if Q, then P; therefore P" exemplifies a principle of inference that is similar to its conclusion P but of the third type, and so on.

Now, this analogy leads straightforwardly to the simple idea that avoids the dilemma inherent in any inductive justification of inductive inference. How, after all, would one justify P? Would one not say that P *defines* "implies," that by "implication" we mean at the very least a relation I between two propositions p and q such that if p is true and has I to q, then q is true? If so, it is of course a sheer mistake to ask for a proof of P. To accept P can only mean to use the concept of "implication" that P defines. One may conceivably have reasons for not using this concept, but one cannot possibly have reasons for questioning the truth of P. If anyone had a reason for doubting P, then he would have to be able to specify the meaning of "implies" (or of "if, then")[12] in such a way that it remains an open question whether P is true after this meaning has been specified. But this cannot be done because the relevant meaning of "implies" is just defined by P. Similarly, it cannot be reasonable to doubt the validity of R unless the meaning of "probable" can be specified independently of R. But is not R just as analytic of the meaning of "if ... , then probably ..." as P is analytic of the meaning of "if ... , *then* ... ?" Suppose I say, "Probably these peaches are very good."

12. Grammatical accuracy requires that "implies" be inserted between quoted sentences—p implies q—whereas "if, then" is inserted between sentences without quotes: If p, then q. But it is grammatically correct to use the form "(The proposition) that p implies (the proposition) that q." The latter form is intended when we write "p implies q." Some subtle problems of semantics lurk here, but we suppress them deliberately because they would detract from the point here made.

You ask me, "On what evidence do you say that?" and I reply, "These peaches have been sold to me by farmer Jones: I, as well as friends of mine, have bought peaches from farmer Jones many times, and under widely different relevant circumstances (different times of the year, when Jones was prosperous as well as when he was broke, and so on), and they have invariably been good." If you are satisfied that the present situation is, in the respects known to be relevant to the prediction, like the past situations in which peaches were bought from Jones, then you *must* assent to my statement "Probably these peaches are very good" simply because a statement of the form "Probably E will happen" *means* that the present conditions are in the relevant respects like conditions that in the past have usually been followed by E. It would be reasonable to voice such a doubt as "Well, in the past he depended on your business, so it was in his interest to satisfy you, but now he is so prosperous that he does not care whether you continue to be his customer or not." This is a doubt pertaining to the similarity of relevant conditions. But to admit that all the known relevant conditions have been repeated and that under those conditions E usually happened, and yet to deny the probability of E's happening again now, is just as much to contradict one's self as to admit that p is true and that p implies q and yet to deny that q is true.

Even if the expectation expressed by "Probably E will happen" is inductively supported by the best evidence that could be asked for, it may not be fulfilled. It is just because we do not know all the conditions on which E causally depends that we use probability language, and it may happen that E fails to recur in spite of the recurrence of all the conditions we *know* to be relevant because some necessary condition of which we are ignorant is absent in the present situation. But whereas the confident prediction "E will happen" can, of course, be refuted by the course of events, "Probably E will happen" is not refutable by observing that E does not happen. It may be compared to directive statements such as "You ought to buy a new car" in that the speaker may fail to support it properly by good reasons but cannot be refuted by the facts the way a purely descriptive statement, whether predictive or not, may be refuted by the facts. To press the analogy a little further: the statement "If you need a new car and can easily afford to buy one and will not cause any suffering by such a purchase—and, of course, can't get one without buying it, then you ought to buy a new car" is analytic in the sense that no intelligible meaning could be attached to the denial of the ought-statement coupled with an admission of the mentioned conditions. But, of course, if you nevertheless don't do what you ought to do, neither the ought-statement nor the hypothetical imperative "If . . . , then you ought . . ." is thereby refuted. Just so, the statement "If C

has always, or nearly always, been followed by E, and C is present now, and all the other conditions known to be relevant to E are again present, then *probably* E will follow again" is analytic. If E does not follow, one concludes that some relevant condition that is not known failed to materialize; one does not conclude that one was wrong is saying "Probably E will happen"—for the truth of this statement is independent of the actual occurrence of E, nor that one did not properly support that statement—for no better support than "C has always been followed by E and all the other conditions that we know to be relevant to E are present again" is conceivable.

One refinement of this "analytic" justification of induction, as it might be called, is, however, forced upon us by the following objection: if the principle of critical enumerative induction were valid independently of experience, then it would be impossible to describe a world in which intelligent beings did not act in accordance with it. But this is possible. Suppose that experience has shown that whenever a generalization had been confirmed, under widely different conditions, a hundred times, it was subsequently refuted. Would we then still regard it as probable that all A are B or even that the next A to be encountered is B on the ground that a varied sample of one hundred A's turned out to be B's? Would we not, on the contrary, deem it improbable?

Undoubtedly the answer is affirmative. But a closer analysis will show that the principle "What usually happened is, under the same relevant conditions, likely to happen again" would remain valid and would remain the only principle of predictive inference. Let us call the rule "If a sample, however varied, of 100 A's have been found to be B's, predict that the next A will not be a B" *counterinductive*. Now, if one were to justify this rule, one could only say that in the past runs of 100 confirmations of "All A are B" were usually followed by a disconfirmation, and that one expects future runs of 100 confirmations of a generalization to be *like* the past ones in this respect. But then the justification one would offer for the prediction "Probably the next A is not B" would still conform to the principle "What has usually happened is, under the same relevant conditions, likely to happen again," for what has usually happened in our hypothetical universe is just that runs of 100 confirmations have been followed by a disconfirmation. An accurate formulation of probability statements must include all the evidence on which the expectation expressed by "probably" is based, and the evidence we actually state is usually less than the total evidence "in the back of our minds."

Thus, we judge it as extremely probable that a fruit that has a shape, color, and texture very similar to thousands of fruits that turned out to taste like oranges and that has been grown the same way will likewise have that distinctive taste. But we would not make the prediction with the same high confidence if we had frequently found that other fruits that were similar in the mentioned respects nevertheless differed in taste. The probability judgment, therefore, is based not only on the evidence referring to oranges but also on the analogous evidence referring to the other species of fruit. In general, the evidence on which the prediction "*x* is *B*" is highly probable is not just "*x* is *A* and most observed *A*'s were found to be *B*'s" but further "Most generalizations of such and such kinds that were already confirmed by samples as varied and as large as the examined sample of *A*'s continued to be confirmed." And if the world were such that in our past experience most generalizations that were confirmed by *n* instances were disconfirmed thereafter, this very general evidence about past experience would become part and parcel of the evidence on which "counterinductive" predictions would be based. But the latter would be counterinductive only relative to the narrow evidence that *n* members of the specific class *A*, whatever it may be, have turned out to be *B*'s; relative to the total evidence that makes the prediction *analytically* probable, it would still be an inductive prediction.

Selected Readings
for Chapters 9 to 13

Ambrose, A., "The Problem of Justifying Inductive Inference," *Journal of Philosophy*, 1947.

Ayer, A. J., "The Conception of Probability as a Logical Relation," in S. Körner (ed.), *Observation and Interpretation* (London, 1957).

Barker, S. F., *Induction and Hypothesis* (Ithaca, N.Y., 1957), chap. 3.

Bergmann, G., "The Logic of Probability," *American Journal of Physics*, 1941.

———, "Frequencies, Probabilities, and Positivism," *Philosophy and Phenomenological Research*, 1945.

Black, M., "The Justification of Induction," in M. Black, *Language and Philosophy* (Ithaca, N.Y., 1949).

———, "Induction," in M. Black, *Problems of Analysis* (Ithaca, N.Y., 1954).

Braithwaite, R. B., *Scientific Explanation* (Cambridge, 1953), chap. 5–8.

Broad, C. D., "On the Relation between Induction and Probability," *Mind*, 1918, 1920.

Brodbeck, M., "An Analytic Principle of Induction?," *Journal of Philosophy*, 1952.

Brown, G. S., *Probability and Scientific Inference* (London, 1957).

Buchler, J. (ed.), *The Philosophy of Peirce* (New York, 1940), chap. 14.

Bures, C. E., "The Concept of Probability," *Philosophy of Science*, 1938.

Burks, A. W., "The Presupposition Theory of Induction," *Philosophy of Science*, 1953.

———, "Presuppositions of Induction," *Review of Metaphysics*, 1955.

Carnap, R., "On Inductive Logic," *Philosophy of Science*, 1945.

————, "The Two Concepts of Probability," *Philosophy and Phenomenological Research*, 1945. [Reprinted in H. Feigl and W. Sellars (eds.), *Readings in Philosophical Analysis* (New York, 1949).]

————, "Remarks on Induction and Truth," *Philosophy and Phenomenological Research*, 1946.

————, "On the Application of Inductive Logic," *Philosophy and Phenomenological Research*, 1947.

————, "Probability as a Guide in Life," *Journal of Philosophy*, 1947.

————, *Logical Foundations of Probability* (Chicago, 1950).

————, *Probability and Induction* (Chicago, 1950).

————, *The Nature and Application of Inductive Logic* (Chicago, 1951).

————, *The Continuum of Inductive Methods* (Chicago, 1952).

————, "Statistical and Inductive Probability" (Brooklyn, N.Y., 1955). [Reprinted in E. H. Madden (ed.), *The Structure of Scientific Thought* (Boston, 1960).]

Coburn, R. C., "Braithwaite's Inductive Justification of Induction," *Philosophy of Science*, 1961.

Cohen, M. R., *Reason and Nature: An Essay on the Meaning of Scientific Method* (New York, 1931), pp. 115–125.

———— and E. Nagel, *Introduction to Logic and Scientific Method* (New York, 1934), chap. 8, 14, 16, 17.

Copeland, A. H., "Predictions and Probabilities," *Erkenntnis*, 1936.

Creed, I. P., "The Justification of the Habit of Induction," *Journal of Philosophy*, 1940.

Darlington, J., "On the Confirmation of Laws," *Philosophy of Science*, January, 1959.

Edwards, P., "Bertrand Russell's Doubts about Induction," *Mind*, 1949. [Reprinted in A. Flew (ed.), *Logic and Language* (Oxford, 1955), vol. I.]

Ewing, A. C., *The Fundamental Questions of Philosophy* (London, 1951), pp. 159–181.

Feigl, H., "The Logical Character of the Principle of Induction," in H. Feigl and W. Sellars (eds.), *Readings in Philosophical Analysis* (New York, 1949).

————, "Scientific Method without Metaphysical Presuppositions," *Philosophical Studies*, 1954.

————, "On the Vindication of Induction," *Philosophy of Science*, 1961.

Hay, W. H., "Professor Carnap and Probability," *Philosophy of Science*, 1952.

————, "Carnap's Continuum of Inductive Methods," *Philosophical Review*, 1953.

Harrod, R., *Foundations of Inductive Logic* (New York, 1957), chap. 4.

Helmer, O., and P. Oppenheim, "A Syntactical Definition of Probability and Degree of Confirmation," *Journal of Symbolic Logic*, 1945.

Hempel, C. G., and P. Oppenheim, "A Definition of 'Degree of Confirmation,'" *Philosophy of Science*, 1945.

Hosiasson, J., "Why Do We Prefer Probabilities Relative to Many Data?," *Mind*, 1931.

Hospers, J., *An Introduction to Philosophical Analysis* (New York, 1953), chap. 3.

Hume, D., *A Treatise of Human Nature*, ed. by L. A. Selby-Bigge (Oxford, 1888), Book I.

Jeffreys, H., *Scientific Inference* (Cambridge, 1931).

————, *Theory of Probability* (Oxford, 1939).

————, "The Present Position in Probability Theory," *British Journal for the Philosophy of Science*, 1955.

Jevons, W. S., *The Principles of Science* (New York, 1905).

Kaufmann, F., "Symposium on Probability," *Philosophy and Phenomenological Research*, 1945–46.

——, "Scientific Procedure and Probability," *ibid.*, 1947.

Keynes, J. M., *Treatise on Probability* (London and New York, 1921).

Kneale, W., *Probability and Induction* (Oxford, 1949), sec. 7–15.

Kyburg, H. E., Jr., "The Justification of Induction," *Journal of Philosophy*, 1956.

——, "R. B. Braithwaite on Probability and Induction," *British Journal for the Philosophy of Science*, 1958.

Laplace, P. S., *A Philosophical Essay on Probabilities*, trans. by F. W. Truscott and F. L. Emory (New York, 1951).

Lenz, J. W., "Carnap on Defining 'Degree of Confirmation,'" *Philosophy of Science*, 1956.

——, "The Frequency Theory of Probability," in E. H. Madden (ed.), *The Structure of Scientific Thought* (Boston, 1960).

——, "The Pragmatic Justification of Induction," *ibid.*

Madden, E. H., "The Riddle of Induction," *ibid.*

Margenau, H., "On the Frequency Theory of Probability," *Philosophy and Phenomenological Research*, 1945–46.

Mill, J. S., *A System of Logic* (London, 1893), Book III.

Miller, D. S., "Professor Donald Williams versus Hume," *Journal of Philosophy*, 1947.

Mises, R. von, *Probability, Statistics and Truth* (rev. ed., New York, 1957).

—— and H. Pollaczek-Geiringer, "Probability," in *Encyclopedia of Social Sciences* (New York, 1932).

Moore, A., "The Principle of Induction," *Journal of Philosophy*, 1952.

Nagel, E., "The Frequency Theory of Probability," *Journal of Philosophy*, 1933.

——, "The Meaning of Probability," *Journal of the American Statistical Association*, 1936.

——, *Principles of the Theory of Probability* (International Encyclopedia of Unified Science, I, no. 6, Chicago, 1939).

——, "Probability and Non-demonstrative Inference," *Philosophy and Phenomenological Research*, 1945.

——, "Probability and the Theory of Knowledge," in E. Nagel, *Sovereign Reason* (New York, 1954).

Neyman, J., *First Course in Probability and Statistics* (New York, 1950), chap. 5.

——, "Inductive Behavior as a Basic Concept of Philosophy of Science," *Review of the International Statistical Institute*, 1957.

Nicod, J., "The Logical Problem of Induction," in J. Nicod, *Foundations of Geometry and Induction* (London, 1930).

Pap, A., *Elements of Analytic Philosophy* (New York, 1949), chap. 9b.

Popper, K., *The Logic of Scientific Discovery* (London, 1958), chap. 8, 10.

——, "The Propensity Interpretation of Probability," *British Journal for the Philosophy of Science*, 1959.

Ramsey, F. P., *The Foundations of Mathematics* (New York, 1950), chap. 7–9.

Reichenbach, H., "The Logical Foundations of the Concept of Probability," *Erkenntnis*, 1932–33. [Trans. by M. Reichenbach and reprinted in H. Feigl and W. Sellars (eds.), *Readings in Philosophical Analysis* (New York, 1949) and in H. Feigl and M. Brodbeck (eds.), *Readings in the Philosophy of Science* (New York, 1953).]

——, *Experience and Prediction: An Analysis of the Foundations and the Structure of Knowledge* (Chicago, 1938).

———, "On the Justification of Induction," *Journal of Philosophy*, 1940. [Reprinted in Feigl and Sellars, *op. cit.*]

———, *Theory of Probability* (2nd ed., Berkeley, Calif., 1949).

———, "Philosophical Foundations of Probability," *Proceedings of the Berkeley Symposium on Mathematical Statistics and Probability*, 1949.

Russell, B., *The Problems of Philosophy* (London, 1912), chap. 6.

———, *Human Knowledge, Its Scope and Limits* (New York, 1948), part V.

Ryle, G., "Induction and Hypothesis," *Aristotelian Society Proceedings*, supp., 1937.

Salmon, W., "The Short Run," *Philosophy of Science*, 1955.

———, "The Predictive Inference," *Philosophy of Science*, 1957.

———, "Should We Attempt to Justify Induction?," *Philosophical Studies*, 1957.

Smart, H. R., "The Problem of Induction," *Journal of Philosophy*, 1928.

Strawson, P. F., *Introduction to Logical Theory* (London, 1952), chap. 9.

Tintner, G., "Foundations of Probability and Statistical Inference," *Journal of the Royal Statistical Society*, series A, CXII, part III (1949).

Urmson, J. O., "Some Questions Concerning Validity," in A. Flew (ed.), *Essays in Conceptual Analysis* (London, 1956).

Venn, J., "Difficulties of the Classical View of Probability," in J. Venn, *The Logic of Chance* (1st ed., 1866). [Reprinted in E. H. Madden (ed.), *The Structure of Scientific Thought* (Boston, 1960).]

Wang, H., "On Scepticism about Induction," *Philosophy of Science*, 1950.

Will, F. L., "Is There a Problem of Induction?," *Journal of Philosophy*, 1942.

———, "Will the Future Be Like the Past?," *Mind*, 1947. [Reprinted in A. Flew (ed.), *Logic and Language*, vol. II (Oxford, 1959); and in P. Edwards and A. Pap (eds.), *A Modern Introduction to Philosophy* (New York, 1957).]

Williams, D., *The Ground of Induction* (Cambridge, Mass., 1947).

———, "Induction and the Future," *Mind*, 1948.

——— and others, "Challenging Situation in the Philosophy of Probability" (symposium), *Philosophy and Phenomenological Research*, 1945–46.

Wisdom, J. O., *Foundations of Inference in Natural Science* (London, 1952).

Wright, G. H. von, *A Treatise on Induction and Probability* (London, 1951).

———, *The Logical Problem of Induction* (rev. ed., New York, 1957).

Part Four

CAUSALITY

AND LAWS

OF NATURE

CHAPTER 14

Causation
as Regular
Succession

The conception of science as a search for causal connections dominated the scientific methodology of John Stuart Mill, which was examined in Chapter 10. If "causal connection" is used very broadly for any kind of order or lawfulness in the course of events, then it is indeed true and truistic to say that science, or at least sciences dealing with change (as distinct from purely classificatory sciences), aim at the discovery of causal connections. In a stricter sense, however, a causal connection is a law of invariable succession and thus a stronger connection than a probabilistic correlation. It is with this stricter, or stronger, sense of "cause" that the present chapter is concerned.

A. THE CONTINGENCY
OF CAUSAL PROPOSITIONS

Anybody with a rudimentary understanding of the meaning of "cause" knows that "*a* caused *b*" is not synonymous with "*a* preceded *b*." Perhaps "*a* caused *b*" entails "*a* preceded *b*" but surely the converse entailment does not hold, otherwise *Post hoc, ergo propter hoc* would not be a fallacy. Right before my car started to move I stepped on the gas pedal, but even if we confine attention to events in the spatial neighborhood of the starting movement we can find many other antecedent events which we judge to be causally unrelated to it: the person in the back seat lighted a cigarette, I myself uttered the words "Let's go" and clasped the steering wheel, and so on. Our problem of analysis is to discover what distinguishes a causal antecedent from a merely temporal antecedent, and therewith discover how we can justify the assertion that I caused the starting movement by stepping on the gas pedal and not, say, by saying "Let's go." David Hume maintained that the verifiable content of a causal assertion is exhausted by an assertion of "constant conjunction" of the kinds of events called "cause" and "effect." Hume defended this analysis in a polemical context: against rationalistic philosophers who dominated the academic chairs he argued that causal connections are contingent, not necessary, i.e., that it is impossible to discover a priori, by pure thinking uncontaminated with observation and experimentation, what is the cause of what. You cannot help expecting that the glass will instantly be shattered when you see a stone approaching it at great speed, but that is, said Hume, because you have frequently observed that an event like the one presently witnessed was followed by an event like the expected effect. If you had never observed such a "conjunction" of events, you would not be able to predict what would follow the stone's impact.

We must certainly agree with Hume's negative thesis that causal connections are not logically necessary. However impressive may be the empirical evidence supporting a causal generalization, such as "If a block of ice is subjected to a temperature exceeding 90°F at standard atmospheric pressure, it will melt," its negation can be conceived without self-contradiction. If this insight of Hume's is still occasionally questioned, it must be owing to one or the other of the following simple confusions:

1. Scientists often redefine their concepts of natural kinds *after* an empirical discovery in such a way that the same sentence that originally expressed a contingent generalization subject to disconfirmation becomes analytically true. Thus Galileo had to discover by experiment that freely falling bodies fall with constant acceleration, i.e., in such a way that the velocity increases in direct proportion to the time. In the context of that experimental inquiry, "freely falling body" meant "body falling under the sole influence of gravity (i.e., all other forces, such as friction, buoyancy of the air, deflecting magnetic forces, and so on are supposed to be eliminated)." But *after* the discovery it is natural to use the constancy of acceleration as a defining criterion of a "free fall," so as to refuse to recognize a descending motion with variable acceleration as a "free fall." Still, the causal generalization that is a statement about the course of nature and not about the meaning of a word can be formulated without using the ambiguous expression "freely falling body" at all: a

body that falls under the sole influence of gravity falls with constant acceleration.[1] The generalization expressed by this sentence remains contingent no matter how the expression "free fall" may have been redefined. Similarly, after having observed that absorption of arsenic has a poisoning effect on an animal, one may include the property of having poisoning power in the definition of "arsenic," i.e., refuse to apply the term "arsenic" to a substance otherwise just like arsenic if it lacks poisoning power. But even if a scientist should so resolve (it is doubtful whether one ever would), he would not thereby establish the logical necessity of the following proposition: a substance that has all the characteristics of arsenic that were known before its poisoning power was discovered also has poisoning power.

2. After succeeding in *explaining* why an event *A* is regularly followed by an event *B* one often says that now he knows why *A must* be followed by *B*. One who plays the piano without the slightest knowledge of the mechanics of a piano knows empirically that different sounds invariably follow the depressions of different keys. Should he one day take a look at the piano's inside, in order to solve the mystery, he would discover that little hammers are set into motion by his fingers, in such a way as to strike wires of different length and thickness. Should he, moreover, know something about the theory of sound production, he could then claim to know, for example, that a depression of a key to the right of a key whose depression was followed by a sound of relatively low pitch *must* be followed by a sound of higher pitch. But if one thinks that an explanation of an observed regularity of succession of natural events enables us to see that it is logically necessary for one event to be followed by another, one has been misled by an ambiguity of ordinary language. We often put the word "must" into the conclusion of an argument though what is logically necessary is not the deduced proposition itself but the implication from the premises to the conclusion. "Giovanni *must* sing Verdi arias well, for he is an Italian tenor and all Italian tenors sing Verdi arias well": but, of course, there is no contradiction in supposing that Giovanni does not sing Verdi arias at all, let alone sing them well. What is a contradiction is only the supposition that he does not sing such arias well although he is an Italian tenor and all Italian tenors sing them well. Similarly, the pianist who has studied acoustics and gained insight into the workings of the piano can still conceive without contradiction that a key to the right of middle C gave rise to a sound of lower pitch than a key to the left of middle C; what is contradictory is only the conjunc-

---

1. In the context of Newton's theory of gravitation, which was not known to Galileo, this law appears to be true only if "constant" is replaced by "approximately constant," since the force of gravity increases infinitesimally as the falling body approaches the earth.

tion of the latter proposition with the propositions about the mechanics of the piano and about the relevant laws of sound production.

B. REFINEMENT OF A REGULARITY ANALYSIS

But, granted that causal generalizations must in the end be inductively confirmed no matter how they may be organized into a deductive system in which many special generalizations are deducible from a few fundamental ones, we are still faced with the task of clarifying the *positive* contribution of the regularity theory of causation. To say that a cause of an event is an event that is regularly followed by the latter is too crude to be illuminating. Thus it surely is not the case that the car starts moving whenever the gas pedal is stepped upon, yet it is a perfectly proper use of the word "cause" to say that it was my stepping on the gas pedal that caused the starting movement. What we mean is that the former event is followed by the latter whenever certain other conditions, too well known to require mention, are fulfilled. Similarly, we say that striking a match causes a flame, knowing that a flame will follow the striking movement only if certain conditions are fulfilled: there must be enough oxygen, the match must be dry, and so on. It is true that in accordance with the dictum "same cause, same effect" we usually deny that A is the *complete* cause of B when we discover a case where A is not followed by B. According to this usage, it is analytic to say that every instance of A is followed by an instance of B if A is the complete cause of B. This sense of "cause" was called "sufficient condition" in Chapter 10. But this is rarely what "cause" means in a singular causal statement "a caused b" or "a will cause b." What we mean is rather "a was (will be) followed by b, and the conditions under which a occurred (will occur)— call them C—are such that any event like a is *in the presence of* C followed by an event like b." In our first example of everyday causation, C is the presence of gasoline in the car's tank, a running motor, and so on; in the second example C is the presence of oxygen, dryness of match and matchbox, and so on.

Does "cause" in this everyday sense, then, mean a *necessary* condition of the occurrence of an event, so that "a caused (will cause) b" entails "Every event like b is preceded by an event like a"? No, such an analysis is again an oversimplification owing to oversight of the conditions C that are usually not explicitly mentioned. Clearly, cars sometimes start moving though the gas pedal is untouched—for example, if starting on a hilltop the driver lets his car "coast." And it is common knowledge that a flame very similar to the kind of flame produced by a match can be produced by manipulating a cigarette lighter. On the other hand, it is very unlikely that a car will start moving on a horizontal surface if it is not pushed and the gas pedal is not stepped on. We are, therefore, justified in asserting that stepping on the gas pedal is a necessary condition for a starting movement *provided* the car is not pushed, the ground is horizontal, and so forth. In this sense a cause of a particular event may be defined as a *conditionally necessary condition*. Denoting by A and B the repeatable kinds of events of which the particular events a and b are instances, we may analyze a singular causal statement "a caused (will cause) b" as follows: a was (will be) followed by b in the presence of C, and an instance of A is followed by an instance of B whenever C is present. C represents the sum total of conditions whose presence is presupposed when one asserts "a caused (will cause) b" and is judged necessary in order for A to be certainly followed by B.

C. THE PLURALITY OF CAUSES

A condition that is thus necessary for the occurrence of an effect E provided certain other conditions are realized may be called a *contributing condition* of E. It is important to understand that "A is a contributing condition of E" does not entail "E is invariably preceded by A." Neither the inference from "An instance of A occurs" to "An instance of E will follow" nor the converse inference from "An instance of E occurs" to "An instance of A occurred" is warranted unless certain other conditions are fulfilled. In the case of the inference from contributing condition to effect these presupposed conditions are usually positive; in the case of the converse inference they are usually negative. Thus the inference from "The windows are wet" to "It rained a short time ago" is highly probable provided there is but a negligible chance that someone turned a hose on the windows or washed them without subsequently drying them. When we feel a movement of air in a previously uncomfortable room we are inclined to infer that it is a sudden breeze that brought relief, but this inference is probable only if it is unlikely that a fan was set into operation.

This complication of causal inference is traditionally called the *plurality of causes*. A repeatable effect (i.e., a *kind* of event, a universal) E is said to have a plurality of causes if it has several logically independent sufficient conditions. Thus unnatural death is an effect that can be produced alternatively by ingestion of poisonous food, strangulation, shooting, drowning, and so on in the sense that the generalizations "Any organism that is shot through the heart dies," "Any human being who stays under water—unprotected by an artificial source of oxygen— longer than thirty minutes dies," and so on are well confirmed. A schematic illustration of plurality of logically independent sufficient conditions is provided by mechanics. Any accelerated motion is, according to Newton's second law of motion, uniquely determined in direction and magnitude by a force acting in the same direction. The latter is, however, resolvable into pairs of component forces, according to the law of vector addition. These component forces may be just conceptual constructions, as when a force is resolved into its components along the x-, y-, and z-axis. But sometimes it is the other way around; i.e., it is the components that are real, physical forces, and their resultant is constructed. For example, if to test the relative strength of two horses one were to have them pull a cart simultaneously in opposite directions, the resultant acceleration of the cart would be produced by the joint action of two real and opposite forces, call them F_1 and F_2, and their resultant would be only a mathematical construction. If the opposing forces were doubled, by reinforcing each horse by one of equal strength, the resulting acceleration of the cart should be the same, but it would be produced by a conjunction of different component forces. Again, consider a straight movement of a billiard ball on a billard table. Let us identify the "effect" with the billiard ball's passage from location A to location B in t seconds (t may be a fraction). A physicist could in principle predict this effect if he measured the impulse received by the ball as well as the frictional resistance of the table top. But he could also calculate the impulse and direction that would result in the same effect if the passage from A to B involved a reflection, either from a table edge or from some other billiard ball. Thus, there is more than one sufficient condition for this effect.

The simple logic of plurality of causes is illustrated in Figure 14.1.

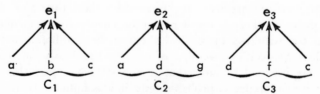

Figure 14.1   Plurality of causes.

Note that the contributing conditions that are jointly sufficient for the occurrence of *some instance or other* of E may be said to be necessary for a *particular instance*, e_1, of E, in the sense that we can say, in retrospect, "e_1 could not have happened without a," "e_2 could not have happened without g," and so forth, *presupposing* that other conditions that might have resulted in an instance of E at the same time and place were absent. "If you had kept a sufficient distance from the car in front of you, you would not have hit it": in making such an assertion, the accuser presupposes, among other things, that the accused driver did not exceed, say, 40 miles per hour, when the car in front suddenly stopped; for had his speed been, say 55 miles per hour, the accident would have been unavoidable even if the distance separating the two cars had exceeded the actual distance at the time of the accident. This illustrates that just because of the plurality of causes, a contributing condition is a necessary condition (a condition "without which the effect would not have occurred") but *relative* to a number of presupposed conditions which equally contribute to the effect. To add an illustration: An expansion of a given mass of gas may be said to be caused by a diminution of the pressure on it in the sense that its expansion always would follow a diminution of the pressure, and the latter change always would precede the former, provided the same relevant conditions were repeated. The proviso refers, of course, to the constancy of temperature. It is well known that a rise of temperature will produce the same effect even if the gas is kept at constant pressure. It is, therefore, equally wrong to say that a diminution of pressure is a sufficient condition of expansion (the pressure drop might be neutralized by a temperature drop) and that the former change is a necessary condition of the latter change (the pressure might be unchanged while the temperature rises).

An argument against the apparent plurality of causes that has been advanced is that plurality of causes is an appearance arising from insufficiently specific descriptions of the effect. If e_1 and e_2, different instances of the same kind of effect, E, seem to be caused by different conditions C_1 and C_2, a closer analysis will reveal, according to this argument, a corresponding dissimilarity between e_1 and e_2. Thus the kind of death due to shooting differs from the kind of death due to strangulation; the kind of pleasure produced by a lovely sight differs from the kind of pleasure produced by good food; the wetness of the ground produced by rain differs from the wetness of the ground produced by artificial irrigation, and so on. But this is an exceedingly weak argument. Obviously e_1 and e_2 will differ in some respect, since they are, after all, *different* instances of the same kind of effect. Visual pleasure is different from gustatory pleasure, nor is the possibility to be excluded that an analysis of earth watered by rain would reveal a difference from earth watered by a sprinkler. As a last resort, one could always point to the causal differences, that the death caused by strangulation was not, after all, caused by a bullet, and that the pleasure produced by staring at a beautiful woman was not, after all, produced by eating! But all this is irrelevant, since any causal statement, by the very meaning of "cause" and "effect," involves abstractions of recurrent features from the concrete, individual event. That e_1 is an instance of the more specific kind of event EA, and e_2 an instance of the more specific kind of event EB, is surely compatible with saying that both are instances of the less specific kind of event E. Thus, the description (D) "a billiard ball moving from P to P' in t seconds" is, of course, less specific than the description (D') "a billard ball moving in a straight line from P to P' in t seconds." But if one is asked to mention a sufficient causal condition of an event described by D one will be perfectly justified in citing several such conditions, though some of them may not produce an event of the more specific kind described by D'. If, on the other hand, an effect were, *per impossibile*, described in complete detail, its sufficient condition would be unique only in the trivial sense that the effect itself would be unrepeatable. The particular collision of cars that happened on a particular parkway X at a particular time was, of course, caused by one and only one collocation of various circumstances, but the moment we abstract from this concrete occurrence a repeatable kind—such as "car collision on parkway X," "a car colliding with a car in process of illegally passing a car going 60 mph," and so forth and so on—we are faced with a possible plurality of sufficient conditions.

D. COINCIDENTAL AND CAUSAL SEQUENCES

We have seen so far that an accurate analysis of causal connection in terms of regular succession is by no means simple. In particular, a strictly sufficient condition is usually so complex that it is difficult to be sure one has discovered one, and because of the "plurality of causes" it is not easy to formulate strictly necessary conditions without making a host of qualifications. When we claim that a condition C that in our experience was always followed by E *will* be followed by E whenever and wherever it recurs we presuppose that C will continue to be accompanied by the same relevant circumstances—though the latter may not be known in full detail, and the prediction may accordingly be put in the cautious form "C will always be followed by E, *other things being equal.*" The reference to "the same relevant circumstances" is, of course, required only if E, the antecedent picked out from the total complex of determining conditions, is not by itself a sufficient condition—as is usually the case in causal talk. But it has been questioned whether "C is invariably followed by E" will do even as an analysis of the concept of a strictly sufficient condition. Bertrand Russell pointed out long ago that the 4 P.M. factory sirens in Manchester are causally unconnected with the nearly simultaneous departure of the workmen from the London factories. One may try to get around counterexamples like this one by stipulating spatial proximity of cause and effect as a defining condition of direct causation, but counterexamples will arise even to this amended definition. Imagine two nearly synchronized and juxtaposed clocks that keep time forever. We judge their corresponding states to be causally unrelated though *whenever* one clock is in a given state, the other clock is in the corresponding state as well. Again, suppose it so happened that whenever a man who suffered from a rare disease—so rare, indeed, that only five cases of it happened during the entire existence of mankind— was persuaded by some witch doctor to eat some rare sort of herb, he was cured within half an hour; would such a regularity of succession, if it should exist, be equivalent to a causal connection?

Such objections are valid as against a simple-minded identification of "*A* is a sufficient causal condition of *B*" with "Every instance of *A* is in fact followed by an instance of *B*." Advocates of the regularity analysis of causation usually defend their analysis in terms of the verification principle of meaning (cf. Part I): since regularity of succession, they argue, constitutes conclusive empirical evidence for a causal proposition, this, and no more, is what is asserted by a causal proposition. But in fact a sound inductive justification of a hypothesis of causal connection involves not just the observation of numerous instances of *A*'s being followed by an instance of *B* but the observation that *A*'s continued to be followed by *B*'s while the presumably relevant circumstances were varied. Even though every instance of *A* is in fact followed by an instance of *B*, *A* may not be a sufficient causal condition of *B*; for every instance of *A* may, by "coincidence," be accompanied by a condition *C* that is necessary for *B*, in which case it would not be true to say that *A would* be followed by *B*, at any time, no matter what other circumstances might exist at that time. Thus we know that the blowing of the factory sirens in London would not be followed by a homeward departure of the workmen in the Manchester factories if the sirens in the latter factories were out of order, or the workmen there were suddenly stricken with deafness, or the working hours there were prolonged for another hour, and so on.

It is true that in thus arguing against the causal nature of a given *de facto* regularity, we presuppose other causal connections, especially *necessary* causal conditions. But we have already emphasized that critical inductions presuppose some tentative hypotheses about causal dependence and independence that were suggested by previous experience. A principle that is especially helpful in forestalling invalid inferences to causal connections from *de facto* conjunctions of events is what may be called the *principle of analogy:* relevantly similar sufficient conditions have similar effects. It may have happened again and again that whenever a picture fell off a living room wall, some misfortune shortly thereafter befell the people who saw the picture fall. Superstitious people may accordingly become fearful when they witness such an ominous event. But by the principle of analogy, there can be no causal connection between two such events, because—to mention just one reason—pictures have fallen off dining room or bedroom walls without any dire consequences for the people who witnessed the accident, and if we claimed a causal connection to hold in the former set of cases and not in the latter set, we would have to be able to explain the difference in the effect in terms of the difference in the conditions. But this we could not do, since there just is not any relevant difference between a picture falling off a living room wall and a picture falling off a bedroom wall. Again, suppose that a certain woman suffered a rash all over her skin whenever she was haunted by great fear. According to the principle of analogy the conclusion that the rash was caused by the state of fear would be warranted only if other people who were relevantly similar to this woman reacted similarly to a similar emotional tension.

The principle of analogy is, of course, vague, but so is the concept of "cause" that it implicitly defines. We can make this concept precise by the definition "A is a cause of B if A is invariably followed by B whenever the circumstances are *exactly identical*," but the price to be paid for such precision would be practical uselessness: the circumstances just never are exactly identical (whether or not such exact recurrence be at least logically possible). An applicable concept of cause must be defined vaguely as "A is invariably followed by B whenever similar relevant circumstances recur." In fact, causal talk in everyday life as well as in pretheoretical sciences is characteristically vague, and reflects a partial ignorance of determining conditions. Once a scientist has formed a pretty definite idea as to *which* circumstances must accompany A in order for B to be predictable with practical certainty, he need not use causal language any longer; he is in a position to assert a definite proposition of the form "Whenever A occurs in the presence of $C_1, C_2, \ldots, C_n$, A is followed by B"—a proposition which, unlike the vague proposition it supersedes, is definitely refutable by contrary instances.

E. CAN A CAUSAL CONNECTION
BE ESTABLISHED
BY A SINGLE OBSERVATION?

That causal connections must, as contended by the regularity analysis, be inductively inferred from many cases in which A is followed under different circumstances by B, may seem to conflict with scientists' practice of pronouncing a causal connection after a single well-controlled experiment. Thus an experimenter who observes that the removal of oxygen from the air breathed by a confined animal is followed by the death of the animal will conclude that the death was *caused* by the removal of oxygen, provided he has satisfied himself that all the relevant conditions except the chemical composition of the air remained unchanged during the experiment. But it is easy to see that the experimenter's argument, "The removal of oxygen from the space within which the animal was confined was the only relevant change immediately preceding the animal's death, therefore it must have caused it," is an argument from elimination of alternative explanations (cf. Chapter 10) that is quite consistent with the regularity analysis of the meaning of "cause."

In order to show this formally, let us analyze the idea of one change's being caused by another change in "thing language" as follows: The fact that a thing A has property Q at time t_1 (which property A did not have at the slightly earlier time t_0) is caused by A's having property P at t_0 (which A did not have immediately before t_0). Suppose now, that this causal proposition in turn were analyzed as follows: A had P immediately before it acquired Q, and for any t, and for any x, if x has P at t, then x has Q at $t + dt$. From this analysis it follows at once that if x has P at some time t_i without having Q at $t_i + dt_i$, then the fact that x has Q at some time cannot be caused by the fact that x had P immediately before. In other words, the analysis entails that x's having Q cannot be caused by x's having P if there is a finite time interval (more exactly, a time interval that is large relative to dt) during which x has P invariably but does not have Q. If, for example, it should have occurred to our experimenter that his guinea pig perished from malnutrition, he could have refuted that suggestion by making sure that it was supplied with exactly the same quality and quantity of food before and after the removal of oxygen. In general, if $R_1, R_2, \ldots, R_n$ are properties with respect to which x does not change during a certain time interval within which x acquires Q, i.e., within which there are instants when x does not have Q and later instants when x has Q, then no hypothesis of the form "For any t, if x has R_i at t, then x has Q at $t + dt$" can be true. On the assumption that some change of A (with respect to some property) that immediately preceded A's acquisition of Q caused the latter, and that P is the only property with respect to which A changed immediately before, it does indeed follow that it is *this* change that caused the effect. A single experiment, then, may highly confirm a causal hypothesis interpreted as an assertion of regular succession, provided one has made sure that all the relevant variables except one remained constant during the experiment.

Another argument against the regularity analysis is that although we must, admittedly, infer causal connections between *physical* events inductively from an observed "constant conjunction," we have, as it were, direct access to the causal nexus in our experience of volitional efficacy. When one pushes an object, lifts it from the ground, kicks it, or whatever, he knows immediately, so the argument goes, that his own volition caused the physical movement; but a law of regular succession cannot be known immediately, since it must be inductively inferred; therefore "cause" does not have the meaning ascribed to it by the Humeans in this context. Now, we certainly have immediate, introspective knowledge of our volitions, and being conscious of one's own volition is surely different from perceptual knowledge of what happens in the physical environment. But does it follow that our knowledge of the causal nexus between volition and bodily movement is any different? The proposition that my volition to lift the glass to my lips caused the desired action is certainly different from the proposition that my volition immediately preceded the desired action, for although my neighbor may have desired the same event at the same time, still it was my desire, not his, that caused it to happen; again, at just the same time I may have crossed my legs, but nobody believes that the latter event caused the effect in question. It is difficult to see, therefore, what the proposition asserting volitional causation of a bodily movement can mean if not "The volition was followed by the action, and the relevant conditions C (such as the possession by the agent of healthy limbs, the agent's implicit belief that he was capable of performing the desired action, the glass' being freely movable and not fastened to the table top) were such that the same kind of volition under the same conditions C is invariably followed by the same kind of overt action."

That regularity of succession must be implicitly asserted by the causal proposition is further evident from a simple reflection: Suppose that, by a strange coincidence, your telephone had rung several times just when you wanted it to ring, and that, in a moment of superstition, you inferred that you had power over the telephone, that you could make it ring at will. Or, to make the story more fantastic still, suppose that, a number of times, your friend called you up just when you consciously desired that he call you up, but that he (or she) had no way of knowing about your desire. How would you *test* your superstitious inference that you had direct volitional control over your friend's manipulations of his telephone? Clearly, you would repeat the experiment, making sure that your friend remained ignorant of your desire. And if, by a very unlikely coincidence, this sort of thing happened again, you would in your moments of critical, scientific reflection still remain unconvinced of such a mysterious causal nexus because the principle of analogy speaks against it: Why should you be capable of volitional control of your friend's phone calls to you and not of any other actions of his (or hers)?

And why not of your other friends' phone calls to you? In short, the overwhelming indirect evidence against the causal hypothesis under discussion bestows such a negligible antecedent probability on it, that the extent of the supposed coincidence would have to be quite extraordinary before that causal hypothesis would acquire the slightest degree of objective credibility. But this method of testing the hypothesis of volitional control would be utterly irrelevant if the latter could be established by direct insight. And if I cannot know by direct insight that by wishing the telephone to ring I can make it ring, or that by wishing my friend to call me up at this moment I can make him do so, it is not by direct insight either that I know that my desire to stretch out my arm caused my arm to be stretched out.

F. MOTIVATIONAL CAUSATION

A psychologist or social scientist who wishes to discover causal explanations of human behavior that are useful for the prediction and control of human behavior cannot possibly ignore subjective motivations. But are motives—such as the desire for prestige, jealousy, the fear of ruining a friend by testifying truthfully about his communist affiliations, the desire to harm a professional rival—causes in the Humean sense? This is often denied by philosophers and social scientists who think that human behavior defies analysis and explanation by the methods that have led the physical sciences to spectacular successes. To bring some clarity into this methodological controversy, let us attempt a dispassionate analysis of a simple explanation of behavior in terms of subjective motivation. Chairman X of philosophy department Y has been observed to assign to assistant professor Z in his department the worst possible hours for his course on "logical positivism"; that is, every year he schedules it to meet on Saturday morning, a time known to be detested by the majority of students. Other courses, taught by other members of the department, are occasionally scheduled for Saturday morning but no other course is invariably scheduled to meet at that unpopular time. It is further known that chairman X is a passionate metaphysician who detests logical positivism and who allows this school of thought to be taught at all only because it is taught at all other colleges of high reputation and because his suppressing it openly would too plainly belie the principles of free inquiry and education he so proudly proclaims in his course on "man and freedom." Z naturally infers that his chairman is afraid that logical positivism might become too popular with the students who elect philosophy courses, and that he attempts to keep the enrollment in Z's favorite course minimal in order to prevent such contagion. Our problem is the analysis of the proposition "Chairman X's discriminatory action against assistant professor Z is caused by his desire to minimize the spread of the doctrines of logical positivism."

We note at once that the specified desire is not, of course, a sufficient causal condition of the assignment of Saturday morning classes to the token positivist in X's department; for, unless X moreover *believed* that this action would serve his purpose he would not act that way. Just as the person who asserts that the light went on because someone turned the switch presupposes the fulfillment of such necessary conditions as that a bulb that is not yet burnt out was tightly screwed into the socket, so an explanation of an action in terms of a motive, or desire, always presupposes that the agent has certain relevant beliefs as to the instrumentality of his action to his aim. But just because the two types of causal explanation—the physical and the psychological—are entirely comparable in this respect, it is no argument against the regularity analysis to point out that the desire, after all, is not the complete cause of the observed action.

However, one might object that after the hypothesis that X had the specified desire as well as the specified belief has been sufficiently confirmed, the correctness of the motivational explanation has been established though no other instance of similarly motivated behavior may ever have been observed. It would, indeed, be odd if one were to demand that the motivational explanation be justified by citing other instances of the generalization "If a department chairman wants to minimize the impact on the students' mind of a course on logical positivism and believes that he will reach this aim by scheduling it for Saturday morning, then he schedules it for Saturday morning," or even of the broader generalization "If a department chairman wants to minimize the popularity of a certain course—because he disapproves of the ideas expressed in it—and believes that he will reach this aim by scheduling it at an unpopular hour, then he will do so." The point is that we all presuppose as a *truism* the vague and abstract generalization: If an agent desires an end E and believes that action A is likely to conduce to E and does not believe that the other consequences of A are so undesirable as to outweigh the desirability of E—i.e., does not believe that A will have other consequences he fears more strongly than he desires E—then he is likely to perform A. And since we presuppose this "law," we are completely satisfied that the proffered explanation of A in terms of motive E is correct once it has been established that the agent desired E, believed that A would lead to E, and did not believe that A would have consequences he feared more strongly than he desired E. The question is whether for this reason the regularity analysis of motivational causation must be rejected.

The question may be reduced to the question whether this very general law of human behavior asserts anything that might conceivably be refuted by observations, like a generalization of physics, or whether it is a mere tautology. Is it at all informative to say that people do what they believe will lead to a net satisfaction of their desires? Can we tell what a man desires without observing what he does? Can we tell what a man believes without observing his overt behavior? Certainly, one test of whether x believes that A leads to E is whether he performs A when he desires E. Thus, if we know that x wants to get to a certain city and we observe that at an intersection he turns right, we infer that he believes the road to the right will lead him to that city. But we also use as a criterion of whether x desires E, whether he performs A when he may be expected to know that A leads to E and is not likely to have consequences outweighing the advantage to be reaped from the attainment of E. It is easy to apply these considerations to our illustration of the chairman's discriminatory action. If we already know that the chairman desires to frustrate assistant professor Z's educational endeavors, we infer from his action—assigning Z's course to an unpopular hour—that he believes it to have that effect. And if we were asked how we know that the chairman has such a desire, we might point out that he could easily have assigned a more popular hour, at least once, to that course and that he undoubtedly knows that very few students will take it at that time. It is this sort of *circularity* in the testing of a generalization connecting overt action with beliefs and desires that prompts the deprecatory remark that it is a mere tautology that does not explain anything.

But a closer analysis will show that the very question "Is it a tautology (an analytic statement) or is it empirically testable?" is rooted in an artificial dichotomy. We certainly need behavioral criteria for the application of the concepts "belief" and "desire" to other persons and to animals, but there is a multiplicity of such criteria permitting independent tests. A conditional statement "If p, then q" is, of course, empty of empirical content if it is impossible to confirm p independently of confirming q. But if it enjoys the company of another conditional statement "If p, then r" (where p represents the same hypothesis), it may acquire empirical content because it is entirely a question of fact whether a hypothesis that has been confirmed by one consequence will continue to be confirmed by another, logically independent, consequence. Thus the inferred hypothesis that driver x believes a right turn will lead him to his destination would be confirmed independently of an observation of his actual course if the man who filled his gas tank before he reached the intersection testified that he told him to turn right. And chairman X's desire could certainly be inferred from a variety of other actions indicating his hatred, or fear, of logical positivism. To be sure, it is difficult to see how any behavioral criteria of belief and desire could have developed to begin with, unless some introspective knowledge of one's own beliefs and desires is conceded. But if the words "desire" and "belief" are taken in a sense in which a person can know immediately, without inductive inference from overt behavior, what his own desires and relevant beliefs are, it is more obvious still that our general law of human behavior is not an empty tautology. I can clearly conceive, without the slightest logical inconsistency, that I desire to have a drink of lemonade, that I believe that the glass in front of me contains good, fresh lemonade and that, consequently, I could satisfy my desire by drinking from it, further that I do not believe this indulgence to have any unpleasant consequences (such as a stomach ache, or intensified thirst) at all, but that I nevertheless do not act so as to satisfy my desire. There can be no contradiction here, because subjective states of desire and belief are clearly *distinct* from any overt action.

There is a famous, much-debated law of learning theory, Thorndike's "law of effect" or "law of reinforcement," which raises the same logical problem. It asserts that if a response has resulted in satisfaction, the probability of its being repeated under similar stimulus and deprivation conditions is increased, this probability being an increasing function of the number of past "reinforcements." How is one to tell whether a response of another organism led to that organism's "satisfaction"? If the only criterion were the subsequent increase of response frequency, the law of effect would assert precisely nothing. But having noted that, say, ingestion of food after prolonged starvation produces "subjective" satisfaction, the psychologist applies the principle of analogy and infers that similar stimuli will produce something like satisfaction in his similarly starved rats. He then observes that the frequency with which the rats subsequently respond in similar choice situations and in a similar state of "food deprivation" in a way that will secure such satisfaction increases with the number of successful responses ("reinforcements"). Henceforth he can operate as a good behaviorist, repudiating any talk about subjective states, and still confirm the law of effect in a noncircular way: for the principle of analogy enables him to supplement the response criterion of satisfaction with the deprivation criterion. He can first infer the subjective state from the fact that the animal is now eating after prolonged starvation, and then test the law of effect by observing whether the animal makes the appropriate response more frequently after it has frequently been "rewarded" by it.[2]

The problem of noncircular testability is not fundamentally different in physics. If the general law of human behavior, vague as it is, strikes

2. For a more detailed discussion of the problem of "intervening variables" in behavior theory, see Chapter 20, **B**.

us as a truism because we have found it confirmed innumerable times, so does a fundamental generalization such as "If a body at rest is acted on by an external force it will move in the direction of that force provided it is not prevented by a counteracting force." Of course we can, and do, infer the presence of a counteracting force if the body is not set into motion by the external force, or moves in a direction different from the latter. If a billiard ball remains motionless after being hit by another billiard ball with considerable force, we infer that it is glued to the table surface, or that it is made of lead, or the like. This is analogous to our concluding that a man who does nothing to satisfy his desire of E though he knows exactly what instrumental actions will lead to E must be haunted by a (rational or irrational) fear of the possible consequences of those actions, rather than admitting that the law "People do what they expect will maximize their net satisfaction" has been refuted. But as long as the inference to such counteracting forces, whether physical or psychological, is *independently* testable, the law is, though vague, not a tautology.

It is impossible to enumerate in exhaustive detail all the possible obstacles that might prevent a given type of external force from producing its normal effect, and for this reason the mentioned law of motion cannot be said to be refutable in a simple, straightforward way. Still, as a genuine empirical law, presupposed in such everyday explanation as "The ball moved because it was kicked," it may not be saved by just postulating counteracting forces *ad hoc* whenever it seems to have been refuted. Such counteracting forces must subsequently be discovered: "See, I told you, it is made of lead," or "See, I told you, it is nailed to the table top." Similarly, we may temporarily postulate that a man who refuses to do what he believes to serve his purposes better than any alternative action is swayed by some irrational fear, but sooner or later we must provide independent evidence that such an emotional factor deflected him from the path of enlightened self-interest. To say that the general law of human behavior is empirically confirmable is, indeed, to say that its apparent refutations can be revealed as merely apparent by producing *independent* evidence that some of the conditions described by its "if" clause were not fulfilled.

G. CONTIGUITY AND MEMORY

According to Hume's analysis, a cause must not only be "regularly" followed by its effect but must also be contiguous to it in space and time. Of course, Hume imposed this requirement only on *direct* cause.

When a locomotive exerts a pull, it is communicated in "chain reaction" fashion to the caboose through a considerable distance, and the time interval separating the initiation of the pull from its accelerating effect on the last car is not infinitesimal either. But this is a case of indirect causation—in metaphorical expression a "causal chain." The model from which this conception of contiguous causation was obviously derived is causation of changes of motion—including starting accelerations —by impact. Understandably, scientists and philosophers who were accustomed to this model of direct physical causation found it hard to accept gravitational "action at a distance"—instantaneous exertion of gravitational attraction through enormous distances—as irreducible to contact action. It so happens that the principle of contact action won out in the later development of mechanics; in Einstein's theory of gravitation, which superseded Newton's, gravitation—like light—is propagated at a finite though enormous speed. It is the requirement of *temporal* contiguity, however, which raises a more interesting philosophical problem.

Bertrand Russell once remarked that temporal contiguity of cause and (immediate) effect is a straight consequence of the idea that the cause *necessarily* produces its effect. For, as long as a finite time interval separates the cause from the effect, some occurrence is always conceivable that might prevent the effect. We cannot say that ingestion of arsenic will necessarily lead to death, for the victim might survive if his stomach were pumped out immediately. We cannot say that a stone thrown toward a window will necessarily break it, for some force might deflect it just in time. But, as Russell noted, if the causes and effects we require to be temporally contiguous were point events, i.e., events that happen instantaneously, without finite duration, they could not possibly be contiguous, since the series of point instants is dense: no element is strictly "next" to any other, just as there is no fraction that is the immediate successor of, say, $\frac{1}{2}$. "Cause" and "effect," then, are terms applicable to processes, not point events, which a finer scientific analysis conceptualizes as continuous sequences of point events. If these point events are conceived as genidentical, i.e., as phases in the evolution of the same *thing* or *system*, they are called *states*. A law of regular succession of qualitatively distinguishable processes then is superseded by a *law of changes of state*.

The purest illustration of such a law is, of course, a differential law of motion. Here temporal contiguity of cause and (immediate) effect is mathematically expressed by the differential form of the law—except that it is inadvisable to speak of infinitesimally close states of a physical system as "causes" and "effects" at all. Consider a particle that moves under the influence of gravity, such as a planet in our solar system. (The word "particle" is applied by the physicist to a physical system, however large, if its dimensions are negligibly small as compared with its distances from other bodies that determine its motion; in this sense astronomers idealize heavenly bodies of enormous size as "points.") Its acceleration is uniquely determined by its distance from the sun; at least this assumption is a practical approximation, since the gravitational attraction exerted on it by other planets is very small in comparison with the solar attraction. It is mathematically represented as the rate of change of the instantaneous velocity with respect to time; hence, if the acceleration is known (as a function of relative position), and the velocity at a to t_0 is known, the velocity at $t_0 + dt$ can be computed, where dt is an arbitrarily small time interval. But an instantaneous velocity is in turn a rate of change, viz. the rate of change of position with respect to time. A position x_0 at t_0 and a velocity dx/dt at t_0 determine the position at $t_0 + dt$. A differential equation of motion, therefore, expresses the successive positions of a moving particle as functions of their immediate predecessors. Idealizing a planetary revolution, for example, as a circular motion—according to Kepler's first law the orbit is an ellipse, but it is an ellipse of such small eccentricity that this simplification yields a fairly good approximation—we can assume a constant acceleration directed towards the sun. This means that the change of velocity in very small time intervals is constant. Having inferred this constant rate of change of velocity from the equation expressing it as a function of relative position, and having measured the particle's initial state at t_0, i.e., its position and velocity at t_0, we could in principle first compute its position at $t_0 + dt$ from its position and velocity at t_0, next its velocity at $t_0 + dt$ from its velocity at t_0 and its constant acceleration, next its position at $t_0 + dt + dt$ from its velocity and position at $t_0 + dt$, next its position at $t_0 + dt + dt$ from its velocity at $t_0 + dt$ and its constant acceleration, and so on, till the entire path is calculated. Fortunately, the mathematical technique known as integral calculus saves us such infinite tedious labor: by integration of the differential equation we obtain an equation expressing at once any future state as a function of the initial state and the time separating the states.

Now, that differential equations should be successful tools for the prediction of states could not have been foreseen a priori. For it is a contingent fact that the mechanical states of a particle are uniquely determined by their immediate predecessors, that a knowledge of the particle's *history*, in other words, is not required for a successful prediction of its future. In order to predict the time it will take a stone of known mass to reach the ground after it is dropped from height h, it is not necessary to know what mechanical states preceded the stones' present mechanical state (h units of length above ground at zero velocity); it is not necessary, for example, to know the path it described before reaching its present position. To be sure, if each state is uniquely determined by an earlier state infinitesimally close to it—assuming a closed system in which the total energy remains constant—it follows that any state is uniquely determined by any earlier state, whether just elapsed or long past. (Indeed, the integrated equations contain the time variable explicitly, and any finite value is substitutable for it.) But the point is that a knowledge of the present mechanical state is *sufficient* for the prediction of future mechanical states, that historical knowledge here, although obtainable by means of the very same equations, is not necessary for the purpose of prediction.

In this respect the causal laws governing the behavior of animals and human beings are prima-facie fundamentally different. Two physiologically similar animals may respond differently to exactly similar stimuli. It follows from the definition of "sufficient condition" that the present stimulus cannot be the sufficient condition of the immediately following response. But once we take into account the animal's past, the explanation of the observed difference in response is easy. The rat that did nothing to secure the presented food, though it had been trained on the path to food by the method of "reinforcement," had just had a plentiful meal and hence was in a state of satiation. In this case the principle of contiguous causation does not break down, because the response difference is correlated with an observable physiological difference at the time of the stimulation, viz. a difference in stomach contents. But the principle seems to break down once we attempt to explain why of two equally hungry rats one pulled the lever that had to be pulled in order to secure food and the other did not. The explanation lies, of course, in the difference of learning background, of conditioning, but thus a prediction of a successful response, or even a weaker statistical prediction of a probability of successful response, seems to require historical knowledge of the number, or relative frequency, of past reinforcements.

Since intelligent responses, i.e., responses that are appropriate relative to present desires or impulses, of an animal thus seem to be determined not only by the present values of stimulus and physiological variables but also by *memories* of past rewards and frustrations, this type of causation has been called *mnemic* causation. Memories and expectations are states elicited by perceptions in accordance with the laws of association, and it is conceivable that laws of contiguous causality could be formulated that express responses as functions of the organism's immediately preceding state provided these memories or expectations are included in the state description. But how is the memory itself caused? If the dog has not repeatedly perceived food smells in close conjunction with the sounds of the dinner bell, he would not now expect to be fed; hence his present expectation or memory is but partly caused by the present perception; his past perceptions are, it seems, necessary conditions of his present internal state, and causality seems to jump a temporal distance. Some philosophers hold such mnemic causality to be entirely unintelligible, not because they follow Hume or because they accept differential laws of motion as the very paradigms of causal laws, but because they confuse the scientific meaning of "cause" with its anthropomorphic connotation. A nonexistent event, they argue, cannot cause anything, let alone an effect that occurs now. But a past event no longer exists; hence it cannot have any effect. A naive semantic fallacy underlying such a metaphysical "proof" is the treatment of pastness as an intrinsic property. Unless we have reason to anticipate a last event, an end of the world, we must admit that *every* event is past relative to some later event. To say, therefore, that past events do not exist is either a tautology—if it means that events that are past relative to the present moment are not present relative to the present moment—from which no informative conclusion can be drawn, or else entails the absurdity that there are no events at all, that nothing ever happens. Secondly, if this metaphysical argument against mnemic causation had any force, it would equally be an argument against mechanistic causation, since whatever mechanical state of a closed system may be identified as "present" by an observer is uniquely determined by whatever state of the system is past relative to that present state. In the scientific sense of "cause," an event *A* causes an event *B* in the sense that there is a law, *L*, such that from the conjunction of *L* and a description of *A* the occurrence of *B* is logically deducible. There is, therefore, no justification for the assertion that a present event cannot be caused by a long past event in this scientific sense of "cause." Very likely a metaphysician is misled into such untenable claims because he thinks of causes, on the analogy of volitional causation, as of pushes or pulls, and finds himself unable to visualize the past pushing the present into the future.

Whether the causal laws that enable us to make predictions satisfy the principle of contiguous causality or have "mnemic" character is, then, entirely a question of scientific fact. It is true that the successful description of the physical universe by means of differential laws has produced in many biologists and pyschologists the belief that mnemic laws of animal and human behavior are not ultimate, that they will in time be superseded by laws conforming to the principle of contiguous causality. But this belief, like the slightly less sweeping belief in universal determinism, is subject to the test of experience and cannot be established by an a priori proof from the "nature" of causality. As an empirical hypothesis it has, as a matter of fact, been very fruitful, for it has led to the theory of brain traces, which has quite recently been confirmed through electrical stimulations of the brains of living subjects.

Selected Readings

Ayer, A. J., *The Foundations of Empirical Knowledge* (London, 1940), chap. 4.

Broad, C. D., *The Mind and Its Place in Nature* (London, 1929).

Cohen, M. R., *The Meaning of Human History* (La Salle, Ill., 1947).

Ewing, A. C., *The Fundamental Questions of Philosophy* (New York, 1951), chap. 8.

Feigl, H., "Notes on Causality," in H. Feigl and M. Brodbeck (eds.), *Readings in the Philosophy of Science* (New York, 1953).

Flew, A., "Motives and the Unconscious," in H. Feigl and M. Scriven (eds.), *Minnesota Studies in the Philosophy of Science* (Minneapolis, 1956), vol. I.

Goetlind, E., *Bertrand Russell's Theories of Causation* (Uppsala, 1952).

Hartshorne, C., "Causal Necessities: An Alternative to Hume," *Philosophical Review*, 1954.

Hospers, J., *An Introduction to Philosophical Analysis* (Englewood Cliffs, N.J., 1953), chap. 4.

Hume, D., *An Inquiry Concerning Human Understanding*, Sec. 7, 8.

Meehl, P., "Law and Convention in Psychology," in H. Feigl and M. Brodbeck (eds.), *Readings in the Philosophy of Science* (New York, 1953).

Mill, J. S., *A System of Logic* (London, 1893), Book III, chap. 5.

Pap, A., "Philosophical Analysis, Translation Schemas, and the Regularity Theory of Causation," *Journal of Philosophy*, 1952.

Peters, S., *The Concept of Motivation* (London, 1958).

Ramsey, F. P., *The Foundations of Mathematics* (New York, 1950), chap. 9.

Reichenbach, H., *The Rise of Scientific Philosophy* (Berkeley, Calif., 1951), chap. 10.

Russell, B., "The Notion of Cause," in *Mysticism and Logic* (New York, 1918). [Reprinted in H. Feigl and M. Brodbeck (eds.), *Readings in the Philosophy of Science* (New York, 1953).]

———, *The Analysis of Mind* (London, 1921).

———, *Human Knowledge, Its Scope and Limits* (New York, 1948).

Schlick, M., "Causality in Everyday Life and in Recent Science," in H. Feigl and W. Sellars (eds.), *Readings in Philosophical Analysis* (New York, 1949).

Silberstein, L., *Causality* (London, 1933).

Stebbing, S. L., *A Modern Introduction to Logic* (London, 1933), part II.

Weinberg, J. R., "The Idea of Causal Efficacy," *Journal of Philosophy*, 1952.

CHAPTER 15

Counterfactuals & Dispositions

A. MATERIAL, ANALYTIC, AND CAUSAL IMPLICATION

Early in this book it was mentioned that symbolic logicians have seen fit to interpret implications, i.e., statements of the form "If p, then q," in obvious and unconcealed departure from ordinary usage, as meaning "It is not the case that p and not q," or equivalently, "Not p or q." In this they followed Bertrand Russell, who introduced this concept of *material implication*—usually symbolized by "$\supset$"—mainly because it was required by a truth-functional theory of deductive inference. As explained in Chapter 6, a deductive inference in the two-valued propositional calculus is valid, according to that theory, if the implication corresponding to it is a tautology, and whether or not it is a tautology is mechanically decidable by a truth table. But such a test of tautology presupposes rules assigning truth-values to compound statements, such as negations, conjunctions, disjunctions, implications, as functions of the truth-values of their components (hence the term "truth-functional"). In particular the rule of detachment, "If A and (if A, then B) have been asserted, B may be asserted as well," is easily shown to correspond to a tautology, and hence to lead invariably to true conclusions from true premises, if the statements in the object-language of the form "If p, then q" are interpreted as material implications.

It is, however, obvious that conditional statements expressing causal connections are not intended as material implications. "If you jump out of the window, you will be killed," construed as material implication, would be just as true as "If you jump out of the window, you will feel better" provided the warning was heeded, for, as is easily seen from the above definition, any material implication with a false antecedent is true. Clearly the connection between antecedent and consequent, here, is stronger than the truth-functional one; that is, although "It is not the case that p and not q" follows from "If p were the case, q would be the case," it does not in turn entail the latter, the subjunctive conditional. On the other hand, causal connections are, as we have seen, weaker than *analytic* connections, since we cannot discover them just by reflecting on the meanings of words and applying formal logic. It happens occasionally that the subjunctive mood is used to express an analytic connection, as in "If she were a widow, she would have been married at least once," but as a rule the connection is synthetic. Now, the majority of contemporary philosophers of science who apply symbolic logic for the clarification of scientific concepts hold that subjunctive conditionals[1] expressing causal connections are, nevertheless, analyzable by means of the truth-functional language of *Principia Mathematica* provided it is supplemented with the metalinguistic term "formally deducible" or "logically true"—or "analytic" in a somewhat broader sense. Let us see whether that position is tenable.

As we have seen, the antecedent that ordinary causal talk focuses on as the "cause" of a specific effect is almost never a sufficient condition for the effect. The actual fulfillment of certain other conditions is usually presupposed by the speaker; for example, the warning "If you jump out of the window, you will be killed" presupposes, among other things, a hard pavement and the absence of a safe net held out by firemen. This suggests the following analysis of "If a had happened (were to happen), then b would have resulted (would result)": there are conditions C that were fulfilled when and where a is supposed to have happened (will be fulfilled when and where a is supposed to happen) and there is a true generalization G such that "b happens at $t + dt$" is deducible from "a happens at t and conditions C are fulfilled at t and G." The weakest generalization that would enable such a deduction is "whenever an event exactly like a happens at a time and place where conditions C are fulfilled, it is followed by an event like b." But such a generalization may not be supported by direct instantial evidence; it may be accepted because it follows from a more comprehensive gen-

1. A subjunctive conditional may be asserted without presupposing that its antecedent is false. The subjunctive mood is often used to express suspension of judgment as to the truth-value of the assumption, as when a *strategy* is worked out. For this reason the contemporary use of "counterfactual" as initiated by N. Goodman is rather too broad, but we follow it here, since the reader is likely to encounter it in the literature anyway.

eralization for which there is instantial evidence. Thus we might have good grounds for asserting, "If this piece of iron were heated, it would expand," even if no iron objects had ever been heated, provided the law of thermal expansion had been confirmed by observing that other metals behaved in accordance with it. This point is important because the question is sometimes raised how a counterfactual statement whose false antecedent describes a *unique* event can be empirically confirmed at all. I can easily establish "If that piece of butter had been left on the stove (while the latter was hot), it would have melted" even though that particular piece of butter has been irretrievably consumed, by subjecting a very similar piece of butter to the same conditions. But it is far different with a historical counterfactual such as "If Chamberlain had not appeased Hitler by signing the pact of 'nonaggression' that betrayed Czechoslovakia, Hitler would not have dared invade Poland so soon." For history does not record any other case of closely similar appeasement resulting in closely similar aggression. Still, it should be noted that whereas every event is unique in the trivial sense that the *numerically* same event cannot recur, no event is unique in the sense that it is impossible to abstract a class of events that contains it along with others that more or less resemble it. And if a wider generalization about such a class of similar events seems sufficiently warranted, the counterfactual can be asserted with some warrant provided the presupposed conditions are sufficiently like the conditions mentioned by the generalization.

Our logical difficulties, however, are not yet over; indeed, they have only begun. For how is G to be formulated? In the truth-functional language that is favored by most symbolic logicians, "All cases of A are cases of B" is rendered as $(x) (Ax \supset Bx)$, which reads "There is no case of A that is not a case of B." But if true generalizations of this sort are admitted, then our analysis will justify counterfactuals that everybody recognizes as absurd. Suppose that the window from which a lunatic threatens to jump is on the fourth floor of an insane asylum and that nobody ever actually jumps from a window on the fourth floor of an insane asylum. The *formal* implication—as Russell called generalized material implications—"Anybody who jumps from a fourth-floor window of an insane asylum feels better thereafter" will then be true simply because there are no instances of its antecedent. And it is easily seen that with this choice of a true G our analysis would justify the counterfactual (addressed to the lunatic) "If you were to jump from this window, you would feel better." Further, that a formal implication is not what one intends to assert when one asserts a *lawlike* generalization —as we shall call an inductively confirmable generalization on the basis of which predictions are made and which, if true, expresses a *law of nature*—is evident from the following consideration. Suppose I asserted "If wood were denser than water, it would not float," and were contradicted by one ignorant of physics: "No, if wood were denser than water, it would still float." Even if he were right, the proposition he asserted would at any rate be incompatible with the proposition he contradicted. But the corresponding formal implications are perfectly compatible; indeed, they are both true, for since there is no wood that is denser than water, it is equally true to say "There is no wood that is denser than water and that floats" and to say "There is no wood that is denser than water and that does not float."

B. THE PROBLEM OF THE "SQUARE OF OPPOSITION"

Whatever our final analysis of the concept "lawlike generalization" may turn out to be, it is clear that "All A are B" is lawlike only if it is incompatible with "No A are B." The former generalization warrants inferences from "x is an A" to "x is a B," the latter warrants inference from "x is an A" to "x is not a B," and such rules of inference are in obvious conflict. This incompatibility holds in the Aristotelian "square of opposition" (see Figure 15.1) where, for fixed subject- and

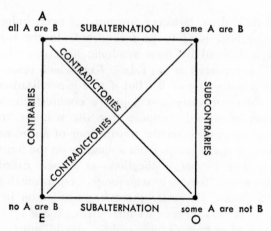

Figure 15.1   The square of opposition.

predicate-classes A and B, the universal affirmative (the A-proposition) and the universal negative (the E-proposition) cannot both be true.

The rules of Aristotelian logic, however, break down for universal propositions about empty classes, such as "All trespassers will be prosecuted," "all bodies that are not acted on by external forces are either at rest or move with uniform velocity," "All perfectly rational humans never regret any of their actions." This is easily seen once we ask ourselves whether, according to Aristotelian logic, "All *A* are *B*" or "No *A* are *B*" is false in case there are no *A*'s. One or the other must be false, according to that logic. But if the former is false, then its contradictory, "Some *A* are not *B*," must be true, and if the latter is false, then its contradictory, "Some *A* are *B*," must be true. Either one of these particular propositions, however, entails the existence of *A*'s, which contradicts our hypothesis. The Aristotelian square of opposition, therefore, becomes inconsistent once we introduce universal propositions about empty classes: in order to solve the above contradiction, we must either (*a*) allow that corresponding *A*- and *E*-propositions may both be true, or (*b*) reject the inference from the negation of a universal proposition to a particular proposition, or (*c*) deny that a proposition of the form "Some *A* are ..." necessarily asserts that there are *A*'s.

The course taken by modern symbolic logic was (*a*). Universal propositions are interpreted as denying that there are objects that are members of the subject-class without being members of the predicate-class; that is, "All *A* are *B*" is interpreted to mean "There are no *A*'s that are not *B*'s," and "No *A* are *B*" is taken to mean "There are no *A*'s that are *B*'s." (Universal propositions so interpreted are generalized material implications; following Russell they are called "formal" implications, though they need not be *formally* true.) If there are no *A*'s altogether, it follows that there are no *A*'s of any kind, neither such as are *B*'s nor such as are not *B*'s; hence any universal proposition about an empty class, whether affirmative or negative, becomes automatically true. Let us call this interpretation the *Boolian*, after Boole, the founder of the algebra of classes, and let us see what becomes of Newton's first law of motion on the Boolian interpretation. Since there are no bodies that are entirely isolated, according to Newton's own law of universal gravitation, the first law of motion is clearly true, simply because its subject-class is empty. But unfortunately it would then be equally true to say "All isolated bodies move with a constant acceleration." Similarly, whereas according to Aristotelian logic we cannot assert that all trespassers will be prosecuted without implying that someone will trespass, the Boolian interpretation makes it impossible for us to assert truly that all trespassers will be prosecuted without also asserting truly that no trespassers will be prosecuted, in case there are no trespassers.

Aristotelian logic was not designed to deal with assertions about empty classes, and since counterfactual generalizations, such as the first law of motion, are indispensable to modern science, a logic that is to be adequate for science has to emancipate itself from Aristotle and his satellites. But as regards counterfactual generalizations, Boolian algebra is just as useless. The point is simply that "For any x, if x *were A*, then x *would be B*" is not synonymous with "There is no x such that x is A and x is not B" (the Russellian formal implication, equivalent to the Boolean equation: $A \cdot \overline{B} = 0$). A contemporary Oxford analyst, P. F. Strawson, has attempted a rehabilitation of the Aristotelian square of opposition by distinguishing between what a speaker *asserts* and what he *presupposes* when he makes a statement. Suppose I see a "baby-sitting" woman in the park with three handsome children, and believing her to be the mother, say to my friend, "All of her children are handsome." If in fact she has no children at all, this proposition is true according to the Boolian interpretation which is favored by symbolic logicians. But Strawson points out correctly that one would not normally call this statement true, nor false; since the speaker presupposed, erroneously, that the subject-class has members, the question of truth or falsehood does not arise. Similarly, if a plain man were asked by a logician whether "All unicorns live in the Bronx zoo" is true or false, his most likely reaction would be "Why, there are no unicorns, so how can you sensibly ask whether all of them live in the Bronx zoo?" And Strawson is right in saying that the square of opposition can be rescued as perfectly consistent if we assume that the nonemptiness of the subject-class is presupposed whenever one asserts any of the four kinds of "categorical" propositions, whether universal or particular. Yet, this valuable distinction between asserting and presupposing does not immediately solve our problem. The subjunctive form "For any x, if x were A, then x would be B" may be wholly noncommittal on the question of the existence of A's, as when an instructor announces reassuringly to his class, "If any of you makes an A in the final examination, he will surely pass the course." It could not be said that the speaker here presupposes that at least one student will make an A, nor that he presupposes the opposite. And in those cases where a universal subjunctive conditional is strictly counterfactual, it is just the emptiness, not the nonemptiness, of the subject-class that is presupposed.

C. THE PROBLEM
OF EXPLICIT DEFINITION
OF DISPOSITION CONCEPTS

The pervasiveness of counterfactual expressions in scientific discourse should be evident from the frequency of dispositional statements—such statements as "Sugar is soluble in water," "The melting point of iron is

2790°F," "The electric field strength at space-time point (x, y, z, t) equals F dynes per unit charge," "Rubber is highly elastic," "All metals are electrical conductors," "Wood floats on water," "This person has a high I.Q.," and so on. Dispositional statements are condensed counterfactual conditionals: "Any sample of sugar would dissolve, if placed in water," "Any sample of iron would melt, under standard pressure, if it were heated up to 2790°F," "If a unit charge were placed at (x, y, z, t), it would be acted on by a force equal to F dynes," "If a piece of rubber were stretched, it would return to its original size and shape after the stretching force was removed," and so on. It is often asserted that modern science differs from Aristotelian science in that it formulates laws of the observable behavior of things that are useful for predictions instead of offering pseudo-explanations of the observed facts in terms of occult "powers" ascribed to things. Such pseudo-explanations were ridiculed by Molière, the French playwright, when he had a learned physician "explain" that opium addicts tend to fall asleep after eating opium because opium has a "sleep-inducing power." We cannot now enter into the question of what a scientific explanation is (cf. Chapter 18), but we certainly cannot agree that modern science does not ascribe powers, as distinct from manifest states, to things. It is true that positivistically inclined scientists, such as Mach and Hertz, tried to eliminate the concept of *force* from physics on the ground that it is an anthropomorphic projection into nature of feelings of muscular tension, as devoid of explanatory value as the Aristotelian concept of the "natural" place of a body, i.e., the place where it strives to be. But even a forceless system of mechanics cannot do without the concept of *mass*, and the mass of a body is, after all, its power to resist changes of its mechanical state. If the word "power" has too animistic a flavor, let us replace it by the more technical term "disposition" in the generalized sense in which it is used in contemporary philosophy of science. A body's mass is a dispositional property in the sense that to ascribe a particular mass to a body is primarily to assert that in such and such situations it would undergo a specified acceleration.

Our present problem is the analysis of such dispositional statements. Offhand this seems to be no problem at all. To say, for example, that sugar is soluble in water is just to say that *if* at any time a lump of sugar were immersed in water, *then* it would dissolve therein. But suppose I said, "That thing is soluble in water," without characterizing the thing pointed at as sugar. This statement has the form "x is D," where x ranges, not over kinds or species, but over particular things that may belong to this or that kind, and D represents a particular disposition ascribed to x. The definition schema for "x is D" is, idiomatically, simply "If Ox, then Rx," where Ox means "x is subjected to operation O," and

Rx means "x reacts in fashion R." To be more accurate, we should introduce a time variable, since a thing may have a disposition at one time and not at another time; for example, a body may become electrically charged, or magnetized, an organism may acquire a habit and lose it, a wire may lose its elasticity because it is overstrained. Our tentative definition schema thus becomes

$$D(x, t) = O(x, t) \longrightarrow R(x, t)$$

where the arrow represents causal implication, a counterfactual if-then connection that is neither truth-functional nor analytic.

Now, since by a causal implication we mean a synthetic connection that is stronger than material implication, we must define the arrow, explicitly or implicitly, in such a way that "$p \longrightarrow q$" entails "$p \supset q$." But then "$O(x, t) \longrightarrow R(x, t)$" cannot be rendered idiomatically as "If x were O-ed at t, x would R at t (or at $t + dt$)" or as "Subjecting x to O at t would cause reaction R at t (or at $t + dt$)." To see this, just recall that the events we identify as causes are rarely sufficient conditions of their effects, that in asserting a causal counterfactual we usually presuppose that certain other conditions besides the "triggering" events are fulfilled. Indeed, any statement of the form "x is immersed in water at $t \longrightarrow x$ dissolves in water at t" is obviously false, because if immersion of a solid thing in water were sufficient to cause its dissolution, it would be easy to cause wooden, iron, or glassy objects to dissolve just by immersing them in water. Our analysis must be restricted in such a way that we can say that sugar is soluble in water but not wood, that rubber is highly elastic but not glass, that hungry rats with the relevant learning background are likely to make the response needed to secure food but not hungry rats that have not been trained nor well-trained rats that are not hungry, and so on. And the restriction must concern primarily the *kind* of thing whose exposure to O leads invariably to R. Formally:

1. $D(x, t) = x$ has at time t some property, P, such that for any y and for any t,

$$[P(y, t) \text{ and } O(y, t)] \longrightarrow R(y, t)$$

But we must investigate further the sort of properties that are admissible values of the variable "P." In the case of solubility, the relevant properties seem to be *kind-properties*, such as "sugar," "gold"; similarly, when we ascribe to a solid thing the capacity to float, we mean that it is of a natural kind, K—such as wood, or cork—such that any instance of K would float when immersed in water. In this way dispositional properties seem intimately tied to natural kinds; that is, we ascribe dispositions to things just to the extent that we classify them into kinds. At once, however, two difficulties appear:

(a) It hardly makes sense to suppose that the *same* thing could at one time be an instance of kind K and at another time not be an instance of K. We cannot say "This animal is *now* a dog" as we can say "This animal is now eating," we cannot say "This is *now* sugar" as we can say "This is now being dropped into the coffee," we cannot say "This flower is *now* a rose" as we can say "This flower is now in full bloom." It is true that physicists talk of transmutation of elements in processes of nuclear fission, such as the transmutation of hydrogen into helium on the sun, but such a statement is meaningful in the context of a theory postulating microentities and microevents, whereas what is here under analysis is pretheoretical discourse about things and their kinds, as in qualitative chemistry. It should be clear, then, that the time variable in "$P(y, t)$" is out of place if the sort of property represented by P is a kind-property, such as wood, gold, sugar. If so, the time variable must be omitted from the definiendum, $D(x, t)$, as well. Indeed, this result is perfectly consistent with ordinary language, for just as it is odd to say "This match is *now* made of wood" so it is odd to say "This match is *now* capable of floating on water," just as it is odd to say "This thing is *now* gold" so it is odd to say "This thing is *now* soluble in aqua regia," and so on. Dispositions that are defined in terms of kind-properties may, accordingly, be called *time-independent*, and the modified definition schema looks as follows:

2. $D(x) = x$ has some kind-property, P, such that for any y and for any t, $[P(y)$ and $O(y, t)] \longrightarrow R(y, t)$.

(b) We seem to be caught in a logical circle because we are defining "disposition" in terms of "kind-property," whereas it seems impossible to explain kind-properties without invoking dispositions. Thus one of the tests one might perform in order to determine whether a thing is sugar is just the solubility test; one of the tests for wood is whether the thing floats; a chemist might determine whether a solid substance is mercury by heating it and seeing whether it eventually turns red; and so on. Indeed, the vast majority of properties in terms of which material substances are identified are dispositional. Even colors, as attributed to physical objects, are dispositions to produce certain, not further analyzable, visual impressions in an organism under specified conditions of perception. Nevertheless, this is not a genuine difficulty; the objection that the definition of "disposition" in terms of "kind-property" is circular rests on a confusion. For, from the fact that specific kind-properties are defined in terms of specific dispositions it does not follow that the general predicate "kind-property" is defined in terms of the general predicate "disposition." We might define a kind-property as a property, P, of particular things such that "x is P at time t" is meaningless—as a property, in other words, with respect to which a thing cannot meaning-fully be said to change—and such that many predictions, including predictions of how the thing would interact with other things under specified conditions, are derivable from a statement of the form "x is P."[2] And since the word "disposition" does not appear at all in this definition, the definition of "disposition" in terms of "kind-property" is not circular.

Time-dependent dispositions, such as "magnetic," "highly elastic," "irritable," and all sorts of learned response dispositions of animals and people, are the sorts of dispositions adequately defined by schema 1, but the property-variable in terms of which they are defined does not range over kind-properties. To judge from the tendency of theoretical science, the changeable properties anticipated by ascriptions of time-dependent dispositions are *structural microproperties*. Locke already knew this when he defined the secondary qualities of things, such as colors and temperatures, as their powers to produce certain kinds of "ideas" (sense-impressions) *by virtue of* the primary qualities of their constituent molecules, i.e., mass, size, and shape of the molecules, their relative positions, and their relative motions. A blue surface differs from a red surface, according to physical theory, in reflecting light of dif-ferent wavelength, and this again results—nobody knows why—in dif-ferent visual impressions when the light waves reach normal eyes. But this difference in reflective capacity must be due to a difference in micro-structure. Again, the difference between hot and cold, considered as dispositional states of tangible things (including liquids and gases) rela-tive to sentient organisms, is correlated by the kinetic theory of heat with differences of molecular motion. An electrically charged body is assumed to be a body with either a surplus (negative charge) or a deficit (positive charge) of electrons, by virtue of which it attracts a body of opposite charge and repels one of like charge.

In psychology, there is the tendency already mentioned (p. 270) to assume that brain modifications are correlated with acquired response dispositions. Perhaps dispositional statements may be said to mark a transition from purely empirical science that gathers reliable correlations without attempting a theoretical unification to theoretical, unifying sci-ence, because in subsuming an observed regularity under a disposition concept one anticipates an explanation in terms of the intrinsic, struc-tural microproperties of the things involved.

This holds also for ascriptions of time-independent dispositions to

2. "Kinds" in this sense may be artificial as well as natural. For example, "has good mileage" is a disposition, since to say that a car has good mileage is to say that it consumes a relatively small quantity of gasoline *if* driven a mile. And the kind-property to which it is relative is the property of being a car.

observable kinds, such as "All sugar is water-soluble," "All iron melts, under standard pressure, at 2790°F." For consider the analysis, in accordance with schema 1, of the former generalization: For any x, if x is sugar, then there is a P such that x is P and such that anything that is P dissolves when immersed in water. If in this context P represented a kind-property, would not "sugar" be the most likely candidate? But such a substitution would yield the simple generalization "Anything that is sugar would dissolve at any time when it was immersed in water," which lacks the anticipatory feature we take to be characteristic of dispositional talk. And this would suggest, moreover, that whereas a property-variable is involved in singular dispositional statements it is absent from generalized dispositional statements (i.e., dispositional statements about kinds). But it is hard to believe that the analysis of D in the context "x is D" differs from the analysis of D in the context "For any x, if x is K (where K is a kind-property), then x is D." It is, therefore, plausible to assume that in making an assertion such as "All sugar is water-soluble" we are not just generalizing the observed regularity that things with the secondary qualities of sugar dissolve when immersed in a liquid with the secondary qualities of water, but express our belief that this empirical law admits of theoretical explanation in terms of the microstructures of sugar and water and indirectly confirmable postulates about the interactions of their constituent particles.

A special problem of analysis may seem to be presented by quantitative dispositions, such as mass. Certainly part of what we mean by a statement such as "The mass of x is 2 pounds" is "If x were weighed on a spring scale, the scale pointer would be deflected to the point marked 2 pounds." But since the event of weighing a body on a spring scale is not sufficient to bring about such a deflection—otherwise any body could be argued to weigh 2 pounds—some property distinguishing x from bodies whose mass is not 2 pounds must be implicitly referred to. And is not that property just the property of having a mass of 2 pounds? If so, the explanation "x deflected the scale pointer to the point marked 2 pounds because the mass of x is 2 pounds" should be on a par with the explanation "This white solid thing dissolved when immersed in water because it is sugar." And one may feel that the former explanation, unlike the latter, is purely tautological since whatever else we may mean by ascribing a particular mass to a manipulable body, we at least mean that it would deflect the pointer of a spring scale a definite amount. Yet, this again is not a genuine difficulty once we recognize the multiplicity of criteria for empirical concepts we have already had occasion to call attention to (cf. p. 33). After all, if the former explanation were tautological, so would the latter be, since undoubtedly solubility-in-water is one of the criteria of sugarhood. But when we accept it as an explanation, we think of other manifestations of sugarhood, such as tasting sweet when touched by a healthy tongue. Just so, we shift to a different possible test of mass when we explain that the scale pointer behaved as it did because the spring was stretched by a body whose mass equals 2 pounds.

To summarize: When we ascribe a qualitative disposition to a particular thing we anticipate a causal law of the form "Anything of the kind K reacts in fashion R to operation (or stimulation) O." When we ascribe that same disposition to all the members of K we anticipate, in a sort of groping for theoretical explanation, that K is characterized by some microstructural property (at least this follows from the assumption that the form of the analysis of D is the same for atomic statements and for generalizations). The explanation of an observed regularity in terms of a relatively constant quantitative disposition may involve anticipation of a microstructural property—examples: the amount of electrical charge on a body, degree of magnetization, degree of elasticity—or it may, as in the discussed case of mass, refer to alternative "manifestations" of the same quantitative disposition. Only the latter can, of course, be intended by a quantitative dispositional statement about ultimate particles, such as "The mass of an electron (at rest) equals 9.11×10^{-28}gram." Similarly, when a physicist explains that a body with a charge of Q electrostatic units is acted on by a force of F dynes at space-time point (x, y, z, t) *because* the electric field intensity there equals F/Q dynes per unit charge, his explanation is not tautological, provided some alternative test of electrical field strength is anticipated.

D. PROBABILISTIC DISPOSITIONS

We have seen that, since the operation of testing a thing for a disposition D is never by itself a sufficient cause of the response we take as indicative of D, a property variable must be introduced into explicit definitions of disposition concepts. This variable may be said to range over *intrinsic* properties in a sense not easy to analyze with precision. In the case of time-independent dispositions, they are intrinsic in the sense that one could not without contradiction suppose that the *same* thing did not have that property; it is for this reason that such expressions as "This is now salt," "This is now water" would sound odd. If to a glass of water we add some syrup, we might, of course, say, "This liquid is not pure water any more," but what this means is "This glass does not contain pure water any more," not that the same mass of liquid that a moment ago was pure water is now diluted syrup.

In the case of dispositions that a thing may acquire and lose, the intrinsic properties may be roughly defined as those which determine, during the time under consideration, a variety of responses to a variety of possible stimulations. In this respect they differ, in spite of their time-dependence, from transient relations of the thing to its changing environments. The latter were represented in our definition schema by the symbol "$O(x, t)$." But the definition schema is oversimplified in the following respect: even the conjunction of O and some intrinsic property P is not, as a rule, a strictly sufficient condition for the response R. To say that turpentine is inflammable is to say that the chemical constitution of turpentine is such that raising it to high temperature will cause it to burn, but we know that even at very high temperature it would not burn if not enough oxygen were present. To say that a thing is objectively red is to say that the microstructure of its surface is such that looking at it when it is illumined by good white light would cause a visually normal observer to see red, but we know that it still would not look red if it were looked at through a discoloring medium. Again, it is no contradiction at all to suppose that a light iron particle placed in the vicinity of a highly magnetized body is not attracted to the latter, because it is deflected by some other force.

The point is simply that we are rarely, if ever, in a position to claim justifiably that we know *all* the environmental conditions that, together with some intrinsic property, are jointly sufficient for a given response. It is for this reason that a determinist, i.e., one who believes that for every event there is a strictly sufficient condition of its occurrence, whether we know it or not, will provide his definitions of disposition terms with the escape clause "other things being equal." Even a behavior theorist who frowns on the subjective connotation of a term like "hungry" as irrelevant to science, and who accordingly wants to introduce it into scientific psychology as a disposition term, will admit that it is no contradiction to suppose that a given rat who has been deprived of food for a long time and has been "trained" on the path leading to food is now hungry and nevertheless does not respond to the stimuli in the appropriate way; there are all sorts of inhibiting variables, such as anxiety, some of them unknown, that might frustrate not only the rat but also the predicting psychologist. At any rate, what holds for rats holds to an even greater extent for humans.

Now, if a scientist does not want to commit himself to such a sweeping article of faith as strict determinism, the appropriate method of taking such ignorance of determining conditions into account is to substitute for the escape clause "other things being equal" a *probability implication.* If by "*x* has *D*" he means the weaker proposition that *x* has some intrinsic property, *P,* such that anything that has *P* and that is subjected to test operation O under conditions C is *likely* to react in fashion R, then he can without contradiction maintain that x has D and whatever intrinsic property is correlated with D although there are cases where x failed to respond in fashion R to O under conditions C. Although this is not the place for a logical analysis of behavior theory (cf. Chapter 20, B), it is appropriate to mention that most behavior theorists treat "intervening variables" such as "hunger" as just such probabilistic dispositions. That is, the behavior scientist can safely make the statistical prediction that a hungry rat that has undergone the relevant conditioning will, in a series of exposures to a choice between a path leading to food and another path leading to, say, a sex partner, take the former path more frequently, the frequency increasing with both the deprivation time and the number of reinforcements already experienced as a result of this kind of response. He does not presume to predict with certainty what the rat's response in a particular case will be.

Again, when we ascribe to a coin a particular probability of falling heads we ascribe to it a probabilistic disposition. According to the frequency theories of von Mises and Reichenbach, which we have discussed in detail, "The probability of throwing heads with this coin is ½" means the relative frequency of heads in a very long sequence of tosses of this coin will be approximately ½. But what if after a few tosses the coin falls down a drain and is never found again? Is the probability statement then refuted? Or is it meaningless if no long sequence of trials with the object to which the probability is assigned ever comes off? A little reflection will convince the reader that neither of these alternatives agrees with his meaning when he makes a statistical probability statement. If the inference from "x jumps from the roof of a house of a height of 40 feet" to "x will be hurt" can be warranted, in the sense that there is good evidence for the corresponding counterfactual, even if nobody else ever jumped from the roof of a house of that height, then likewise an inference of the form "x is A, therefore x is probably B" may be warranted, by analogical reasoning, though the class A have just one or very few members. What we mean is not that this coin has been tossed a large number of times and has come up heads approximately half the time, nor that it will exhibit approximately that proportion of heads in a future long sequence of tosses, but that such *would* be its statistical behavior *if* it *were* tossed a great many times.

Yet, in spite of the various qualifications we have made in order to achieve a plausible method of explicitly defining disposition concepts— the latest consisting in a loosening of the connection between the antecedents and the consequents of the defining implications—it must in the end be admitted that probabilistic reduction sentences[3] do more

3. The concept of "reduction sentence" was explained in Chapter 2, F.

justice to the multiple anchorage of dispositions in mutually correlated tests than explicit definitions, however sophisticated. Consider again our simple example of the body weighing 2 pounds. Having weighed it several times on a beam balance and having observed the sum of the standard weights required for equilibrium to be 2 pounds each time, we conclude that the body has a property—namely, a weight of 2 pounds— such that any body with the same property would probably behave similarly in a similar situation. But it does not strictly follow that the true weight of the body is 2 pounds, for some source of systematic error, such as a magnetic field acting on the standard weights but not on the weighed body, may have falsified the results. Indeed, if a physicist subsequently discovered that the body did not weigh 2 pounds on a spring scale at the same location as the beam balance, it is unlikely that he would declare Hooke's law refuted; he would probably suspect that the one or the other set of measurements were spoiled by some unknown source of systematic error. The point is that the induction that similar tests would probably yield similar results may be perfectly justified and still it does not *analytically* follow that the indicated weight is the body's true weight.

Now, let us take a psychological example: belief considered as a dispositional state of a human being. In saying that a person's belief that the glass before him on the table contains milk is a *dispositional* state we imply that he need not be thinking about the proposition that the glass contains milk at the moment and still may be said to believe it at the same time. It would, indeed, sound odd were one to say that the belief was *acquired* the moment his mind happened to turn to that proposition. The statement "He believes the glass to contain milk" may, therefore, be provisionally analyzed by some such counterfactual as "If he were asked, in his own language, whether the glass contained milk, he would probably reply 'Why, yes,' or 'Why, of course.'" Moving a little closer to our definition schema for probabilistic dispositions, we obtain "He is in a brain state—resulting from relevant associations of perceptions in the past—such that anybody in that same brain state would probably reply affirmatively to the question in a language he understood, whether the glass contained milk." The qualification "probably" is unavoidable because we can easily think of conditions under which a person holding that belief might nevertheless respond negatively or just fail to respond: there might be a sudden desire to deceive, or to be facetious, or the question might be shrugged off as not deserving an answer. But even supposing him to be in a brain state B such that most people in state B respond affirmatively to such a question most of the time, does it analytically follow that he believes the proposition? It does not, because it cannot be analytically inferred that he would satisfy all the other tests for the same disposition. As a matter of empirical fact, the verbal test just described will usually correlate with what might be called the surprise test of belief: if he tasted the liquid and found that it did not taste like milk, he would be surprised. But there is no logical contradiction in supposing that the man would fail to be surprised in experiencing, say, a taste of sugary water, though he believed the proposition according to the verbal test. And if so, he and his interrogator might well doubt whether he really believed the proposition.

The use of a complex disposition concept, one might say, presupposes an empirical correlation of various tests. If in a given instance they do not correlate, one is either too baffled to draw any conclusion, or concludes that at least one of the tests is not reliable. It is this feature of multiply anchored disposition concepts that a neat explicit definition in terms of one selected test conceals.

Selected Readings

Burks, A. W., "The Logic of Causal Propositions," *Mind*, 1951.

———, "Dispositional Statements," *Philosophy of Science*, 1955.

Chisholm, R., "The Contrary-to-Fact Conditional," *Mind*, 1946. [Reprinted in H. Feigl and W. Sellars (eds), *Readings in Philosophical Analysis* (New York, 1949).]

———, "Law Statements and Counterfactual Inference," *Analysis*, 1955.

Diggs, B. J., "Counterfactual Conditionals," *Mind*, 1952.

Goodman, N., "The Problem of Counterfactual Conditionals," *Journal of Philosophy*, 1947. [Reprinted in L. Linsky (ed.), *Semantics and the Philosophy of Language* (Urbana, Ill., 1952.)]

———, *Fact, Fiction and Forecast* (Cambridge, Mass., 1955).

Kneale, W., "Natural Laws and Contrary-to-Fact Conditionals," in M. Macdonald (ed.), *Philosophy and Analysis* (Oxford, 1954).

Lewis, C. I., *An Analysis of Knowledge and Valuation* (La Salle, Ill., 1946), chap. 8.

Nagel, E., *The Structure of Science* (New York, 1961), chap. 4.

Pap, A., "Disposition Concepts and Extensional Logic," in H. Feigl, M. Scriven, and G. Maxwell (eds.), *Minnesota Studies in the Philosophy of Science* (Minneapolis, 1958), Vol. II.

Popper, K. R., "A Note on Natural Laws and So-Called Contrary-to-Fact Conditionals," *Mind*, 1949.

Ryle, G., *The Concept of Mind* (New York, 1949), chap. 5.

Sellars, W., "Counterfactuals, Dispositions and the Causal Modalities," in H. Feigl, M. Scriven, and G. Maxwell (eds.), *Minnesota Studies in the Philosophy of Science* (Minneapolis, 1958), Vol. II.

Storer, T., "On Defining 'Soluble,'" *Analysis*, 1951.

CHAPTER 16

What Is a Law of Nature?

A. LAWLIKE GENERALIZATIONS AND COUNTERFACTUAL INFERENCE

In the last two chapters we have attempted to elucidate the causal and counterfactual meaning of "if-then." We have argued, in the spirit of Hume, that a belief in the existence of a logically contingent law, whether strict or probabilistic, is involved in counterfactual conditionals such as "If the match were struck (with the right amount of force), it would light." But what exactly is the if-then connection asserted by a lawlike generalization, i.e., a generalization that, if assumed to be true, is said to express a law of nature? Causal implication, we said, is stronger than material implication because it rules certain kinds of events out as *impossible;* it does not just deny their actual occurrence. On the other hand, it is weaker than analytic implication. Can we say anything more positive about the relevant senses of "(causally) impossible" and "(causally) necessary"?

An intuitive criterion of lawlikeness proposed by both Nelson Goodman and Roderick Chisholm[1] is that a lawlike generalization supports counterfactual inferences. Suppose I come upon a fruit that looks like an

1. N. Goodman, "The Problem of Counterfactual Conditionals," reprinted in L. Linsky, ed., *Semantics and the Philosophy of Language* (Urbana, Ill.: University of Illinois Press, 1952) and in N. Goodman, *Fact, Fiction, and Forecast* (Cambridge: Harvard University Press, 1955), chap. 1; R. Chisholm, "The Contrary-to-Fact Conditional," reprinted in H. Feigl and W. Sellars, *Readings in Philosophical Analysis* (New York: Appleton-Century-Crofts, Inc., 1949).

orange but then turns out to taste like tangerines. If my friend insisted that, just the same, it is an orange, it would be quite proper for me to exclaim, "But if it were an orange, it would taste like an orange!" We do not, in such a case, admit that the generalization "All oranges taste like oranges" has been refuted, for we have such confidence in it that we refuse application of the term "orange" to a thing that does not taste like an orange. This does not mean that the generalization is merely analytic of the meaning of "orange," as long as we can conceive of circumstances under which we would admit that a thing that does not taste like most things that are normally called oranges still *is* an orange. Suppose the thing before us not only satisfies the visual and tactual tests of orangehood but also grew on an orange tree and has just the same anatomy as fruits growing on orange trees; in that case one may be strongly inclined to admit that there are "freak" oranges that do not taste like "normal" oranges.

Similarly, if a physicist came upon an apparently freely falling body whose acceleration fluctuated considerably, he would say, "This body cannot be falling freely; if it were falling under the sole influence of gravity, it would fall with constant acceleration; there must be some disturbing force that is responsible for this deviation from the norm." Again, this does not mean that he treats the law of freely falling bodies as an irrefutable analytic statement, as a definition of "freely falling body." As a responsible scientist, he would search for disturbing forces; that failing, he might examine the body to see whether in some conceivably relevant respects it differed from the bodies whose gravitational behavior was normal, and whatever the outcome of this examination might be he would either have to abandon the law of freely falling bodies in its present form or else would have to abandon some other physical principles that are logically involved. If the abnormally behaving body had, say, a chemical property P, and other bodies with P were found to fall similarly, he might restrict the law to "All freely falling bodies fall with constant acceleration unless they have P," even though this course would compel him to abandon the very important principle that the effect of gravity on a given body does not depend on any intrinsic properties (but only on the location) of that body. And if no relevant difference were discovered, the law could not even partially be saved by restricting its scope, unless one or the other of the following assumptions were given up instead: (1) That the clocks employed in measuring the time lapses corresponding to the successive positions were accurate. He might assume that unknown forces disturbed, not the falling body, but the clock (even though the postulate of causality would not allow him to rest satisfied with such an ad hoc assumption until the postulated "disturbers" were actually tracked down). (2) That the measuring rods employed in measuring the displacements were not rigid but contracted and expanded—again by forces unknown for the time being—so as to produce the appearance of fluctuating acceleration. The point is that unlike a simple analytic statement ("All freely falling bodies fall under the sole influence of gravity," for example) a physical law can be maintained under the pressure of apparently disconfirming evidence *only* by abandoning other factual assumptions that are logically involved in the process of testing it.

By contrast, if on examining the contents of my purse I announce, "All the coins in my purse are nickels," this statement, though universal in form, cannot support a counterfactual such as "If that coin—it looks like a dime from where I stand—were in my purse, it would be a nickel." It would be more natural to infer the counterfactual "If that coin were in my purse, then not all the coins in my purse would be nickels." Similarly, though it may be true that all the people who ever sat on a certain park bench as long as the park bench existed were redheads, this true universal statement could hardly support the counterfactual "If Cary Grant had been sitting on that park bench, he would have been a redhead"; the proper inference is rather "If Cary Grant had been sitting on that park bench, then not all the people who sat on it would have been redheads."

Although this intuitive test of lawlikeness of a generalization, as contrasted with merely *accidental* universality, has some surface appeal as a criterion, it obviously will not do as an *analysis* of lawlikeness. For, as we have seen, we need to invoke the concept "lawlike generalization" in order to explain how a counterfactual conditional can be asserted with warrant; hence it would be running around in a circle to define a lawlike generalization as a universal statement that warrants a counterfactual conditional. But even its value as a criterion of distinction is open to doubt. According to deductive logic, the premises "All A are B" and "x is an A" entail the conclusion "x is a B" in any case. Let us assume that the constants that may be substituted for x are just indexical signs, i.e., expressions that "point" or identify without characterizing the object, such as "that thing" or "the thing at place P at time t." Then the universal premise "All A are B," whether lawlike or not, entails any statement of the form "If x is an A, then x is a B." And if we assume that all A are B, we can justifiably assert "If x were an A, then necessarily x would be a B," the necessity being relative to that assumption.

Thus, if I have made quite certain that all the coins presently in my pocket are nickels, I am perfectly justified in asserting "If that object—whatever it may be—were a coin presently in my pocket, it would be a nickel," for the subjunctive mood here really expresses a logically necessary connection between "All the coins presently in my pocket are nickels" and "If that object is a coin presently in my pocket, then it is a nickel." To say "If that dime were in my pocket now, it would be a nickel" sounds paradoxical because in *characterizing* the object as a dime, I have already excluded its being a nickel, and then my statement suggests that by being transferred to my pocket the dime could be converted into a nickel. In inferring, on the contrary, ". . . , then not all the coins presently in my pocket would be nickels," I drop the assumption that all the coins presently in my pocket are nickels and perform the necessary deduction of the proposition "Some of the coins presently in my pocket are not nickels" from the supposed proposition "That dime is presently in my pocket." But surely there would be just the same justification for the counterfactual "If that dog were a raven, then some ravens would not be black," or "If the moon were a planet, then at least one planet would not revolve in an elliptical orbit around the sun." In each of these cases of inferring the negation of the universal statement "All *A* are *B*" from the counterfactual assumption the object of the counterfactual assumption is tacitly characterized by a property that is incompatible with *B*. And if this is permitted, the universal statement will, of course, be unable to support a counterfactual inference whether or not it be accidental. This holds as well for our example of Cary Grant and the redheads: if Cary Grant were just indexically identified, and all other knowledge about him—such as that he never sat on the park bench in question! —were suppressed, then one who had made sure that all the people who ever sat there were redheads would be perfectly justified in saying, "Well, if this man were one of those who sat there, he would be a redhead." The statement can have a paradoxical ring only for one who knows that Cary Grant's hair is not red and hence is puzzled by the suggestion of a causal connection between a man's hair color and his sitting accidentally on some park bench.

B. THE CRITERION OF UNRESTRICTED GENERALITY

Those who believe that empirical science can be adequately expressed in a language having the structure of *Principia Mathematica*, i.e., an object-language devoid of such modal expressions as "necessarily" and "possibly" (though the notion of logical consequence can be formulated in the meta-language), face a trying test of their faith. They must, of course, admit that lawlike generalizations cannot be simply equated with synthetic formal implications, nor can they invoke the criterion just criticized.

Some have proposed *unrestricted generality* as the mark of lawlikeness, in a sense to be explained forthwith.

Some universal statements seem to refer essentially to a particular object or to a particular place or to a particular time. Thus the examples discussed in the preceding section refer to a particular trouser pocket, a particular time, a particular park bench. Let us call expressions by which we designate particular objects, times, or places *individual constants,* and predicates by means of which we talk about repeatable qualities or relations and that are not defined in terms of individual constants *purely general* (for convenience, we shall extend this term also to physical functors). And an individual constant will be said to occur essentially in a statement *p* if it occurs in *p* and *p* is not translatable without change of meaning into a statement in which it does not occur. As a first approximation one might then define a lawlike generalization as a synthetic universal statement in which no individual constants occur essentially. It is true that with some luck we might always succeed in eliminating individual constants from the formulation of a mere coincidence because we might find that the particular in question could be *uniquely described* by means of purely general predicates. Thus, if it so happened that the park bench mentioned in our example was the only park bench ever sat upon by a toothless drunkard, we could formulate the following true formal implication: For any *x*, if there is a time at which *x* sits on a park bench on which a toothless drunkard sits at some time, then *x* is a redhead.[2] Nevertheless, it would not follow that the individual constant "that park bench" occurred inessentially in the original statement, for the supposition on the basis of which the individual constant was eliminated is factual, not analytic. If it is true, the purely general statement will have the same truth-value as the original statement, but not the same meaning.

On the other hand, there are many statements containing individual constants essentially that we would want to characterize as lawlike: (1) "All the ice cubes now in this refrigerator will turn into water when heated," (2) "All the planets continually revolve around the sun in elliptical orbits," (3) "All freely falling bodies near the earth fall with a constant acceleration of 32 ft/sec^2," (4) "All freely falling bodies near the earth fall with the same acceleration, regardless of differences of mass." In the case of (1) and (4), a deduction from universal statements that contain no individual constants at all is feasible, and this has suggested to some the definition of a *fundamental* lawlike statement as a synthetic universal statement in which no individual constants occur essentially, and of a *derivative* lawlike statement as one that is deducible from a fundamental lawlike statement though it contains individual constants essentially. The so-called laws of motion and the law of universal gravita-

2. "Sits" is here meant as the tenseless form of "to sit," not as the present tense.

tion, from which (4) is easily deducible, are obvious examples of fundamental lawlike statements in the defined sense: they do not mention any particular body nor any particular time or place. Yet, unfortunately, (2) and (3) are not lawlike at all according to this criterion. Kepler's first law of planetary motion follows from the axioms of Newtonian mechanics only on the assumption that the motion of a given planet is determined by solar attraction alone, but this assumption can be justified only by information concerning the relative masses of the bodies in the solar system: it is because the masses of the other planets are small in comparison with the mass of the sun that the gravitational attractions they exert are negligible and the problem of planetary revolution can be treated as a so-called "two-body problem." Without singular premises about the bodies in the solar system, therefore, (2) is not deducible from the general axioms of Newtonian mechanics. Similarly, in order to establish (3) deductively within the Newtonian theory, we have to know the earth's radius and mass.

A further difficulty facing this approach is that it is not entirely clear that the predicates and functors in the postulates of an empirically interpreted theory are purely general. Length is operationally defined in terms of the standard meter, weight in terms of the standard gram. These units of measurement can, of course, be indefinitely duplicated once an appropriate relation of equality has been defined, but unless some *particular* body were designated as "the" standard meter or "the" standard gram, measurement could not begin at all. One may perhaps reply that though a particular body must be conventionally chosen as the standard body, the scientist can choose between it and any other body that is in the relevant respect equal to it. Just so we can defend the claim that "red" is a purely general predicate though it must be ostensively defined in terms of some red particular or other, because it is not necessary that one refer to *this* rather than *that* red particular. But this line of defense would seem to break down for a very fundamental concept of mechanics: the concept of an inertial system. It is, of course, involved in the law of inertia: any isolated body is at rest or in uniform motion relative to any inertial system. It is also involved in the postulate of the special theory of relativity that the velocity of light (*in vacuo*) is the same in all inertial systems. What is meant by an inertial system? Three definitions may be considered:

1. A system relative to which an isolated body is either at rest or in uniform motion. The obvious objection to (1) is that it turns the law of inertia into an innocuous tautology, whereas it has in fact a significant predictive and explanatory use. It is used, for example, jointly with the law of freely falling bodies and the law of independence of forces to derive the parabolic trajectory of a projectile.

2. A system in which no inertial forces, such as centrifugal forces, manifest themselves. But the test of inertial force is (*a*) a subjective one, pulls or pushes experienced by an observer, such as the centrifugal outward pull on a merry-go-round, or the forward pull experienced by the passengers when the bus suddenly slows down. If so, the defined concept of inertial system would be inapplicable to physical systems in outer space, but the laws of motion *are* used in astronomy. Or else (*b*) inertial forces are *definitionally* inferred when the observed accelerations cannot be fitted into the formula "$F = m \cdot a$" on the assumption that only what Newton called "impressed" forces are involved. Thus, if a ball were rolled on the floor of a moving train in the direction of motion and at that very moment the train came to a sudden stop, the resultant acceleration of the ball would exceed the ratio of the force that was "impressed" on it to its mass; hence the action of an inertial force (due to an "absolute" acceleration of the train) could be inferred by just measuring the ball's total acceleration and noting that it exceeds the amount entailed by the second law of motion. Clearly, this definition of inertial force, and therewith inertial system, is again irreconcilable with the factual import of the laws of motion.

3. A system that is not accelerated relative to the fixed stars. This last definition is the one usually adopted by physicists, probably because it is "operational" and prevents the laws of motion from collapsing into idle tautologies. But since "the fixed stars" is an individual constant, "inertial system" is not, then, a purely general predicate, and the laws of motion, as well as the law of the constancy of the velocity of light in all inertial systems, would not be fundamental laws.

C. TEMPORAL INVARIABILITY

Some have contended that a law of nature is essentially a functional relation that remains constant in time. That nature is "uniform" means, on this view, just that there are relatively simple functional relations between physical variables that do not vary as time goes on. The type of law that has suggested this definition is, of course, a differential law of mathematical physics. Thus the law of gravitation expresses the acceleration of a gravitating body as a function of its distance from the attracting body: $d^2r/dt^2 = f(r)$. But it is not clear why the functional relations invariance in time should be deemed more "essential" than its invariance in space. When the law is fully stated, it says: For any body x that revolves around a central body of mass M under the sole influence of gravity emanating from that central body, no matter *where* in space the revolving motion occurs, and *for any time t*, if d^2r/dt^2 is the (gravitational) acceleration of x at t and r the simultaneous distance of x from the central body, then

$$d^2r/dt^2 = G \cdot M/r^2$$

In the terminology of symbolic logic, a universal quantifier binding a space-variable is just as essential for a complete statement of the law as a universal quantifier binding time-variable; otherwise one might ask, for example, whether this functional relation is meant to hold only for our solar system or for any region of space.

Again, it has been asserted that it is definitory of "law of nature" that the time-variable is not one of the arguments on which the function depends, that it does not occur "explicitly" in the equation though, of course, it may occur "implicitly" through the definitions of derivatives (such as acceleration). In our example, in order to calculate the planet's acceleration at a given moment the physicist must know the value of r at that moment but he need not know what time it is. But the time-variable does occur explicitly in the equations of motion that are derived from the differential equations by integration. Thus, consider the simplest case of a differential equation of classical dynamics, that describing a falling motion under a constant force:

$$\frac{d^2z}{dt^2} = g$$

Integration yields first:

$$\frac{dz}{dt} = g \cdot t + v_1$$

where v_1 is the velocity at an initial instant t_1—which may or may not be zero, and t is the time lapse; and next:

$$z = \frac{1}{2}g \cdot t^2 + v_1 t + z_1$$

(If z_1, the initial position, is taken as zero, and the body falls from rest, this equation reduces to $z = \frac{1}{2}g \cdot t^2$, Galileo's law, where g represents a constant to be determined by measurement.) And it seems somewhat arbitrary to withhold the title "law of nature" from integrated equations of motion and to restrict it to differential equations of motion.

A more acceptable criterion recognizing that space and time are on a par as regards the postulated uniformity of laws of nature is Maxwell's criterion: neither space-coordinates nor time-coordinates should occur "explicitly" in equations expressing laws of nature. Obviously "coordinates" here must mean particular values of the variables x, y, z, t, not the variables themselves. So understood, Maxwell's criterion is simply the criterion of unrestricted generality applied to the functional laws of physics: if no individual constants are to occur essentially in a lawlike statement, then coordinate descriptions of particular regions of space-time are excluded. From what has already been said in Section A it follows, however, that only what may be called *fundamental* laws satisfy this condition.

D. RELATIVISTIC INVARIANCE

A functional relation between physical magnitudes may be invariant in several respects. The greater the range of invariance, the more likely is the physicist to accord to it the status of a fundamental law of nature. Indeed, the belief that only functional relations that are invariant in a certain precise sense can be recognized as fundamental laws of nature is the heart of the theory of relativity. We have already had occasion to mention the restricted principle of relativity in Newtonian mechanics: if a law of mechanics holds relative to a reference-frame R (i.e., coordinate system in which measurements are made), then it holds relative to any other reference-frame that is at rest or in uniform motion relative to R. This principle does not, of course, tell us relative to *which* reference-frames the laws of Newtonian mechanics are valid. Experience shows that the laws of Newtonian mechanics (including the laws of Galilean kinematics) are valid to a fair degree of approximation relative to inertial reference-frames, defined as systems that are nonaccelerated relative to the fixed stars. But is it likewise a question of experience whether a given law of mechanics that holds relative to an inertial system R also holds relative to any other inertial system? In other words, is the restricted principle of relativity an empirical generalization or is it simply a statement analytic of the meaning of "law of mechanics"?

It is easy to become confused about this matter. On the one hand, it seems undeniable that the principle describes a contingent feature of mechanical phenomena, as the following simple illustration will show. When two perfectly elastic bodies of equal mass collide directly, approaching each other with equal velocities v_1 and v_2 relative to a system R, then they will rebound with equal velocities u_1 and u_2 after impact, the velocities of rebound being measured in the same system R. Let R be a train at rest. If the experiment is repeated when the train moves uniformly, so that the velocities are now measured in a system in uniform motion relative to R, the same result will be obtained, in conformity to the restricted principle of relativity. But it is surely conceivable that the stated law of impact of perfectly elastic bodies not hold when the collision of billiard balls takes place in a uniformly moving train. After all, a uniform motion of R *might* produce certain forces acting on the bodies in R, just as in the case of accelerated motion; though we assume this to be *empirically* impossible, it is *logically* possible. On the other hand, it seems to be mathematically demonstrable that the simple law of impact we are considering satisfies the Newtonian principle of relativity, as follows:

Let v_1 be the positively directed velocity before impact, u_1 the negatively directed velocity after impact, similarly v_2 negative and u_2 positive, and let R move with a constant positive velocity V equal in magnitude to v_1 relative to the earth. Then, relative to an observer on the earth,

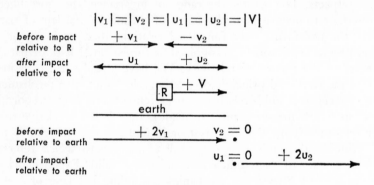

$$|v_1| = |v_2| = |u_1| = |u_2| = |V|$$

Figure 16.1

body 1 approaches body 2 with a positive velocity $2V$ while body 2 is at rest, and after impact body 1 is at rest while body 2 moves with a positive velocity $2V$. Generalizing, we can deduce from the simple "symmetrical" law together with the relativity principle that if, in a perfectly elastic impact, a body collides directly with a body of equal mass at rest, the latter will pick up the former's velocity and the former will be at rest. But the premised and the deduced law are simply special cases of the more general law that in a direct collision of perfectly elastic bodies of equal mass their *relative speed*, i.e., speed relative to each other, is conserved. And it may seem self-evident that if this law is valid relative to one inertial system, then it is valid relative to any inertial system, since it does not mention a third system from which speeds are measured at all. However, such an argument is fallacious. What is, of course, demonstrable without experiment is that if two bodies A and B move with a given constant relative speed when their individual speeds are measured in R, they move with the same constant relative speed when their individual speeds are measured in a system in uniform motion relative to R. But it does not in the least follow that the equality of their relative speed *before and after impact* is independent of the coordinate system in which the measurements are made. It is not self-contradictory to suppose, for example, that the described symmetry obtains when the train is stationary but breaks down when it moves with perfect uniformity.

The Newtonian principle of relativity, therefore, is not tautological if "law of mechanics" is defined by examples, and the invariance is then predicated of those specific relations. It might be held, on the other hand, that there is a deep reason why the physicist would hesitate to call an equation a law if it were not invariant in the explained sense. It is often said that physics strives to formulate uniformities that do not depend on the observer. This tendency began, of course, with the Copernican revolution: Copernicus suspected that the complexities of the epicyclic orbits of the heavenly bodies were due to the observer's own motion. By shifting to the sun as center of the coordinate system, he managed to produce a far simpler system of celestial kinematics. The same tendency culminates in Einstein's theory of relativity. Let us call a shift from one inertial reference frame to another that is nonaccelerated relative to the first a "Galilean transformation." Then the special theory of relativity may be characterized as an extension of the Newtonian postulate of invariance (of physical laws) with respect to Galilean transformations from mechanical to optical and electromagnetic phenomena. Einstein's conception of a law of nature as a relation that holds independently of the accidents of observation led him to argue as follows:

According to the Newtonian principle of relativity, if a physical law holds relative to an inertial coordinate system S in which the position of a particle at a time t is expressed by an ordered triplet of coordinates x, y, z, it will also hold in an inertial coordinate system S' that moves with a constant velocity v relative to S and in which the coordinates of the same particle at the same t' are x', y', z'. For the case of motions along the x-axis, the positions in S' are related to the positions in S by the Galilean transformation equation: $x' = x - vt$ (assume $t = 0$ when the origins of S and S' coincide; the generalization for motion in space is obvious). But the proposition that the velocity of light in vacuo has the constant value 186,000 miles/sec is of fundamental importance, especially since the same value turned out to characterize the velocity of propagation of electromagnetic waves. It ought, therefore, to receive the title "law of nature." But it is in obvious conflict with the Galilean transformation equation: if c is the velocity of a light beam along the positive x-axis as measured in S, and c' the velocity of the same light beam as measured in a system S' that moves with positive velocity v along the x-axis relative to S, then we should have $c' = c + v$. Einstein concluded that the transformation equations must be modified in such a way that the postulate $c = c'$, which to his mind was dictated by the very meaning of "law of nature," would be satisfied. There resulted the Lorentz-Einstein transformation equations with their well-known consequence that measured lengths and times depend on the state of motion of the coordinate system relative to the measured objects or processes. The new transformation equations are still restricted to inertial coordinate systems, but they unify the laws of mechanics, optics, and electromagnetics as being invariant with respect to the same group of transformations.

To explain how the general theory of relativity lifts even this last restriction to the class of inertial coordinate systems would be entirely out of place here. The point to be made is that though invariance in some sense is part and parcel of what a scientist—or, for that matter, a scientific philosopher—means by "law of nature," this does not necessarily mean independence of observers or measuring apparatus.[3] What it means is rather, in the language of symbolic logic, that a formula expressing a law must not contain a free variable such that it holds for some values of that variable but not for others. Thus, we can imagine without self-contradiction the mechanical behavior of bodies to be such that the relative speed of two directly colliding, perfectly elastic[4] bodies of equal mass is the same before and after collision *only* if the speeds relative to the coordinate system do not exceed a certain limit. Such a law would obviously violate the postulate of restricted relativity. But if the condition "The velocities of A and B relative to whatever coordinate system the measurements are made from do not exceed x" is explicitly included in the antecedent of the conditional, there is no justification for the assertion that this "law" is not valid for all inertial coordinate systems. The latter statement makes sense only if by the "law" is meant an incomplete formulation to which truth cannot be significantly ascribed. There is no objection to a loose way of speaking, such as "Boyle's law holds provided the temperature of the gas is constant," if one realizes that what in this loose mode of speech is called "law" is not a complete proposition. At any rate, there is no contradiction in the concept of a law of physics that is not independent of the "choice" of coordinate system, provided these restrictions are formulated in a perfectly general way in the antecedent of the lawlike generalization. Our hypothetical law of impact is still a perfectly *general* proposition (except for the implicit occurrence of the individual constant "the fixed stars"): "For any perfectly elastic bodies A and B, and *for any inertial coordinate system S:* if the speeds of A and B relative to S do not exceed x, and the masses of A and B are

3. It is, of course, assumed throughout this discussion that there is an independent criterion of perfect elasticity—in accordance with the requirement of multiple criteria for theoretical concepts.

4. Such a definition would anyway clash with the revolutionary developments in quantum mechanics. (See Chapter 17.)

equal, then the relative speed of *A* and *B* after impact is equal to their relative speed before impact."

E. DEGREE OF LAWLIKENESS
AS DEGREE OF CONFIRMATION

We have not succeeded in capturing any *formal* characteristic of lawlike hypotheses that would reliably distinguish them from accidental statements. Unrestricted generality, in the sense of absence of individual constants, may be a necessary condition for a statement to express a fundamental law of nature (waiving the difficulty created by the operational interpretation of the theoretical concepts). But there are lawlike hypotheses, such as Kepler's and Galileo's laws, that do not satisfy this condition and yet are not deducible from statements that satisfy it by straight substitution of individual constants for universally quantified variables. Further, we have seen that unrestricted generality is not a sufficient condition of lawlikeness either. The statement "All the coins in the left trouser pocket of a six-foot carpenter on a day when an armistice is signed are nickels" is purely general, but it may be purely accidental in the sense that nobody would with any confidence base a prediction on it. One cannot, to be sure, know that it is true, since one cannot know that there will never again occur an armistice, and a fortiori that there will never occur an armistice at a time when a six-foot carpenter holds a coin other than a nickel in his left trouser pocket; but the point is that, even assuming such knowledge, one would not claim to have any *inductive support* for the subjunctive conditional: for any *x* and for any *t*, if *x* were a coin in the left trouser pocket of a six-foot carpenter at *t* and *t* were a time when an armistice was signed, then *x* would be a nickel. Accordingly we shall suggest that a universal conditional is lawlike just to the degree that it is inductively supported, or confirmed.

That lawlikeness, subjunctive expressions, and inductive confirmation are, so to speak, tied together becomes evident once we ask ourselves why a counterfactual statement such as "If that coin had been in your pocket, it would have been a nickel" sounds odd. It sounds odd because we assume that there is no causal connection between a coin's location in, say, Jones' pocket and its being a nickel. And this assumption would be well supported by the evidence that at different times Jones' pockets contain different kinds of coins, or that other people's pockets contain different kinds of coins though these people and these pockets do not differ relevantly from Jones and his pockets. By contraposition, suppose we knew that Jones never put any coins other than nickels into his trouser pocket. We would then be inclined to infer that somehow he had acquired the habit of allocating different coins to different places, perhaps for reasons of expediency. In that case there would be an indirect causal connection between the location and the character of Jones' coins. If someone claimed to have just found a dime that had dropped out of Jones' pocket, one might then quite reasonably protest, "Oh no, if it had been in Jones' trouser pocket it would have been a nickel, for Jones the pedant is known never to put any other coins into his trouser pockets (he keeps the dimes in his shirt pockets, the quarters in a special purse, and so forth)." Generalizing: let "All A are B" be a universal statement whose subject-class is small, and let it be a deductive consequence of an extensively confirmed generalization "All C are B" about a larger class including A; then "All A are B" derives indirect inductive support—by the principle of analogy—from the instances that confirm "All C are B" without directly confirming "All A are B," and to this extent it acquires the power of supporting a counterfactual inference "If x were an A, then x would be a B." A universal statement is lawlike to the degree that it is indirectly confirmed by instances that directly confirm more general hypotheses from which it follows or less general statements that follow from it. The latter condition of lawlikeness refers to fundamental hypotheses that by the very meaning of "fundamental," are accepted because they imply directly confirmed generalizations, not because they are implied by independently confirmed principles. It is thus the concatenation of inductions by means of unifying, comprehensive generalizations that confers lawlike character on statements of restricted generality as well as on statements of unrestricted generality.[5]

It is, however, a mistake to suppose that by thus justifying counterfactual expressions in terms of the process of indirect inductive confirmation one renders them dispensable in a scientific language. For though the observational evidence for a law of nature can be recorded in truth-functional language, the law itself must be expressed by a subjunctive conditional. The laws of physics would not possess the mathematical simplicity that renders them manageable for predictions if they referred to the highly complex conditions we encounter in any actual case. They owe their simplicity to idealizing suppositions that such and such variables are constant, that such and such "disturbing" forces are absent or negligibly small, or that their subject-matter is ideally uniform in specified respects: the principle of conservation of mechanical energy

5. On this point we are, except for a reservation expressed below, in full agreement with R. B. Braithwaite's analysis of lawlikeness, in *Scientific Explanations* Cambridge: Cambridge University Press, 1953), chap. 9.

refers to frictionless motions, the general principle of conservation of energy (first law of thermodynamics) refers to isoloted systems, but the only strictly isolated system is the universe and the significance of a speculative extension of the principle to the entire universe is doubtful; the laws of hydrodynamics refer to incompressible and internally friction-less fluids; Ohm's law states that the current established in a metallic circuit is directly proportional to the electromotive force of the source, *assuming* that no other electromotive forces are acting in the circuit; Boyle's law refers to gases whose molecules do not attract or repel each other and that are ideal point-masses that do not rotate; the law of freely falling bodies refers to bodies that fall under the sole influence of gravity, and so on.

It is true that laws referring to ideal conditions that were first estab-lished by extrapolation from experimental data may subsequently be deduced as "special cases" from more general laws. It was by extra-polation to an imagined fall in a vacuum that Galileo came to assert that bodies of widely different mass would fall with the same acceleration if dropped in a vacuum; it was by the same sort of extrapolation to the limiting case that he first came upon the law of inertia. And we know that both of these laws are mathematical consequences of the general axioms of Newtonian mechanics. The law of inertia, in particularly, is contained in the formula "$F = m \cdot a$" as the special case "If $F = 0$, then $a = 0$." Similarly, Boyle's law which holds accurately only for (non-existent) gases whose molecules are point-masses that exert no forces on one another, is contained as a special case in van der Waals' general equation of state for "real" gases. But this observation does not support the truth-functionalist's case. For a functional equation expresses, in the unparalleled conciseness of mathematical symbols, an infinite family of subjunctive conditionals. To say, for example, that the current, I, in a metallic circuit of fixed electrical resistance R, is proportional to the electromotive force, E, of the source, is to say: for any x and y, if x represents the electromotive force of the source at time t, and y the current in the circuit at time t, then $y = x/R$ (where x and y range over real numbers used to measure physical quantities). If this were a formal implication (cf. p. 275), then we could easily insure its truth for a given metallic body, say a zinc wire, by making sure that it was never connected with a source of electricity. And the fact that no physicist would regard such an omission of experimentation as a conclusive verifi-cation of the conditional proves that Ohm's law as he intends it cannot be formulated in truth-functional language.

Let us contrast the meaning of "if-then" in lawlike generalizations with material implication by calling it *nomological* implication. The truth-functionalists' complaint is that "nomological implication" is just a dignified label under which an obscure notion of necessary connection between natural events is smuggled into an allegedly empiricist philosophy of science. But their complaint can easily be silenced—or, at least, answered—by specifying exactly the properties that distinguish nomological implication from material implication. In order to do this, we have to use the concept of analytic entailment, for to define a concept, whether explicitly or postulationally, is to lay down analytic entailments that involve it. Symbolizing analytic entailment by ⊰ , we first lay down analytic entailments that are satisfied by material implication and likewise by nomological implication:

(1) $[p \text{ and } (p \supset q)] \dashv q$
(2) $[(q \supset r) \text{ and } (p \supset q)] \dashv (p \supset r).$
(3) $(p \supset q) \dashv (\text{not-}q \supset \text{not-}p)$
(4) $[(p \supset q) \text{ and not-}q] \dashv \text{not-}p$

Entailment (1) is the principle of modus ponens, (2) the principle of the hypothetical syllogism (also called "transitivity of implication"), (3) the principle of transposition, (4) the principle of modus tollens. The following analytic entailments, however, are satisfied by material implication but not by nomological implication:

(5) $\text{not-}p \dashv (p \supset q)$
(6) $q \dashv (p \supset q)$
(7) $[(p \text{ and } q) \supset r] \dashv [p \supset (q \supset r)]$

Entailments (5) and (6) are formulations of the so-called "paradoxes of material implication" that a false proposition materially implies any proposition and that a true proposition is materially implied by any proposition. Entailment (7) is the principle of exportation. That (5) and (6) do not hold for nomological implication is obvious. The following illustration will show that (7) likewise breaks down: Let a be an indexical name of a thing, hence a name that does not connote any specific properties of the thing. Then the conjunction of the propositions "a is sugar" and "a is immersed in water" nomologically implies "a dissolves." But "a is sugar" does not nomologically imply that "a is immersed in water" nomologically implies "a dissolves." For if it did, then, given the truth of "a is sugar," modus ponens would yield that "a is immersed in water" nomologically implies "a dissolves," which is not the case.

To say that nomological implication satisfies entailments (1)–(4) but not entailments (5)–(7) is not a sufficient postulational definition of nomological implication, because analytic entailment has just the same properties. We must add that a nomological implication can be established only by induction, not by analysis of meanings and formal deduction alone. A complete postulational definition, therefore, involves the rules of critical inductive generalization in accordance with which the acceptance of a nomological implication is justified by "confirming" empirical evidence. He who, after all this has been done, still complains of the obscurity of nomological implication must have burdened himself with standards of clarity that are themselves none too clear.

Selected Readings

Alexander, H. G., "General Statements as Rules of Inference," in H. Feigl, M. Scriven, and G. Maxwell (eds.), *Minnesota Studies in the Philosophy of Science* (Minneapolis, 1958), Vol. II.

Ayer, A. J., "Laws of Nature," *Revue Internationale de Philosophie*, 1956.

Bergmann, G., "Outline of an Empiricist Philosophy of Physics," *American Journal of Physics*, 1943.

Braithwaite, R. B., *Scientific Explanation* (Cambridge, 1953), chap. 9.

Bunge, M., "Kinds and Criteria of Scientific Laws," *Philosophy of Science*, 1961.

Campbell, N. R., *Foundations of Experimental Science* (New York, 1957), chap. 2, 3.

Darlington, J., "On the Confirmation of Laws," *Philosophy of Science*, 1959.

Duhem, P., *The Aim and Structure of Physical Theory* (Princeton, N.J., 1954), part II, chap. 5.

Einstein, A., *Relativity, the Special and General Theory* (New York, 1947).

Goodman, N., *Fact, Fiction and Forecast* (Cambridge, 1955).

Hempel, C. G., and P. Oppenheim, "Studies in the Logic of Explanation," *Philosophy of Science*, 1948. [Reprinted in H. Feigl and M. Brodbeck, (eds.) *Readings in the Philosophy of Science* (New York, 1953).]

Kneale, W., "Universality and Necessity," *British Journal for the Philosophy of Science*, 1961.

Koerner, S., "On Laws of Nature," *Mind*, 1953.

Lindsay, R., and H. Margenau, *Foundations of Physics* (New York, 1936), chap. 1.

Mach, E., "The Significance and Purpose of Natural Laws," in *Erkenntnis und Irrtum* (Leipzig, 1908). [Reprinted in A. Danto and S. Morgenbesser (eds.), *Philosophy of Science* (New York, 1960).]

Meehl, P. E., "Law and Convention in Psychology," in H. Feigl and M. Brodbeck (eds.), *Readings in the Philosophy of Science* (New York, 1953).

Mehlberg, H., *The Reach of Science* (Toronto, 1958), part 2, chap. 2.

Meyerson, E., "Law and Causal Explanation," in *Identity and Reality*, trans. by K. Loewenberg (London and New York, 1930). [Reprinted in P. P. Wiener (ed.), *Readings in Philosophy of Science* (New York, 1953).]

Nagel, E., *The Structure of Science* (New York, 1961), chap. 3–5.

Presley, C. F., "Laws and Theories in the Physical Sciences," *Australasian Journal of Philosophy*, 1954. [Reprinted in A. Danto and S. Morgenbesser (eds.), *Philosophy of Science* (New York, 1960).]

Reichenbach, H., *Elements of Symbolic Logic* (New York, 1947), chap. 7.

———, *Nomological Statements and Admissible Operations* (Amsterdam, 1954).

Sellars, W. S. "Concepts as Involving Laws and Inconceivable without Them," *Philosophy of Science*, 1948.

Suppes, P., *Introduction to Logic* (New York, 1957), pp. 246–291.

Toulmin, S., *Philosophy of Science* (London, 1953), chap. 3.

Werkmeister, W. H., "Science, Its Concepts and Laws," *Journal of Philosophy*, 1949.

CHAPTER 17

Determinism & Indeterminism

Next to the theory of relativity, the quantum theory has stimulated more philosophical interest in science than has any other scientific development of the twentieth century. The theory of relativity, especially the "special" theory challenged the classical conceptions of space and time; the quantum theory went further and challenged the Laplacian conception of physical causality or determinism. It claims that the principle "Every event has a cause," proclaimed by Kant as an a priori presupposition of all science, has broken down in the subatomic world, since such events as individual electron jumps from one atomic orbit to another, or impacts of individual electrons at particular positions on a screen or disintegrations of individual radioactive atoms, are not predictable. And such prediction is alleged to be not only practically but even theoretically impossible. According to Heisenberg's famous principle of uncertainty it is impossible to measure the position and simultaneous velocity of an electron, or any other subatomic particle, with unlimited precision; hence "states" subatomic particles in the Newtonian sense (position and simultaneous velocity) are not uniquely predictable. As we shall see, this failure of Newtonian causality in the microworld is inseparably connected with the breakdown of the classical concept of "particles," and even the deeply entrenched common-sense concept of "things" that are at any time in a definite state whether or not the latter is observed or measured has become suspect. But before venturing into the technicalities of quantum theory, let us try to become clear about the meaning and function of the principle of causality in the unsophisticated form in which it is usually debated by philosophers: "Every event has a cause."

A. WHAT IS ASSERTED BY "EVERY EVENT HAS A CAUSE"?

If we take "cause" in the sense of a sufficient condition, we get the following analysis: for any event e there is a preceding event a, such that if at any time an event like a occurred, it would be followed by an event like e. This is equivalent to saying that given an event sequence $a \longrightarrow e$, there is a law L such that the occurrence of an event of the same kind as e is deducible from the prior occurrence of an event of the same kind as a together with L. One virtue of this formulation is that brings out the *vagueness* of the principle of causality, a feature often overlooked by philosophers busying themselves with the question of proof or disproof as though the meaning of the debated formula were perfectly clear. Any two concrete events are alike in some respect or other; in other words, for any two concrete events a and b we can abstract a *class* of events C such that both a and b are members of C. Consequently, if the principle of causality merely asserts that for any event sequence $a \longrightarrow e$ there is a true generalization "Every event that is a member of class A is followed by an event that is a member of class E," where A contains a and E contains e, it is trivial; its truth can easily be insured by a suitable choice of classes A and E, even if we impose the further requirement of spatio-temporal contiguity of cause and effect. Reichenbach reports in his *The Rise of Scientific Philosophy* the following example of chance coincidence: A slight earthquake once shook a movie theater in Los Angeles just when the blasting of lumber was shown on the screen. Since the effect of such a blasting is similar to the tremor then experienced by the audience, it is understandable that the latter instinctively assumed a causal connection at first. But, of course, says Reichenbach, there was no causal connection because this particular event sequence was "not repeatable." Yet, a tricky logician might not have too much trouble in defining two classes of events A and E such that A contains the described movie episode and E the associated earthquake, and such that every member of A is in fact followed by a member of E. Or consider a disease whose specific cause is so far unknown, such as lung cancer. Let $e_1, e_2, \ldots, e_n$ be all the instances of this disease, from the very first to the very last victim. Clearly, if we examined the states of these organisms that closely preceded the outbreak of the disease, we would be bound to discover some common property that would be at the same time distinctive in the sense that *only* those who were stricken with the disease at $t + dt$ were in a state of that kind at t. For example, it might happen that all and only the people who caught lung cancer at $t + dt$

(assuming, for the sake of the argument, that the beginning of the disease could be approximately located) smoked the last one of a series of twenty-five Brand X cigarettes at t. We could then take as L the universal statement "Anyone who at t completes a chain of twenty-five Brand XX cigarettes, contracts the beginnings of lung cancer at $t + dt$," and the problem of the cause of lung cancer would be solved.

Now, it is true that the principle of causality cannot be satisfied in such trivial fashion if we observe the distinction between a law, supporting predictions in the subjunctive mood, and a true universal statement, which may not express any causal connection at all. But that it remains nevertheless vague, becomes evident once we remember that the events we call causes are in most cases only "triggering" conditions, not strictly sufficient conditions of their effects. For, in order to take this feature of causal talk into account, we must qualify our causal generalizations by the escape clause "provided the same relevant circumstances are present." The principle of causality must be correspondingly qualified: any event e is preceded by an event a such that any event like a is followed by an event like e *provided* the relevant circumstances are the same. When we formulate a specific causal law we must specify what those relevant circumstances are, and to the extent that we claim to have specified all the conditions that are jointly sufficient for the effect, to that extent we have "stuck out our neck" and risk being refuted by the facts. But the philosopher who, leaving the discovery of specific causal laws to special scientists, pronounces profoundly that every event has a cause does not stick his neck out at all; he need not fear being refuted by the facts because he can always say that some of the relevant circumstances must have been different if he is told—by researchers who venture to rise from the armchair to take a look at what is happening in the world —that closely similar antecedents were followed by widely different effects. Since the principle of causality is thus irrefutable by experience, some positivistic philosophers of science who are noticeably irritated by the apriorism of Kant and his followers have declared that it is an empty tautology that "tells us nothing about the world." Is it a tautology?

It is not, of course, a tautology in the restricted sense of this term in deductive logic (cf. p. 94). But what is intended by the critics of Kant and of other metaphysicians who proclaimed the principle of causality as a synthetic a priori proposition is that it is *analytic*, for the following reason. Suppose that a is the only antecedent of an event e that, in the light of our past experience, can plausibly be supposed to have caused e, but that events closely similar to a are found not to be followed by events like e. May we then conclude that e has no cause? Not until we have ascertained that the events of kind A that were not followed by an event of kind E occurred under *the same relevant circumstances*. Thus the proposition that the lighting of the match was caused by striking it is not refuted if we find that just the same procedure with a wet match-box does not produce the desired effect. But how do we know whether the relevant circumstances were exactly the same? The only criterion, it seems, is whether the "same cause" was followed by the "same effect." The critic accordingly concludes that the statement "If the relevant circumstances are the same, then the same cause is always followed by the same effect" merely analyzes the meaning of its antecedent, just like "If a figure is square, then it is equilateral." Kant was quite right, says the critic, in holding the principle of causality to be irrefutable by ex-perience, but he was wrong in thinking that such irrefutability requires a metaphysical explanation in terms of an elusive entity so awesome that its name must be capitalized: "Reason." It is irrefutable for the same simple reason that "If a figure is square, then it is equilateral" is irrefu-table.

But something must be wrong with this argument. If it were valid, it would prove much more than it was designed to prove: it would prove that any *specific* causal generalization is likewise analytic, since the clause "other things being equal" is part and parcel of causal talk. A cautiously formulated causal generalization is not *simply* refutable the way "All college professors make at least $10,000 a year" is simply re-futable (by just finding a college professor who is not so well off). In the language of symbolic logic, it contains an existential quantifier: there are conditions C such that whenever and wherever an event of kind A occurs in the presence of C, there and then an event of kind E follows. If many instances of A have been observed, under widely different con-ditions, to be followed by an instance of E, one legitimately suspects a causal connection; hence one will conjecture that an instance of A that is not followed by an instance of E occurred under conditions different from C. But this hypothesis of "difference of relevant conditions" would be ad hoc in the pejorative sense only if it were not independently test-able. As pointed out in a previous context (cf. p. 290), a scientist must subsequently justify that hypothesis by actually discovering a relevant difference between the conditions under which instances of A were fol-lowed by an instance of B and the conditions that prevailed when his prediction went wrong. Now, the factual content of the principle of causality is just the contingent fact that a patient analysis of antecedent conditions usually reveals a difference correlated with the observed dif-ference of the effect following apparently similar antecedents. To the extent that such differences are discovered, the condition variable C can be "filled in" and a more reliable, complex hypothesis "If A occurs in the presence of C_1, E follows" replaces the refuted hypothesis "A is invariably followed by E."

The principle of causality, therefore, is not analytic, nor is it an inductive generalization that could be refuted by contrary instances. It is best described as a *guiding principle* of causal inquiry that owes its successes to a contingent feature of the universe. It "guides" the scientist in his search for a difference in antecedent conditions to account for the fact that apparently similar antecedents were followed by dissimilar effects. Whether in this conception it can be claimed to be a true, or at least a well-confirmed proposition, or should be accorded the status of a "rule of procedure" that cannot properly be called true or probably true, is really a matter of taste since the distinction between a proposition and a rule of procedure becomes somewhat fuzzy as we ascend on the ladder of inductive generalization.

Take, for example, the principle of the conservation of energy in the most general form: "In an isolated system the sum of all the different forms of energy (mechanical, heat, electrical) is constant in time." If strict falsifiability by observations is stipulated as a criterion of the factual character of a statement, then this is not a factual statement. As was pointed out by Poincaré and other "conventionalists," the concept of energy was actually generalized in the history of physics in such a way that the property of conservation became *definitory* of "the sum of all the different forms of energy." That is, if the already known forms of energy fail to have an approximately constant sum in an approximately isolated system, the physicist either postulates a new form of energy or (as in the case of the "neutrino" particles) a new kind of particle whose energy accounts for the difference. Nevertheless, the statement is not "merely" analytic, for the assumptions made in order to reconcile it with the observations must be independently confirmed. Thus some mechanical energy is obviously lost in a changing isolated system owing to friction. To say that this lost mechanical energy is regained by the system in the form of heat energy is to say that there is a strict proportionality between the work involved in the frictional dissipation of mechanical energy and the independently measurable heat that the system gains at the same time. The energy principle may accordingly be said to function as a guide to the discovery of quantitative equivalences between independently measurable quantities.

That the contrast "analytic—empirically falsifiable" cannot be imposed without considerable artifice on a science such as physics, can be shown in terms of less general "laws" of physics as well. For this purpose we shall refer again to Hooke's law. If it is taken to assert "For all values of stress and strain, the stress is proportional to the strain," it is obviously false, and no physicist means *that* by Hooke's law. If a certain maximal stress is exceeded—called the "elastic limit" of the material—the relationship breaks down. Is there, then, a true proposition called "Hooke's law" that is not a definitional truth? The sentence "The stress is proportional to the strain, and vice versa" is incomplete, since the range of the variables for which this mathematical relationship holds is unspecified; strictly, it does not express any proposition at all. The obvious way to delimit the ranges of the variables is: "For all stresses that do not exceed the elastic limit of the material, the stress is proportional to the strain." But how do we tell whether or not in subjecting, say, a wire to a certain stress we have exceeded the elastic limit? Is not the very proportionality asserted by Hooke's law a criterion? It is, but since this is not the only criterion, Hooke's law does have factual content. We can test whether a given wire has been subjected to too much stress without assuming Hooke's law by determining whether its elongations are still reversible, i.e., whether the wire will automatically regain its original length after removal of the weight. But what must not be overlooked is that the multiplicity of criteria—the price to be paid for "factual content"—entails the impossibility of a simple falsification by "negative instances." Suppose that the wire were still elastic according to the test of reversibility but that the measurements just did not fit into the formula "stress $= k \cdot$ strain." And suppose that the anomaly could not be explained in terms of systematic errors, such as temperature fluctuations. Would the law then be refuted? Not strictly, for, to mention just one assumption entering into the test, the law implicit in the method of weight measurement might be questioned instead.

The upshot of this digression is simply that the question whether the principle of causality is to be regarded as a rule of procedure or as a well-confirmed empirical generalization rests on an artificial contrast. Any scientific generalization directs inferences to "disturbing" factors; and the more often the scientist succeeds in tracing such factors because of his faith in the provisional generalization, the more reluctant he will become to abandon it when his observations seem to contradict it. Undoubtedly one will try all other avenues of escape before surrendering the principle of causality itself, but the view that an expression such as "The principle of causality does not fit our observations any more" is nonsensical can hardly be maintained in the light of the famous developments in quantum physics. Whether one describes the situation by the words "According to the present state of physics, the proposition 'every event has a cause' is probably false" or by the words "According to the present state of physics, it is fruitless still to be guided in one's investigations by the rule 'try and try again to trace every observed difference in the effect to a difference in the initial conditions,'" is merely a matter of taste.

B. DETERMINATION AS A RELATION BETWEEN STATES

As has been pointed out by Mach, Russell, and others, the word "cause" does not occur in the physicists' formulations of laws of nature at all. The laws of mathematical physics are laws of functional dependence, not causal laws. Accordingly, "Every event has a cause" is not an adequate formulation of what the physicist means by the principle of causality. Causation in the sense analyzed in Chapter 14 is a relation of uniform succession holding between observable changes, but determination is a relation between mathematically conceptualized states of a physical system, not between observable changes of state. It would sound odd to ask what caused a falling apple to be, at time t_1, at position x_1 with instantaneous velocity v_1; it would sound odder still to answer, "Its being at t_0 at position x_0 with velocity v_0." It would, on the other hand, be a proper use of causal language to ask what caused the body to fall at that moment, and to answer, "Someone shook the tree."

But what is meant by the *state* of a physical system at a given time? In the case of a mechanical system that evolves in accordance with the laws of mechanics, it means the positions and velocities, relative to some "inertial" reference frame, of all the constituent particles. This, however, is not a general definition of "state." It is rather a definition of "mechanical state," or "state of a mechanical system." If the system whose internal changes are to be predicted by means of differential equations is a continuous fluid, the variables whose instantaneous values constitute an instantaneous state of the system are the (rectangular) velocity components of the constituent particles. In the case of electromagnetic fields, whose temporal changes are governed by Maxwell's field equations, the state descriptions are again different: a complete description of an instantaneous state of an electromagnetic field consists in the specifications of the electrical and magnetic field strengths at all points within the space-time region in question. The variables whose values at a time t constitute, collectively, the state of the system at t, are called the *state variables*. And the differential laws whose integration permits the deduction of future states from present states, as well as the deduction of past states from present states, are equations expressing the time rates of change of the state variables as functions of the state variables themselves. In the case of continuous systems, such as liquids or gases of electromagnetic fields (phenomenologically described)— contrasted with discrete systems consisting of widely separated particles, such as the solar system—the equations involve partial derivatives: the field strengths, for example, vary continuously not only with the time but also with the spatial coordinates. In order to consider the rate of change of this state variable with respect to the spatial position alone, one assumes the other independent variable, the time, to be constant and considers the space rate of change at a given time; similarly, one may focus attention on its time rate of change at a given place.

But what is the generic meaning of "state"? What are we saying about a set of physical variables in calling them the "state variables"? Clearly this concept of state is tied up with the physicist's purposes of prediction. An astronomer, for example, is primarily interested in predicting the *positions* of the heavenly bodies; hence he must know which variables, the values of which characterize the constituents of the system, are such that from their initial values the positions at future times can be deduced. It is a contingent fact that the desired deductions require him to know not only the initial values of position but also the initial values of velocity. That is, the future positions are not uniquely determined by the earlier positions alone but only by the earlier positions together with the simultaneous velocities. And to say that the "state," at a time t, of a closed mechanical system consists in the positions and velocities at t of the constituent particles is to say that the positions of the constituent particles at some time other than t are uniquely determined by their positions and velocities at t. Note, however, that it is meaningless to say generally that the *future behavior* of the system is uniquely determined by its initial state. For only the values of that variable property of the constituents of the system in which the scientist happens to be interested are uniquely determined, not the values of *any* variable property. Thus Venus changes not only its position as time goes on but also its brightness and, presumably, its average surface temperature, but these changes are not controlled by the same dynamical laws that control the changes of position and of velocity. Deterministic descriptions of physical systems are always selective: certain variable properties are abstracted and the scientist endeavors to formulate laws expressing the rates of change of those properties as fairly simple functions of their own values and of the values of very few other variables. That they do turn out to be fairly simple functions of a small number of variables is a very fortunate contingency. If the universe were not so constituted, Laplacian determinism would, even if it had ever been thought of at all, have remained an idle speculation, though the counterfactual "If only we knew the values of enough relevant variables, we would be able to predict what we want to predict" could not, of course, be refuted.

The following general definition of *state* may be extracted from these considerations: a state of a physical system at time t is the set of values, at t, of a set of variables $x_1, x_2, \ldots, x_n$ such that knowledge of the values of $x_1, x_2, \ldots, x_n$ at some time is necessary and sufficient for the prediction of the values at any other time of any member of the set. The qualification that such knowledge be "necessary" is made in order to exclude redundancies in state descriptions. Thus one might specify a mechanical state in terms of positions, velocities, potential energies, and kinetic energies of the constituent particles, but since the values of the latter two variables are derivable from the values of the former, they are not commonly listed as mechanical state variables. It is clear that on this definition "The future states of a closed physical system are uniquely determined by its initial state" is not a formulation of a *synthetic* principle of physical determinism, for this statement is simply analytic of the meaning of "state." According to the definition given it is just self-contradictory to suppose that the same initial state of a closed physical system could at different times be followed by different states after the same time lapse. To preserve the factual content of the principle of determinism we require an existential formulation: for any (practically) closed physical system S, and for any selected continuously variable property P characterizing S, there is a fairly small set of variables $x_1, x_2, \ldots, P$ (P, that is, is included in the set of "state variables") such that the values of $x_1, x_2, \ldots, P$ at a given time uniquely determine the values of P at any other time; and to say that this relation of unique determination holds means that there are differential laws expressing the time rate of change of one or more of these variables as a fairly simple function of themselves, such that from these laws together with a description of the values of $x_1, x_2, \ldots, P$ at a given time, the values of P at any other time are deducible.

The values of the state variables at some initial moment from which a future or earlier state of the system is deduced are usually called "initial conditions." In the strict sense of "logically deduced," however, a future or past state is logically deduced not from initial conditions alone, but from initial conditions in conjunction with differential laws and assumptions of "closure" of the system. In the case of Newtonian astronomy, the closure assumption is the assumption of which bodies in the solar system must be taken into consideration in calculating the accelerating forces that cause changes of state. If the predictions go wrong, one need not abandon the differential laws (such as the law of gravitation), nor need one infer that the initial conditions were incorrectly measured: one may re-examine the closure assumption. The important logical point to keep in mind is that determination, as a relation between states of a closed system, is not a logically necessary connection; for, from initial conditions alone, without a law of the rate of change of the state variables, the states of the system at other times cannot be deduced. And though these laws are not obtained by inductive generalization from observational data, they are logically contingent: the specific form of functional dependence of the accelerating force on the state variables must be empirically discovered. This would remain the case even if the *general* equation of motion, equating the accelerating force to the product of the mass of the accelerated body times its acceleration, were construed as a "definition," since it is the *specific* laws of force that must be known in order to predict or retrodict the evolution of the system.

Suppose that an evolving system is *deterministic* in the explained sense (keeping in mind that determinism in the scientific sense is always relative to selected state variables characterizing the evolving system); are we then justified in saying that it necessarily *must* be in whatever states it is found to be at given times, and that it could not conceivably have evolved in any other way? Not if by "necessity" is meant an absolute logical necessity. The necessity of a given state is doubly relative: it is relative to earlier states and also to the existence and constancy of the law governing changes of state. Even if the logical contingency of the laws could be reasonably doubted, it would have to be admitted that the initial conditions could always without logical inconsistency be conceived to be different. If, for example, the relative positions and the velocities of the planets in our solar system had been different at whatever time the solar system first acquired its dynamic stability, then their present positions and velocities would also be different. And if by "chance" be meant just such logical contingency of initial conditions, then determinism is not only compatible with, but even inconceivable without chance. For, to repeat, the assertion that a closed system evolves deterministically means that one and only one state at any given future time is compatible with the laws of change *and* a specified initial state; and if it were logically necessary that the initial state is what it is, then a knowledge of the initial state could not be required for the prediction of future states.

It would, however, lead to disastrous confusion if the same word "chance" were used both in this sense of logical contingency of initial conditions and also in the sense of an event that is not uniquely determined by initial conditions. It is, for example, logically conceivable that a penny toss performed under exactly the same mechanical conditions at different times resulted once in heads and once in tails. If (*per impossibile?*) we could know that the initial conditions were exactly identical, we would be justified in calling the outcome of the tosses "chance events" in the sense in which a chance event is an event that is not uniquely determined by the initial conditions. But even if the penny tosses were uniquely determined—though our ignorance of determining conditions makes unique prediction *practically* impossible—they would, like all events, remain logically contingent. There is nothing in the most rigorous scientific determinism that prevents us from keeping on asking why the initial conditions were what they were. Only by introducing the obscure theological notion of a "necessary first event" can the regress be terminated.

C. STATISTICAL REGULARITY
AND MICRODETERMINISM

We have just distinguished practical and theoretical possibility of making unique predictions from given initial conditions. Scientists and philosophers who, like Laplace, believe in a strict determinism of physical events do not regard such challenges as "Predict the exact sequence of heads and tails in the next hundred tosses of this coin" or "Predict which side of this die, which I am about to push over the edge of the table, will lie uppermost when it regains equilibrium on the floor" as serious threats to their belief. The proposition they maintain is the counterfactual conditional "*If* the relevant laws and all the determining conditions were known, then the results could be uniquely predicted." That it is *practically* necessary even for the best human scientists to make only statistical (or "probabilistic") predictions in such cases, they readily admit. Observations of statistical regularities enable us to predict with a fair degree of confidence that there will be between 40 and 60 heads in a random sequence of 100 penny tosses, and that if the experiment with the die is repeated a large number of times, any given side will come up about one-sixth of the times. But our speaking of probabilities with respect to individual events, say the determinists, merely reflects our ignorance of determining conditions; *objectively*, they say, the outcome of any random toss or throw is just as uniquely determined by the physical forces as the motion of a billiard ball is determined, in magnitude and direction, by the motion of the colliding billiard ball and whatever frictional resistance there is.

When statistical assumptions were first introduced into physical theory, in the kinetic theory of gases, the Laplacian determinism that was inspired by the successes of Newtonian mechanics in the realm of large-scale motions remained undoubted. The assumption that gases are composed of similar molecules in random motion was found to explain the experimentally discovered laws of the thermal behavior of gases, especially the general gas law: under certain ideal conditions of temperature and pressure, changes of gas pressure are compensated by changes of volume in such a way that the product of pressure times volume is always proportional to the absolute temperature of the gas. In particular, the gas molecules were assumed to be particles that moved and interacted according to the same laws of Newtonian dynamics as had long been found to account for the observable motions of bodies, both terrestrial and celestial. A superhuman scientist, it was supposed, would be able to measure the initial positions and velocities of all the molecules constituting a given mass of gas and hence could derive any other "microstate," i.e., state of the gas conceived as an aggregate of billions of microcosmic particles, at any other time. What led to the "kinetic" treatment of the behavior of gases—as contrasted with the macroscopic descriptions of experimental thermodynamics—was the breakdown of Lavoisier's "caloric" theory of heat.

Lavoisier had assumed that heat was a highly elastic, weightless fluid whose total quantity was conserved, like matter. But the generation of heat through friction was hard to reconcile with the conservative property of caloric. On the other hand, the fact that the mechanical energy that is lost in frictional processes is proportional to the heat developed suggested that heat is a form of energy and that when molar kinetic energy is lost—as when a bullet is fired into a ballistic pendulum—it is converted into kinetic energy of the constituent molecules. Further, it was known that the pressure of a gas confined within a constant volume increases proportionately with the temperature; that is, as heat is added to the gas its capacity to do mechanical work is increased. These facts suggested the theory that the temperature of a substance, whether gaseous, liquid, or solid, is the macroscopic manifestation of the kinetic energy of the constituent molecules. More exactly, the temperature was postulated to be proportional, not to the total kinetic energy of all the molecules, but to an average of the diverse kinetic energies such that if all the molecules moved with the same velocity corresponding to that average, the temperature would be unchanged.

It is just this *statistical* assumption, reflected in the choice of an average quantity, that distinguishes the procedure of the human scientist from that which would be open to Laplace's superhuman calculator, according to the classical conception. It is not just that ascertaining the positions and velocities of all the molecules at a given time is *practically* unfeasible for human experimentalists, as is often said. A symbol representing a specific position or a specific velocity of an individual molecule does not, in the classical kinetic theory, even have any operational meaning: we don't know what it would be like to measure a mechanical state of an individual gas molecule. But since not all the symbols entering into the postulates of a physical theory need be operationally definable (cf. Chapter 3, A), the assumption that the molecules nevertheless have exact positions and velocities at any given time is scientifically quite in order within the framework of Newtonian mechanics. The method of the classical kinetic theory, in its simplest form, was as follows:

Since there is, a priori, no reason to suppose that a molecule moves with one rather than any other possible velocity, all possible velocities are assumed equally likely. In the frequency interpretation, this means that all possible velocities occur with equal frequency, i.e., that the number of molecules with v_1 is equal to the number of molecules with v_2 and to the number with v_3, . . . , and to the number with v_r. The molecular motions are assumed to be uniform except when a molecule rebounds from a wall of the container. Because of this assumption of equal probability of all possible values of molecular velocity—conceived as a random variable (cf. p. 235)—the constant average by which the theory replaces the unknown individual velocities is the simple arithmetic mean. More exactly, the average velocity $\bar{v}$ is defined as the square root of

$$v_1{}^2 + v_2{}^2 + \cdots + \frac{v_r{}^2}{r}$$

where r is the number of possible velocities.[1] All the molecules, then, are assumed to move with the same average velocity $\bar{v}$, since, on the assumption of uniform velocity distribution, the macroscopic state of the gas, definable in terms of pressure and simultaneous temperature, would be just the same if this assumption were true. Further, if all possible directions of motion occur with equal frequency, then the macrosopic state of the gas would be no different if exactly one-third of the molecules enclosed in a cubical container moved parallel to the x-axis, one-third parallel to the y-axis, and one-third parallel to the z-axis. If we further assume that the changes of momentum that occur at the enclosing walls are governed by Newton's second law of motion and that the instantaneous force on a wall equals the number of molecules striking it times the force due to each molecule, we can deduce that the pressure (defined as force per unit area) equals $nm\bar{v}^2/3V$, where n is the number of molecules, m the mass of a molecule, and V the volume occupied by the gas. The assumption that the absolute temperature is proportional to $\frac{1}{2}m\bar{v}^2$ then leads to the general gas law: $pV = kT$.

A deterministic law of macrophenomena, viz. the general gas law, according to which any two of the thermodynamic variables pressure, volume, and temperature uniquely determine the third, has thus been de-

---

1. As in the definition of "standard deviation," the averaged items are squared in order to avoid cancellations due to differences of sign.

duced from the assumption of complete irregularity of microscopic motions. Temperature and pressure are conceived, by classical kinetic theory, as averages that are insensitive against a large class of changes of the microscopic state of a gas, in essentially the same way in which a wide variety of individual distributions of heads and tails in a sufficiently long sequence will correspond to approximately the same statistical distribution. But the conclusion that the observed regularity on the level of macroscopic experience is therefore the result of microsopic irregularity would be unwarranted: for without the assumption that the molecules are particles that individually move and interact in accordance with the dynamical laws of Newtonian mechanics, the deduction of macroscopic regularity from microscopic irregularity would not have been possible.

D. HEISENBERG'S UNCERTAINTY PRINCIPLE

Newtonian determinism, we have seen, is essentially tied up with the conception of particles whose states are described in terms of position and simultaneous velocity. That this sort of determinism does not govern the behavior of electrons and other subatomic "particles" is now generally conceded. The controversial question is whether for this reason determinism in general has broken down in the revolutionary "quantum" theories of the twentieth century. Those who draw this conclusion usually refer to Heisenberg's uncertainty principle according to which the product of the "uncertainty" in the position of a subatomic particle and the uncertainty of its simultaneous momentum cannot be less than h, the "quantum of action":[2]

$$\Delta x \cdot \Delta p_x \geqq h$$

(The quantum of action is a universal physical constant; the energy radiated by an atom is always an integral multiple of this quantum.) In order to predict a future position of an electron, one would have to know its initial position *and* simultaneous momentum, but according to Heisenberg's principle, so the argument runs, this requirement cannot be fulfilled: if we determine the position within narrow limits of "uncertainty," the simultaneous momentum becomes very uncertain, and if we determine the momentum within narrow limits of uncertainty, the simultaneous position becomes very uncertain. This argument, to be sure, does not strictly refute the belief that the earlier states of an electron

2. This principle applies to any object to which position and momentum are ascribable. But the equivalent formulation $\Delta x \cdot \Delta v_x \geqq h/m$ shows that the uncertainty vanishes for objects whose mass is large.

$momentum = m \cdot v$

$\Delta x \cdot \Delta (mv) \gtrless h \;,\quad \dfrac{\Delta x \cdot \Delta (mv)}{m} \gtrless \dfrac{h}{m}\;,\quad \Delta x \cdot \Delta v \gtrless \dfrac{h}{m}$

$P = \triangle (mv) \overset{?}{=} m(\text{constant}) \triangle v \text{ (variable)}$

$m \triangle v$

uniquely determine the later states; for the assertion that *if* we could measure an initial state without error, *then* we could uniquely predict the future positions of the particle is logically compatible with the admission that the required condition just cannot be fulfilled. Still, since the existence of deterministic laws governing the behavior of subatomic particles could only be *verified* by approximately unique predictions, the argument under discussion does establish that such a generalization of Newtonian determinism for the subatomic world is a metaphysical dogma of no relevance to physical science.

But the crucial question that a philosophical discussion of the uncertainty principle must face is the meaning of "uncertain." This word certainly suggests to the layman that electrons objectively have an exact position and simultaneous momentum at any given time, but that from the nature of measurement an accurate knowledge of their objective states is unobtainable. This misinterpretation is encouraged when the principle under discussion is exhibited as a consequence of the interaction between the process of measurement and the measured object: in order to locate an electron with great accuracy, the observer must illuminate it with light of short wavelength. But the shorter the wavelength, the greater the frequency, and the greater the frequency the greater the energy of the photon that strikes the electron. (A photon is a smallest parcel of light energy, its energy equal to *hn*, where *h* is the quantum of action and *n* the frequency of the light.) Hence the momentum that the electron supposedly had before the act of measurement took place is altered by the act of measurement. If, on the other hand, it is desired to ascertain the electron's momentum with accuracy, light of great wavelength must be used, and in that case no sharp location can be assigned to the electron.

Clearly, this interpretation rests on the particle interpretation of electrons and photons. But physicists seem to be agreed that a consistent particle interpretation cannot be maintained unless one is to mar physical theory with the weirdest ad hoc hypotheses. Thus, when a beam of electrons passes through a hole in a diaphragm the pattern of scintillations on a fluorescent screen behind the diaphragm indicates that the electrons do not move in an inertial path like Newtonian particles but are diffracted when they pass the diaphragm, like light passing through a small hole. As far as this diffraction effect is concerned, one might still stick to the particle model by assuming that the electrons are deflected from the inertial path by certain forces in the vicinity of the hole. But if the same experiment is repeated under the same conditions except that at a certain distance from the already existing hole a second hole is made in the diaphragm, the pattern of scintillations changes completely and cannot be derived by addition of the patterns resulting when only one hole exists.

Were one to stick to the particle model, one would have to make the incomprehensible assumption that the mere existence of the second hole influences the path of the electrons passing through the first hole. If, on the other hand, the electron beam is viewed as a wave motion, the change in the pattern of scintillation can be explained as due to the interference of the waves reaching the screen from the two holes.

When electrons or photons passing through a hole in a diaphragm are diffracted, part of their momentum is communicated to the diaphragm. This interaction with the diaphragm is all the greater, the smaller the hole; hence an exact determination of position entails "uncertainty" about the simultaneous momentum. This derivation of the uncertainty relation from the diffraction effect (verified for both photons and electrons) is totally different from the one we discussed and rejected before, since diffraction is just one of those phenomena that call for the wave model, not the particle model. But this does not mean that the wave model succeeds in making microprocesses intelligible in terms of visualizable processes. Electrons also manifest a particle aspect: the scintillations on the screen suggest the incidence of sharply localized particles though no laws of motion for individual electrons are known, and how it happens that an electron wave suddenly collapses into a particle when it hits the screen is no less mysterious than the action of the distant hole that is entailed by the particle interpretation. An interpretation that somehow mediates between the particle picture and the wave picture and at the same time smoothly leads to the uncertainty relation is that electrons are "wave packets." A number of waves may interfere in such a way that their amplitudes destroy each other everywhere outside of a small region. This packet of interfering waves may then be said to be localized in that region. But in order for the localization to be sharp, a large number of waves must interfere with one another. These waves differ in frequency, and to these different frequencies correspond different momenta of the "particle" represented by the wave packet: the more definite the location, the less definite the momentum.

Whichever of these models be accepted, the important fact with regard to the determinism problem is that physicists know of no deterministic (causal) laws governing the motions of individual electrons and photons. It is not possible to predict, for example, where an individual electron passing through a hole in a diaphragm will strike the screen; only percentages of scintillations in different parts of the screen can be predicted. According to Heisenberg's principle this impossibility of causal prediction of microevents—as contrasted with merely statistical prediction—is theoretical, not just practical, i.e., it is incompatible with a law of physics. Heisenberg's principle itself is usually given a statistical interpretation: if a large number of position measurements on electrons prepared for the same "state" are made, and Δx is the standard deviation with respect to the mean of the measured values, then the standard deviation for the measurements of simultaneous momentum is at least $h/\Delta x$. To avoid the misinterpretation already cautioned against, one should keep in mind that the standard deviation is a measure of dispersion that refers to a computable mean of actual results, not to a metaphysical "objective" value. To be sure, a finite dispersion in a set of repeated measurements of the same quantity was inevitable even in classical physics. But it was not suspected that a decrease in the dispersion for one physical variable would entail an increase in the dispersion for another physical variable.

Determinism, we argued earlier, is a testable hypothesis only relative to a particular method of describing the *states* of an evolving and practically closed system. But if Newtonian, mechanical states are not ascribable to electrons, what sense is there in the question whether their states succed each other in causal fashion? What is meant by the "state" of an electron or, for that matter, of any subatomic particle? The answer given by the quantum theory is unintelligible if one thinks of electrons as substantial entities. For the states of whatever is the subject-matter described by the laws of quantum mechanics are the values of certain mathematical symbols called "ψ-functions," and these symbols are interpreted in the following indirect manner: the square of $\psi(x)$ is proportional to the probability of finding the "particle" at position x. Clearly, if it is to make sense to speak of a probability of finding an electron at position x, then it must make sense to suppose that an electron is exactly at position x, which presupposes the particle interpretation. Further, the relative frequency with which a *given* electron occupies a certain position could be determined only if there were a criterion for determining whether several electron events are genidentical or not, which there is not. It would seem to be mistaken, therefore, to interpret the quantum-mechanical state descriptions as referring to individual particles. And the same difficulty confronts their interpretation as statistical descriptions of ensembles, or swarms of particles. For example, suppose it is asserted that the square of $\psi(x)$ is proportional to the relative frequency with which electrons—not a single electron that is repeatedly prepared for the same "state"—hit the immediate neighborhood of x per unit time. The state description would then be a description of a statistical distribution, comparable to a description of a long sequence of throws of dice in terms of the relative frequencies of the six possible outcomes. But a die is an individual object that, once it is thrown, is in a definite ascertainable and nonstatistical state, whereas no meaning can be assigned to the statement that an individual electron that was wavelike when it passed through the diaphragm—hence had an "uncertain" position—suddenly turned into a sharply localized particle when it hit the screen. The point is that the statistical distributions described by the ψ-function must be taken to refer simply to point-events, not to momentary locations of substantial particles.

These point-events are individually unpredictable, in the sense that no laws are known that would enable their individual prediction. In this sense, and this sense only, quantum mechanics is indeterministic. Also such microevents as "quantum-jumps" within an atom; i.e., discontinuous energy radiations from an atom, are not individually predictable. The law $E_1 - E_0 = hn$ allows us to calculate the final energy state of a radiating atom from its initial energy state and the frequency of the radiation, but no law is known that would permit prediction of the time when a quantum jump will occur. On the other hand, quantum mechanics contains a differential law, "Schroedinger's wave equation," according to which a value of the ψ-function at one time determines the values of that function at any other time.[3] That is, if it is known that with the various possible values of a certain random variable—such as the locations of scintillations on a screen—definite probabilities are associated for a given time interval, the probabilities of the same values for a later time interval are deducible. For this reason the defenders of determinism argue that if only we recognize that determinism is relative to a specific method of describing states and that quantum-mechanical state descriptions are fundamentally different from classical state descriptions, we will see that determinism has not broken down at all in modern atomic physics. But perhaps both parties are right: there may be a deterministic law governing the succession of ψ-states but only statistical laws governing the occurrence of individual events like clicks of a Geiger counter, or scintillations on a screen bombarded with electrons, or disintegrations of individual radioactive atoms.

E. PHYSICAL REALITY, PROBABILITY, AND OBSERVATION

Heisenberg himself believes that the quantum-mechanical indeterminacies have an important bearing on the concept of physical reality. According to common-sense realism, physical measurement discloses properties and states of physical objects that are inherent in the latter whether or not they are revealed by measurement. But quantum-mechanical descriptions refer to the results of interactions of atomic objects with a measuring

3. Strictly speaking, the statistical interpretation of ψ-states requires an abandonment of the classical notion of an *instantaneous* state, for frequency distributions are defined only for a finite time interval, not for an *instant* of time.

apparatus, and the question of the "inherent," "objective" properties or states of the atomic objects has, from this point of view, no operational meaning whatever. Quantum mechanics is, therefore, said to support an idealistic, or at least phenomenalistic, epistemology. This philosophy seems to draw support from the fact that the concept of probability enters into quantum-mechanical state descriptions, or at any rate into their empirical interpretation: for is not probability relative to information? And if so, is not the quantum-mechanical description of microprocesses partly subjective?

That those who allege that physical microprocesses are irrevocably in-deterministic (i.e., only statistically lawful)—however they may deduce the nonexistence of deterministic laws from the human failure, up to date, to detect any—should also question the applicability of the common-sense concept of objective physical reality to the microworld is not accidental; for there is a close logical connection between the belief in causality and the belief in the independent existence of physical objects and processes. If many observed instances of a kind of event *A* have been experienced in conjunction with observed instances of another kind of event *B*, and a new instance of *B* is observed, one infers the occurrence of a new instance of *A* though it may be unobserved. In this way we infer, as Hume noted, that the fire continued to burn in our absence because we observe the same effect we have found to follow observed fires; in the same way we infer that familiar sounds were produced by familiar objects at a time when the latter were not seen by us. The validity of such inductive inferences from observed effects to unobserved causes cannot be established, obviously, in terms of causal laws which themselves are extrapolated to unobserved events and objects by the very same mode of inference. Thus it would be naive to attempt a purely empirical proof of the continued existence of a tree when it is not observed by anyone by pointing to the shadow as an effect that can only be explained by assuming that the tree continued to intercept the sunlight while it was not observed, for this is simply to *assume* that if an observed effect does not have any observed cause of the kind that has been observed to produce it in the past, then it has an unobserved cause of just the same kind. Still, the assumption of permanent objects and unobserved physical processes is forced upon us by the principle of causality, by the desire to account for our sense-impressions in terms of fairly simple laws. How could we account for the observed shadow if we did not assume the continued existence of an opaque thing? The realistic postulate enables us to formulate causal generalizations that are extensively confirmable, whereas a phenomenalistic restriction to sense-impressions makes the formulation of reliable causal laws impossible. For example, we can reliably predict that the release of a heavy body in midair is followed by its fall, but a sense-impression of such a release need not at all be followed by a sense-impression of a fall since the observer may close his eyes or turn around after having released the object. In this sense, therefore, there is a close logical connection between physical realism and causal determinism.

But the question whether physical objects have measurable traits and are in measurable states independently of an actual *measurement* should not be confused with the question whether they exist and have determinate properties independently of *observation*. The statements of physics never mention mental acts of observation, whether they refer to macro-objects or to micro-objects. Without the realistic assumption that all of us make as a matter of "animal faith"—at least when we are not philosophizing—there could be no science of physics, and this is just as true of quantum physics as it was of classical physics. The classical assumption that may be reasonably questioned in the light of quantum mechanics is rather the assumption that we can always make verifiable statements about physical objects without reference to actual measurements conceived as interactions of the objects with measuring apparatus. Is measurement just a process of revealing the traits and states of objects that the latter possess whether they are revealed or not, or is it a process of interaction that yields knowledge only about the result of the interaction?

In order to see more clearly exactly which question is at issue let us analyze a simple classical statement of measurement—say, that the temperature of body A at time t equals 90°F. It obviously does not mean that an actual measurement is carried out at t with the result 90°F. If it did mean that, then it would be false provided the temperature of A at t is not measured; and then all statements ascribing a different temperature to A at t would also be false, with the result that A has no temperature at all at time t! The idea that temperature is a state of a body that exists independently of its actual measurement is preserved, on the other hand, by the conditional interpretation: *if A were brought into contact with a thermometer at time t, then* the latter would register 90°F at t. A direct verification of this conditional statement requires, of course, an actual measurement, but it is clear that the statement does not describe its own direct verification, otherwise the intelligible assertion that the statement might not be directly verified and still be true would be unintelligible.

But is there any way of knowing what a body's temperature is at a time when it is not measured? This is to ask whether one could have grounds for asserting a conditional of the above kind though the operation described by its antecedent remained unperformed. The answer is, of course, affirmative. We have inductive grounds for ascribing a dispositional property P to an object if it has observed properties that are lawfully connected with P. Thus the temperature of a confined mass of gas might be calculated from the gas pressure without actually using a thermometer. Nevertheless, a special problem arises from the circumstance that a measurement of temperature is a process of interaction in which the initial temperature of the measured object may be changed. How do we know what the temperature of the measured object was before it exchanged heat energy with the thermometer? The obvious answer may seem to be that we can calculate this initial temperature on the basis of the principle of the conservation of the quantity of heat within a thermally closed system: the heat gained by the thermometer (assuming it to be initially colder than the measured object) is equal to the heat lost by the measured object, and since the masses and specific heats of the interacting objects can be measured and the initial temperature of the thermometer as well as the equilibrium temperature are known, the initial temperature of the measured object can easily be calculated. But this answer begs the question, for if this fundamental equation of calorimetry is to be used to determine initial temperatures, it must first itself be established by independent measurements of the temperatures that thermally interacting bodies have prior to their thermal interaction, but this requires again a thermal interaction with a thermometer, and how can we ascertain the temperature status of these bodies prior to their measurements without presupposing the equation that is to be established? If the latter, on the other hand, describes only a mathematical relation between *measured* temperatures of thermally interacting bodies, then it cannot be used to compute unmeasured temperatures, i.e., temperatures of bodies before the thermal interaction that constitutes their measurement. Fortunately, however, this is not an inescapable dilemma. It can be experimentally verified that if the mass of the thermometer is very small in comparison with the mass of the measured body, then the equilibrium temperature is practically independent of the initial temperature of the thermometer. In this sense the initial temperature of the measured object is practically "undisturbed" by the process of measurement. Indeed, the doubt whether the temperature disclosed by the measurement is really the "objective" temperature of the body is an idle metaphysical doubt unless it is just the doubt whether a measurement with a different thermometer would have yielded the same result. Hence the fact that such invariance of results is guaranteed by the use of sufficiently small thermometers ought to dissolve it.

Just in this respect, however, measurement of temperature is profoundly different from measurement of position, momentum, or energy of micro-objects. Here, as we have seen, a "disturbance" of the state of the micro-object is inevitable—*if* one conceives of the micro-object as having an objective, classical state at all. And no presently conceivable improvement of measuring techniques could eliminate the "disturbance." A further difficulty is that the concept of dispositional, objective properties or states is logically tied up with the concept of genidentical things. Whenever similar operations, whether just perceptual or measuring operations, repeatedly and consistently lead to similar results, we speak of objects with "inherent" properties. If the apparent shape, size, and color of a penny underwent continual change under constant conditions of observation, we would not speak of a penny with an inherent color, size, and shape at all. It is true that some dispositional properties are such that their manifestation coincides with the destruction of the thing to which we ascribe them: a lump of sugar is destroyed as a thing by its dissolution, a block of ice is destroyed as a block of ice by melting, and so on. But in these cases there is still a genidentical thing to which the dispositional properties are ascribable because other properties remained constant before these particular dispositional properties were manifested: the lump of sugar had a constant shape, size, color, taste and weight; the block of ice a constant weight, size, shape, hardness, and temperature. Now, we have seen that the concept of genidentical particles, or even waves, has suffered shipwreck in microphysics. It is therefore to be expected that the concept of "objective" measurable states of microobjects, in the sense in which temperature, length, and mass are ascribable to macro-objects, will run into trouble. If it is impossible to trace a path, an orbit of an electron or a photon, then the nouns "electron" and "photon" just don't denote particles. That particlehood analytically implies a continuous orbit becomes clear the moment we ask ourselves on what ground successive particle-positions at different places are regarded as successive positions of the same particle. The answer: if the intermediate places are found to be succesively occupied by similar qualities. In this sense particles might even be identified with continuous series of events of such a kind that closely contiguous members are similar. That particles move continuously, i.e., that the position of a persisting particle is a continuous function of the time, is on this conception of particlehood a purely analytic proposition. The idea that matter is composed of substantial electrons (along with other elementary particles) ought, therefore, to have been shaken already when Bohr's theory of the atom had to postulate discontinuous jumps of electrons from one orbit to another, for, as long as the number of planetary electrons remains constant, how is one to tell whether the *same* electron has changed its orbit or whether one electron has been destroyed and another created on a different orbit? At any rate, the experiments with electrons passing simultaneously through distant holes of a diaphragm made the particle model untenable even for those who had not noticed the contradiction in the concept of a "jumping" particle. And in order to avoid the mystery of an electron's metamorphosis from wave into particle, it may be best to abandon the attempt to interpret microphenomena by means of the thing-language adapted to common-sense experience, and to speak instead of wavelike and particlelike electron *events*.

We have seen that we can distinguish a description of an actual measurement from an ascription of a *measurable* property or state to an object by a dispositional analysis of the latter. But dispositions are ascribable only to relatively permanent objects. It is for this reason that the distinction between describing micro-objects as they are independently of measurement and describing their interactions with measuring apparatus had to collapse with the "substantial" interpretation of the microworld. Thus electrons assume a particlelike aspect only when they interact with experimental apparatus such as a fluorescent screen, and there is no reason for supposing even that the *same* electron exists, as a wave or wave packet, before this interaction. How, then, could one expect that a law of quantum mechanics, such as Schrödinger's wave equation, should describe the behavior of swarms of electrons "objectively," without reference to interactions with measuring apparatus? A measurement of a particle-position can be distinguished from the particle-position if there is a particle that has a position whether or not it is measured; and this assumption of the existence of particles, we argued, rests on the experience of genidentical event-series in the macroworld. Since a sharp electron-position is not a position of a genidentical electron, a measurement of a sharp electron-position —whose probability is given by the square of a quantum-mechanical state function—is not a revelation of a position that a substantial particle would have had even if it had not been revealed. In this sense it is true that quantum mechanics does not describe an "objective" reality that is independent of measurement interactions. What has here been suggested is that this epistemological feature of quantum mechanics results from the inapplicability of the concept of genidentical things to the world of subatomic phenomena.

The fact that probability enters into the very description of quantum-mechanical "reality" indicates the collapse of classical determinism, not because a statistical description of large aggregates is incompatible with a causal description of the behavior of the individual elements of the aggregates, but because the aggregates whose states are represented by ψ-functions are not composed of persisting particles describing continuous orbits. Schroedinger's wave equation is deterministic, in the sense that it expresses the rate of change in time of the ψ-function as a function of the ψ-function; but the waves whose propagation it renders predictable are not material waves, like water waves or sound waves. They are *probability waves*. This means that in speaking of waves, physicists use a spatial picture of the probabilities of certain pointlike events, such as bright spots on a screen hit by photons. The spread of the wave symbolizes the range of uncertainty as to the location of such pointlike events; the intensity of the wave at various points within its spread (which according to classical wave theory is proportional to the square of the amplitude) represents the probability of a pointlike event at those points. For example, within a very bright band of the screen hit by photons the intensity of the probability wave is great, which means that the probability that a given quantum of light energy (a photon) would be encountered there is great, which means that the ratio of the number of such quanta in that area to the number in the total area within which a quantum may hit is large. That these probabilities are said to vary in space as well as in time may seem strange in the light of our analysis of the frequency concept of probability in Chapter 11. For a statistical probability was there defined as a fraction that must remain fixed as long as the attribute and the reference class remains fixed. Indeed, in speaking of "fluctuations" of probability in space and time physicists speak loosely, since the alleged fluctuations are due to shifts of the reference class or of the attribute. In the case of fluctuations in space, the attribute is being shifted, viz. the location of the point-events. In the case of temporal fluctuations, the reference class is being shifted: the class of photon impacts somewhere on the screen at time t_1 is, of course, different from the class of photon impacts somewhere on the screen at time t_2; hence the probability of a photon impact at position x may change in the sense that the probability of such an event at t_1 differs from the probability of such an event at t_2.

The following experiment, often mentioned in the literature on quantum mechanics, shows impressively that the waves whose states are represented by ψ-functions cannot be material waves. Let a single photon be shot at the surface of a transparent substance, and let us assume that it has an even chance of being transmitted or reflected. The ψ-states of this minimal beam of light energy right after it reaches the surface are then represented by two waves, one corresponding to the possible paths of reflection, the other to the possible paths of transmission. But suppose that after calculation of the possible paths of reflection a screen intercepting them is set up, and suppose that a luminous spot on that screen is observed just after the photon was shot at the surface. The observer then knows that the photon was reflected, and relative to this new item of information the probability of its having been transmitted is, of course, zero. Since the intensities of the ψ-waves at various places are proportional to the probability of certain atomic events at those places, this means that the ψ-wave corresponding to the possible paths of transmission collapses as a result of that observation. Technically this process is called "reduction of a wave packet" (the probability waves under discussion are really wave packets since, as pointed out earlier, it is only by superposition of waves that a

wave of finite spatial extent, representing the distribution of probabilities in a finite volume, can be generated). But if the ψ-waves were
material waves, the described "reduction of a wave packet" would be a
truly astounding causal action of mind on matter: a mere act of observing a luminous spot on a screen has annihilated a wave a million miles
away! Such an "idealistic" interpretation is, of course, not only fantastic
but also inconsistent: it is only if the ψ-waves are regarded as probability
waves that there is any warrant for ascribing to an observation such
destructive power. But in that case what has been destroyed is not a
material existent, but only a probability—in just the same sense in
which the half chance of throwing heads is "destroyed" and replaced
by certainty when the penny is actually observed to come up heads.

Is what quantum mechanics describes by means of ψ-functions, then,
"objective" or "subjective"? Are the probabilities whose succession is
governed by a deterministic equation of wave mechanics physically real
or an expression of partial knowledge and partial ignorance? This
philosophical issue, the question whether the quantum theory in the
dominant statistical interpretation satisfies the classical ideal of a predictively fertile description of objective, physical reality or whether,
on the contrary, it has rendered physics "subjectivistic," ought to be
decidable without excessive difficulty by a careful analysis of the relevant concept of probability. A relative frequency of occurrence of a
specified attribute within a specified reference class is, of course, a
physical fact independent of observation; at any rate, there is no reason
for doubting that such a relative frequency exists uninfluenced by observation. An initial probability distribution is determined, in a concrete application of wave mechanics, in essentially the same way in
which the probabilities of the various sides of a die are determined. A
probability distribution of scintillations on a screen has no meaning
with respect to, say, a single electron, which may hit the screen here
or there or somewhere else. It can be determined only by emitting a
swarm of electrons from some source and then finding the relative
frequencies of hits in the various parts of the screen. If this is how the
probability distributions that are causally connected by the wave
equation are conceived, they are perfectly objective and there is no
basis for the assertion that they change with the knowledge acquired
by an observer. My knowledge that the penny just came up heads does
not change the probability, in the sense of the frequency definition, of
the penny's falling heads, for that probability is the relative frequency
of heads approached in a long series of penny throws. Similarly, an
observer's knowledge that an electron, or a photon, whose motion was
individually (causally) unpredictable just hit the screen at a specified
point, does not change the probability that the "particle" hits the screen
at that point if the probability in question is the relative frequency with

which such "particles" hit that location when emitted under the same observable initial conditions.

On the other hand, the probability of a *single* event is "subjective" in the sense that it varies with the information that is relevant to the prediction of the event. Suppose I know that a friend of mine arrived in a given city and registered in one or the other of two hotels, *A* or *B*. Relative to this information, the probability that he is presently in the lobby of hotel *A* is not very high; if I subsequently learn that he did not register in hotel *B*, the probability of the same event rises, and, of course, if I then actually meet him in the lobby of hotel *A*, it jumps to certainty. It is in this sense of probability of single events[4] that the probability of events that the physicist interprets as manifestations of micro-objects changes with the relevant observations. But it does not follow that the probabilities represented by ψ-waves change with relevant observations, provided they are consistently interpreted as relative frequencies of specified point-events or impulse-events in *classes of* similar events. To say that each new relevant observation or measurement disrupts the causal succession of ψ-states is to overlook that a statistical probability by its very definition refers to a fixed reference class. The statement, for example, that the solitary photon in the described reflection experiment has an even chance of being reflected, says something about the relative frequency of reflected photons in a long series of experiments with similar initial conditions. This probability statement, therefore, remains valid after the observation of a luminous spot on the screen makes it certain that the *particular* photon in question was reflected. If this new information implies, according to the rules of the probabilistic interpretation of wave mechanics, that the ψ-wave corresponding to possible paths of transmission collapses, then this interpretation simply involves a confusion of objective probabilities defined in terms of fixed classes of similar events and subjective probabilities of individual events, which, as explained, vary with relevant information.

F. IS DETERMINISM COMPATIBLE WITH FREE WILL?

Notoriously, the social sciences, in the broad sense of the sciences of human behavior, cannot as yet pride themselves on predictive and

4. Cf. the analysis of this concept, in terms of the principle of "total evidence," in Chapter 11.

explanatory successes comparable to those of the physical sciences. One argument offered to show that this superiority of the physical over the social sciences is not a reflection on the skill of social scientists (including psychologists) but a consequence of the peculiarity of the subject-matter of the social sciences is that conscious human behavior is an expression of free will and *therefore* not governed by causal laws. As a matter of fact, the most rigorous and mathematical of the social sciences employ statistical methods to arrive at and test statistical generalizations about large populations. Mathematically precise deterministic laws allowing individual predictions are rare in the social sciences. At the time when physics still operated within the framework of classical determinism, this state of affairs tended to throw an unfavorable light on the social sciences. John Stuart Mill, believing in the deterministic character of the ultimate laws of nature, advocated the "concrete deductive" method as the ideal method of the social sciences: to derive laws of human society, including laws of social change, inductively from observations or even experiments is a method doomed to failure; instead the social scientists ought to guess—aided, perhaps, by introspective observation—the causal laws governing individual human behavior (for example, that a human being acts in economic respects so as to maximize his welfare) and hence deduce the expected aggregate behavior in situations of social interaction. But since the twentieth-century developments in quantum physics it is tempting for social scientists to point at physics and to say: If physical microevents exhibit only a statistical regularity, why should it be different with human actions? Why should we expect, like Mill, that as yet undiscovered deterministic laws underlie the statistical regularities that we are discovering with increasing success?

Whether individual human actions are governed by deterministic laws like planetary motions, or whether they are comparable to the behavior of electrons and photons in being only statistically lawful, is a factual question that cannot be settled by a priori arguments. The claim made by some quantum physicists that we now know that the ultimate laws of microphysics are statistical is just as dogmatic as the contrary claim that statistical laws *must* be derivable from deterministic laws. But even if the former claim were well supported, it would have no tendency at all to undermine the search for deterministic laws of human action. Even if quantum jumps occur in the brain when a human being consciously reacts to the environment in a certain way, his reaction might still fall under a deterministic *molar* law of the form "Whenever a human with (acquired or inherited) disposition D_1, D_2, ... , is exposed to an environment of kind E, then he reacts by doing A." The fact that the laws of quantum physics—which, of course, apply also to the microprocesses going on in living brain cells—are statistical, need not inhibit behavior scientists from the search for a more reliable deterministic law of that form when they encounter exceptions to their first, provisional formulation, and in that sense they may still be guided by the principle of causality whatever the latest word of quantum physics may be.

A famous a priori argument against the determinism of human actions is the argument from "free will." The argument alleges that causal predictability of an action is *incompatible* with its being an expression of the agent's "free will." Although this question has been debated for many centuries and continues to be debated, it must be decidable by a careful analysis of the meaning, or meanings, of "free will": whether two propositions are compatible or incompatible cannot remain in doubt after the propositions have been clearly analyzed (unless there be a doubt about the relevant laws of logic, which is rarely the case). Let us consider a simple example of free action, such as a voter casting his ballot for a certain candidate for political office without having been "compelled" to do so in any ordinary sense of this word. Indeed, if the ballot is secret, and the voter believes that it really is secret, it is difficult to see how he could possibly be compelled, in the ordinary sense of this word, to vote for a particular candidate; that he may be compelled—by his desire to be regarded a solid citizen by his neighbors —to vote at all is a different matter, since it is easy to find out whether or not a qualified voter exercised his privilege. The voter's action, then, was free in the sense that it was not coerced—as would be the case, for example, if the ballot were not secret and a voter voting against the candidates put up by the dominant party had reason to believe that he would suffer for such an act of nonconformism. Given the circumstances that existed when he entered the voting booth, however, both the external circumstances consisting in the eligibility of specified candidates and the internal circumstances consisting in the voter's political ideals and beliefs, his vote for candidate X was predictable. None of us, for example, would have hesitated to predict that our friend, whom we know to detest Republicanism, whether of the "old guard" or the "modern" variety, and whom we also know to be an ardent admirer of Adlai Stevenson, would vote for Stevenson and against Eisenhower if he voted at all. Yet, even if his political preference were purely emotional, unsupported by good reasons, it would be odd to deny that his action was free. Since his overt action was a direct and natural expression of his desire, viz. of the election of his favored candidate, and he did not prefer it to its alternatives—not voting at all or voting for a different candidate—because he dreaded its consequences less than those he expected from the alternative actions (as when a hunted criminal "gives himself up" because he expects this action to lead to a milder penalty), it was not a coerced action, and in that sense it was free.

This simple analysis establishes at least that the burden of proof rests on him who claims predictability and freedom to be incompatible attributes of actions. Let us, then, examine some proofs of the alleged incompatibility.

Certainly, some of our actions are in accordance with our desires, others are forced upon us by the circumstances we find ourselves in. And it is, indeed, customary to describe the former as free. But in a profounder sense an action is really free only if under the very same circumstances in which it was performed it *might not* have been performed. It is rather trivial to point out that the voter would not have pulled the Democratic lever if he had not desired to do so. The serious question, however, is whether given his total background, he could have desired otherwise. A determinist must clearly deny this, but then he is committed to the view that the desires that we occasionally express in our actions are really inevitable and predetermined, and in this sense, he must hold, our actions are not free after all. They are, according to determinism, the causal consequents of many antecedent events over which the agent had no control at all, and therefore they are not free in the profound sense of the word.

The sense of "free action," which according to this argument is only superficial, may be rendered by the following definition: A free action is an action that (*a*) is partly caused by the agent's desire to perfom it (that is, if the agent did not want to perform it, he would not perform it and (*b*) is not preferred to the alternative because it appears as the "smaller evil.") Before reflecting on the allegedly profounder meaning of the word "freedom," let us be clear that this definition does succeed in distinguishing different classes of human actions. To say that a person did what he or she desired to do, as contrasted with what he or she was compelled to do, is surely to make an informative statement. Everybody understands the distinction, for example, between making a charitable contribution because one wants to help and making it in spite of desiring to spend the money for entertainment, merely because one fears the neighbors disapproval of one's selfishness. Some confusion may, however, arise if desiring is not properly distinguished from deciding. Deciding to do a certain thing means not just desiring to do it, otherwise it would be contradictory to say that people often decide to do what they would rather not do. Reflection on the consequences of the satisfaction of a certain desire often leads one to *decide* not to satisfy it. The captured soldier who betrays the whereabouts of his battalion under threat of torture certainly carries out a decision inasmuch as he considered the consequences of the two alternatives and deliberated what he should do; but his action was coerced since he would have preferred not to inform (contrast this situation with the case of a soldier who voluntarily gives the information to the enemy because he disapproves of the cause his country is fighting for). If a free action, therefore, were defined as an action that the agent decided to perform, then any action that resulted from a process of deliberation would be free, even actions that the agent was compelled to do against his desires. One may, of course, so use the word "free" that even what people absolutely hate to do is said to be "freely" done by them provided it is a process of reasoning, forecasting of the consequences of the alternatives open to them, that causes them to do it. But in that case many coerced actions would be free, "free action" would be synonymous with "deliberate, or reasoned, action," and another, more restricted word would have to be appropriated as a word of contrast to "coerced."

To those, however, who hold determinism to be incompatible with freedom in the profound sense, it makes little difference whether "superficially" free action is defined in terms of desire or in terms of decision. For their point is that, in the profound sense, an action is free only if the agent *could* have decided not to do it; that he would not have done it *if* he had decided not to do it, they cheerfully concede but dismiss as an unimportant truism. As this argument shows, the central problem of analysis we must face is what "could" means in a context such as "He could have refrained from stealing the money." Those who hold determinism of human behavior to be incompatible with the sort of freedom of decision we presuppose when we pass moral judgments on human actions are not satisfied with the analysis "If he had not desired to steal the money, he would not have stolen it" nor with the analysis "If he had decided (made up his mind) not to steal the money, he would not have stolen it." For, they ask, could the agent have had a different desire, or could he have made a different decision *given* all the causal antecedents, if every event, including mental events, is causally determined? If determinism is true, then an omniscient psychologist who knew the character and the motives as well as the present beliefs of the criminal could have predicted that when confronted with the opportunity to steal he would decide to steal. No physicist would allow that, given all the physical forces determining a particle's motion and given the particle's initial state, it could have moved differently from the way it moved. Similarly determinism entails that given all the causal antecedents, nobody could have desired or decided differently.

Clearly, there are these different uses of "could": When we say of an overt action that it could have been avoided, we refer to its causal dependence on the agent's desire or decision to do it or other things causally related to it. "The automobile accident was avoidable: if the driver had decided to slow down before reaching the intersection, his car would have come to a stop before hitting the pedestrian." Nobody in practical life would contest the avoidability of the accident—and consequently the responsibility of the driver—on the ground that the driver's carelessness could in turn be causally explained. But "could" the driver have decided to slow down? If the question is whether he would have made that decision if he had decided to make it, it is of course nonsensical. What the question must be taken to be is whether his failure to exercise caution was itself a necessary causal consequence of the total set of causal antecedents. And the answer to this question is "Yes, if human actions and their mental causes are subject to deterministic laws—which nobody knows but which it is useful to suppose in our causal investigation of them."

It appears, then, that what some philosophers call the profound sense of "freedom" is simply indeterminacy. Consequently the proposition that determinism of human action is incompatible with freedom in the profound sense of the word is a mere truism. And there is no good reason for departing from the ordinary use of "free action" as meaning either "desired, uncoerced action" or "reasoned action, i.e., action decided upon as a result of deliberation." In either of these two senses, some actions are free and some are not, but all of them are commonly supposed to have causes. In some cases, though, the causal explanation stops at an apparently spontaneous volition. I made a fist right now because I wanted to, but why did I want to make a fist? Nobody knows. If quantum physicists are justified in maintaining that such events as radioactive disintegrations of individual atoms and individual luminous spots on a screen receiving light energy have no causes, then one is equally justified in holding that such spontaneous volitions have no causes. But either claim would be the kind of dogma that stirs up heated but unilluminating philosophical debate. The plain fact is that nobody *knows* whether or not such events have causes

Some have argued that because human beings have the power to *decide* what they are going to do, human actions could never, even for a superhuman psychologist, be predictable in the same sense in which the course of inanimate nature is predictable. For provided I know what volitional action of mine has been predicted, I can deliberately falsify the prediction. If the predictor is truly omniscient, then, of course, he will also know that I have the desire as well as the power to prove him wrong. So he may change his prediction in the light of this additional knowledge about my motivation. But because of my "freedom of decision" I always remain a step ahead of him: knowing that he canceled his first prediction because he believed that I would decide to falsify it, I may now decide to make his first prediction true in order to falsify the contradictory prediction that superseded it. This argument does establish that a *publicized* prediction of a conscious human action can never be based upon a complete set of initial conditions, since the agents' knowledge of the prediction is a further relevant initial condition relative to which the probability of the prediction's coming true may decrease. For this reason a shrewd predictor of human action would proceed dishonestly as follows: He publicizes a prediction to agents whom he knows to be resolved to demonstrate their "freedom of decision" by deliberately falsifying predictions made about them. He knows, then, that the publication of his prediction makes it highly probable that the prediction will be falsified. Therefore he keeps in his hidden files, as it were, the contradictory prediction, which he really believes in view of the calculated effect of the dishonest publicized prediction.

Nevertheless, this argument does not establish that, because human beings have the power of spontaneous decision, their actions cannot be causally determined in the same sense in which physical processes may be so determined. The argument, in fact, involves a confusion of causal determination with practical predictability. An assertion of unique determination is, of course, verified by predictive success, but it says nothing whatever about human acts of prediction, especially not about predictions in the literal sense of assertions in the future tense. If it is true that C uniquely determines E, then it is true regardless of whether or not anybody ever predicts an occurrence of E on the basis of C. This remains the case if E is a future *act*ion of a human being and C includes that human being's belief that someone predicted he would not do E as well as his desire and ability to prove the predictor wrong. The omniscient calculator then knows that E will occur, but he wisely keeps this knowledge to himself—at least until E has occurred. In fact, to say that my actions causally depend on my awareness of a prediction of them is grossly incompatible with the denial of their causal determination.

Selected Readings

Ayer, A. J., "Freedom and Necessity," in A. J. Ayer, *Philosophical Essays* (London, 1954).

Bergmann, G., "The Logic of Quanta," *American Journal of Physics*, 1947.

Birkhoff, G. D., and J. von Neumann, "The Logic of Quantum Mechanics," *Annals of Mathematics*, 1936.

Bohr, N., *Atomic Theory and Description of Nature* (Cambridge, 1934).

——, "Causality and Complementarity," *Philosophy of Science*, 1937.

Born, M., *Natural Philosophy of Cause and Chance* (Oxford, 1949).

Bunge, M., *Metascientific Queries* (Springfield, Mass., 1958), chap. 8, 9.

——, *Causality: The Place of the Causal Principle in Modern Science* (Cambridge, 1959).

Campbell, C. A., "Is 'Free Will' a Pseudo-Problem?" *Mind*, 1951. [Reprinted in P. Edwards and A. Pap (eds.), *A Modern Introduction to Philosophy* (New York, 1957).

Cassirer, E., *Determinism and Indeterminism in Modern Physics* (New Haven, Conn., 1956).

Dear, G. F., "Determinism in Classical Physics," *British Journal for the Philosophy of Science*, 1961.

Destouches, J. L., "Physique moderne et philosophie," in R. Klibanski (ed.), *Philosophy in the Mid-Century* (Florence, 1958), Vol. I.

Eddington, A., *Nature of the Physical World* (New York, 1928), chap. 14.

——, "Indeterminacy and Indeterminism," *Aristotelian Society Proceedings*, supp. Vol. 10 (1931).

Frank, P., *Das Kausalgesetz und Seine Grenzen* (Vienna, 1932).

——, *Interpretations and Misinterpretations of Modern Physics* (Paris, 1938).

——, *Philosophy of Science* (New York, 1957), chap. 11, 12.

Gruenbaum, A., "Causality and the Science of Human Behavior," in H. Feigl and M. Brodbeck (eds.), *Readings in the Philosophy of Science* (New York, 1953).

Hanson, N. R., "The Copenhagen Interpretation of Quantum Theory," *American Journal of Physics*, 1959. [Reprinted in A. Danto and S. Morgenbesser (eds.), *Philosophy of Science* (New York, 1960).]

——, "Five Cautions for the Copenhagen Interpretation's Critics," *Philosophy of Science*, 1959.

Heisenberg, W., *The Physical Principles of the Quantum Theory* (Chicago, 1930).

——, *Philosophic Problems of Nuclear Science* (London, 1952).

——, "The Development of the Interpretation of Quantum Theory, 1912–29," in W. Pauli (ed.), *Niels Bohr and the Development of Physics* (London, 1955).

——, *The Physicist's Concept of Nature* (New York, 1958).

——, "The Representation of Nature in Contemporary Physics," *Daedalus*, 1958.

Hinshaw, V., Jr., "Determinism Versus Continuity," *Philosophy of Science*, 1959.

Hobart, R. B., "Free will as Involving Determination and Inconceivable without It," *Mind*, 1934.

Hook, S. (ed.), *Determinism and Freedom in the Age of Modern Science* (New York, 1957).

Hutton, E., *The Logic of Modern Physics* (New York, 1956).

Koerner, S. (ed.), *Observation and Interpretation* (New York, 1957).

Landau, L., and E. Lifshitz, *Quantum Mechanics* (Cambridge, 1958).

Landé, A., *Foundations of Quantum Theory* (New Haven, 1955).

——, "From Dualism to Unity in Quantum Mechanics," *British Journal for the Philosophy of Science*, 1959.

Lenzen, V., "The Concept of Physical Reality," *Philosophical Review*, 1945.

——, "Philosophical Problems of the Statistical Interpretation of Quantum Mechanics," *Proceedings of the Second Berkeley Symposium on Mathematical Statistics and Probability*, 1951.

Lindsay, R., and H. Margenau, *Foundations of Physics* (New York, 1936), chap. 10.

Ludwig, G., *Die Grundlagen der Quanten-Mechanik* (Berlin, 1954).

Margenau, H., "Reality in Quantum Mechanics," *Philosophy of Science*, 1949.

——, "Conceptual Foundations of Quantum Theory," *Science*, 1951.

Margenau, H., *The Nature of Physical Reality* (New York, 1950), chap. 19.

Mehlberg, H., "The Idealistic Interpretation of Quantum Mechanics," *Studia Philosophica* (Poland), 1949–50.

Nagel, E., "The Causal Character of Modern Physical Theory," in H. Feigl and M. Brodbeck (eds.), *Readings in the Philosophy of Science* (New York, 1953).

——, *The Structure of Science* (New York, 1961), chap. 10.

Northrop, F. S. C., "The Philosophical Significance of the Concept of Probability in Quantum Mechanics," *Philosophy of Science*, 1936. [Reprinted in F. S. C. Northrop, *The Logic of the Sciences and the Humanities* (New York, 1947) chap. 11.]

Novak, S., "Some Problems of Causal Interpretation of Statistical Relationships," *Philosophy of Science*, 1960.

Nowell-Smith, P. H., "Free Will and Moral Responsibility," *Mind*, 1948.

O'Connor, D. J., "Determinism and Predictability," *British Journal for the Philosophy of Science*, 1957.

Planck, M., "The Concept of Causality in Physics," in *Scientific Autobiography and Other Papers*, trans. by F. Gaynor (New York, 1949). [Reprinted in P. P. Wiener (ed.), *Readings in Philosophy of Science* (New York, 1953).]

Popper, K. R., "Indeterminism in Quantum Physics and in Classical Physics, I and II," *British Journal for the Philosophy of Science*, 1950–51.

——, *The Logic of Scientific Discovery* (London, 1958), chap. 9.

Reichenbach, H., *Philosophic Foundations of Quantum Mechanics* (Berkeley, Calif., 1948).

——, "The Principle of Anomaly in Quantum Mechanics," in H. Feigl and M. Brodbeck (eds.), *Readings in the Philosophy of Science* (New York, 1953).

Schlick, M., "Die Kausalität in der gegenwartigen Physik," *Die Naturwissenschaften*, 1931.

——, "When Is a Man Responsible?," in M. Schlick, *Problems of Ethics*, trans. by D. Rynin (New York, 1939). [Reprinted in P. Edwards and A. Pap (eds.), *A Modern Introduction to Philosophy* (New York, 1957).]

——, *Philosophy of Nature* (New York, 1949), chap. 10–13.

Schrödinger, E., "Die gegewärtige Situation in der Quantenmechanik," *Naturwissenschaften*, 1935.

Stebbing, L. S., *Philosophy and the Physicists* (London, 1937).

University of California Associates, "The Freedom of the Will," in H. Feigl and W. Sellars (eds.), *Readings in Philosophical Analysis* (New York, 1949). [Reprinted in M. Munitz (ed.), *A Modern Introduction to Ethics* (New York, 1958).]

Waismann, F., "The Decline and Fall of Causality," in A. Crombie (ed.), *Turning Points in Physics* (Amsterdam, 1959).

Warnock, G. J., " 'Every Event Has a Cause,' " in A. Flew (ed.), *Logic and Language* (Oxford, 1955), Vol. II.

Workman, R. W., "Is Indeterminism Supported by Quantum Theory?," *Philosophy of Science*, 1959.

Part Five

EXPLANATION
AND
JUSTIFICATION

CHAPTER 18

Logical Analysis of Explanation

A. EXPLANATION BY SUBSUMPTION UNDER LAWS

As in our analysis of causation, let us elucidate the common-sense roots of scientific knowledge before focusing on scientific theory. Science can explain and predict far more precisely and reliably than common sense, but in order to gain a preliminary understanding of the process of scientific explanation it is best to begin by analyzing simple everyday examples. Suppose you open the refrigerator and find that the milk has gone sour. This calls for explanation because it is somewhat unusual and hence surprising: milk usually stays fresh in the refrigerator. The explanation, of course, is that you defrosted the refrigerator early in the morning and forgot to turn it on again. The refrigerator did not maintain a sufficiently low temperature for the milk to stay fresh. What has been explained is that the milk turned sour, and the explanation is that the temperature of the surrounding air was too high.

This explanation is, to be sure, superficial, since it is based on observation of an event sequence that the nonscientist just accepts as an empirical regularity but does not really understand. But it is with the first stage of explanation, explanation by subsumption under an empirical regularity, that we are now concerned; the explanation of the presupposed regularities is a different story. The explanation surely involves a rough empirical law, such as "Milk turns sour if kept at average room temperature (say, between 65 and 75°F) for a long time," although there may be a difference of opinion about the exact way in which it is involved. According to one formulation, the law is an indispensable part of the explanation. Let us call the explained fact F_2, the explaining fact (the "cause") F_1, and the law L. Then the formulation in question is not that F_1 by itself explains F_2, but that F_1 does so in conjunction with L. Accordinging to the other formulation, which is patterned after common speech habits, F_1 explains F_2 completely, provided the kind of event of which F_1 is an instance is a strictly sufficient condition for the kind of event of which F_2 is an instance. The law needs to be invoked only in order to justify the claim that F_1 explains F_2, whereas according to the first formulation one has not really given a complete explanation of F_2 without mentioning L. But this is largely a verbal difference. The important point on which both parties will and must agree is that unless there is a law connecting events (or facts) like F_1 with events (or facts) like F_2, the explanation of F_2 in terms of F_1 is not correct.

As the example brings out, subsumptive explanation is a cognitive process that has the same logical structure as prediction. The deductive schema "F_1 and L, therefore F_2" represents an explanation if F_2 is observed first and the cause is inquired into; it represents a prediction if F_1 is observed first and on the basis of this observation F_2 is anticipated. ("You defrosted the refrigerator and forgot to turn it on again; I bet you will find the milk has gone sour.") In other words, in explaining we look for true premises from which the already verified conclusion is deducible, and in predicting we verify the premises before verifying the conclusion. At once, however, we must refine the analysis by clearing up an ambiguity of "verifying." It is obvious that a complete verification of L would include observation of F_2, since this would mean that absolutely all event sequences covered by L had been observed; hence a completely verified law would have no predictive use. Now, in order to justify our claim that F_2 happened because of F_1 we surely must in some sense verify L; that is, we must have grounds for believing L. But if the required grounds of belief were *conclusive* grounds, it would be impossible, indeed logically impossible, ever to justify an explanation claim, since a law, by the very meaning of the word, can only be confirmed, not completely verified. It cannot be completely verified because it applies to an indefinite number of cases. In other words, no matter how many confirming cases of "Whenever A, then B" have been observed, it remains logically possible that there be another instance of A that refutes the generalization. It follows that to justify the claim that F_1 explains F_2 involves the verification of F_1 and the *confirmation* of L in terms of instances other than the sequence F_1–F_2. The better L is confirmed, the better the explanation.

If L, a causal law is well confirmed and F_2 is a deductive consequence of the conjunction of L and F_1, then we have a good *causal explanation*. But it is easy to show that the simultaneous fulfillment of both requirements, the requirement of deducibility and that of a reasonably good confirmation of a relevant causal law, is rarely possible. In order to strictly deduce the "explanandum" (fact to be explained) from the "explanans" (explaining premises) we need a universal premise of the form "All A are B," but such statements usually have known exceptions, so their degree of confirmation relative to the total known relevant evidence is zero. "He slipped because he stepped on a banana peel"; but, of course, it is not true that everybody slips whenever he or she steps on a banana peel. It may be replied that in contrast to the rough explanation sketches that serve the practical purposes of everyday life, at least the precise causal explanations in physical science conform to the model of strictly deductive explanation. For example: The balloon rises because it is filled with a gas that is lighter than air, so that the upward force of buoyancy exceeds the downward pull of gravity. Several strictly universal laws are involved in this explanation: helium's density's being smaller than that of air; Archimedes' principle that a body immersed in a fluid is buoyed up by a force equal to the weight of the displaced fluid; Newton's law that a body accelerates in the direction of the net (resultant) force acting on it. But the more complex a situation in which explainable changes occur, the less applicable are simple, precise laws; the latter usually apply to conceptually simplified, idealized situations. If the methodologist of science holds up the deductive model of causal explanation as an ideal to be striven for by applied scientists, psychologists, and social scientists, he is likely to produce frustration and resignation. That the Democrats scored a landslide victory in a certain congressional election in the United States because after the re-election of Eisenhower the country suffered from a depression with resulting high unemployment and the American electorate tends to blame things that go wrong on the party in administrative power is about as rigorous an explanation as "He slipped because he stepped on a banana peel." It obviously is not deductive, since the "law" it involves is a tendency law, i.e., a statement of the form "*E usually* results when condition C obtains," and from such a statement one cannot deduce that if C now obtains then E will result in that specific situation. Undoubtedly a closer analysis by expert political scientists of the causes of political behavior may produce a more precise and rigorous explanation of the Democratic landslide, but it will certainly not be an explanation satisfying the deductive model, for no strictly universal laws governing political elections are known. And it is surely wiser to recognize *probabilistic explanation* as the best sort of explanation available for complex subject-matters, whether physical or social, than to discourage psychologists and social scientists by identifying scientific explanation with strictly deductive explanation.

We may distinguish vague probabilistic explanation, in terms of tendency laws, from statistical explanation as involving numerical probability implications. The schema of statistical explanation is: m/n cases of A are cases of B; x is a case of A; therefore it is to be expected with probability m/n that x is a case of B. Of course, this is an acceptable explanation only if in classifying x as a case of A we do not omit any information about x that is relevant to the conclusion of the statistical inference. Suppose that in a high percentage of cases an injection of penicillin accelerates recovery from a cold. It may seem superficially that this statistical uniformity justifies the explanation "He recovered from his cold so quickly because he got a penicillin injection." But suppose that in past treatments of this kind the patient in fact has displayed an allergy to penicillin; surely this fact would discredit the explanation, because it puts the patient into a class (say, of people with a physiological characteristic, whatever it may be, that causes a negative reaction to penicillin in the majority of cases) within which the relative frequency of accelerated recovery following a penicillin injection is low. A statistical explanation, therefore, is acceptable only if it satisfies the important principle of total evidence, discussed in Chapter 11 in connection with the problem of the probability of singular statements.

It should further be noted that statistical explanation, just like causal explanation, must involve, either as premise or as justificatory principle, a *lawlike* generalization. If it happens accidentally that nine out of ten people in a certain village whose surname begins with F married a blonde at the age of twenty-five, we would not be justified in arguing "John Farber, inhabitant of that village, *might have been expected* to marry a blonde at twenty-five, for nine out of ten males there whose surname begins with F behaved just like that, as the village statistics show." Since experience does not indicate any significant correlation between the first letters of surnames and the age of marriage of the bearer of the name nor the hair color of the spouse, there is no justification here for the probabilistic counterfactual inference "If x were an inhabitant of that village and his surname began with F, there would be a nine-out-of-ten chance that x would marry a blonde at the age of 25"; therefore the statistical premise cannot function in an explanation.

We have argued that explanation and prediction of individual facts are logically equivalent processes in the sense that if it is correct to say "The fact that F_1 occurred explains the fact that F_2 occurred (a little later)," then it must also be correct to say "If we had observed F_1 before observing F_2 we might have (rationally) expected that F_2 would occur." It is important to understand that this logical equivalence does not depend on whether or not the causal law, which can be equally used to predict and to explain, is symmetrical. Let us call a causal law symmetrical if it authorizes inferences in both directions, from present to future and from present to past. Thus, if we have reason to believe that a certain kind of destruction can be caused only by an atomic bomb, then we can formulate a law in the symmetrical form "If *and only if* an atomic bomb explodes in a certain region, then such and such destruction is wrought in the region." On the other hand, where plurality of causes is involved, the inference from effect to cause is not nearly as reliable as the prediction of the effect from the cause. It is easy to predict that a car hitting an icy piece of road at great speed will go out of control; but since any number of causes can produce the same effect, the inference from the information that the car went out of control to the proposition that it slid on ice is not nearly as certain. Similarly, quantitative laws of physics may be symmetrical or asymmetrical, depending on whether they describe reversible or irreversible processes. The law of freely falling bodies, for example, is symmetrical because the same equation can be used to calculate *later* or *earlier* positions of a freely falling body. (The mathematical expression of this symmetry is that it makes no difference whether positive or negative values are substituted for the time variable, since the latter occurs in squared form.) The law of entropy, on the other hand, asserts that in an isolated system organized states (states of low entropy) are almost always followed by disorganized states (states of high entropy), but it does not say that a disorganized state, such as a state of uniform temperature and density, must have been preceded by more organized states: the information that an isolated system is now in a state of maximal entropy is compatible with the hypothesis that it has always been in that state, that it did not evolve from organization to disorganization.

But this distinction between symmetrical and asymmetrical laws does not affect the logical equivalence of explanation and prediction. Even if the inference from a present occurrence of E to an earlier occurrence of C is, on account of plurality of causes, unreliable, C cannot be a basis for predicting E unless it is correct to say, in retrospect, "E happened because of C." That *other instances* of E may be caused by antecedents other than C is perfectly compatible with explaining the occurrence of *this* particular instance of E in terms of C. Similarly, suppose that we have a vessel divided into two compartments by a wall impervious to heat and water, one compartment filled with cold water, the other with hot water. The law of entropy allows us to predict that if the entire vessel is thermally isolated from the surroundings and the dividing wall is removed, then the cold and the hot water will mix until a uniform temperature is reached. (It will "almost never" happen that the cold water becomes colder and the hot water hotter.) But clearly the same law authorizes the explanation "The water in the vessel has acquired uniform temperature because the cold and the hot mass of water were allowed to diffuse and the vessel remained in thermal isolation from the surroundings." That the same disorganized state of the water system might not have been preceded by an organized state—hence, that the inference from present to past here is less reliable than the inference from present to future—in no way contradicts the logical equivalence of explanation and prediction.

B. SUBSUMPTIVE EXPLANATION
OF LAWS

The laws by subsumption under which individual facts are explained must be confirmable, for otherwise it is not proper to speak of "explanation" in the scientific sense. Theistic explanations of events in terms of the will of God are *formally* quite in order: from "Whatever happens is willed by God" and "God willed that Miller die young" we can deduce that Miller was bound to die young with the same rigor as we deduce that the ice had to melt from "Whenever the sun shines, the ice melts" and "The sun shines." But whereas we can *separately* verify that the sun shines and that the ice melts, and hence confirm the universal premise of the latter argument, we have no independent access to God's will: the only conceivable evidence for the proposition that it was God's will that Miller die young is just that Miller died young—otherwise those who claim to have privileged access to His will ought to be able to predict that Miller would die young instead of just "explaining" it ex post facto— hence the theological "law" here invoked is not confirmable. But although the requirement of confirmability of explanatory laws is inevitably imposed by the very meaning of "scientific explanation," one should be careful not to confuse the confirmation of a law with *its* explanation. The ruling that a law cannot really exercise an explanatory function unless it is itself explained is obviously unreasonable since it precipitates an infinite regress, for to explain a law is to exhibit it as a deductive consequence of more comprehensive laws that are equally contingent and hence would have to be in turn explained in terms of still more fundamental laws, and so on. An inquisitive mind may, to be sure, be dissatisfied with the explanation "The water pipes burst because the temperature dropped below the freezing point and water expands in freezing" because he would like to know why water expands in freezing. Nevertheless this is a perfectly good example of correct subsumptive explanation. The justification of this explanation claim requires confirmation of the law "Water expands in freezing" (in particular, confirmation independently of the explained fact that the water pipes burst when the temperature dropped below the freezing point), but it does not require explanation of that law.

A very common form of this second step in the process of explanation is a syllogism in *barbara;* in the inverted, or explanatory version: all S are P *because* all M are P and all S are M. "Why does iron conduct electricity? Because all metals conduct electricity. (Suppressed minor: Iron is a metal.)" Here again the major premise is confirmable independently of the conclusion: it asserts not only that iron conducts electricity but ascribes the same property to zinc, silver, copper, and so on. Psychologically, however, such a syllogism satisfies the quest for explanation only if the minor premise conveys new information to the questioner. If we had antecedently confirmed that metals conduct electricity but did not know that iron was a metal, then the answer "Because iron is a metal" would satisfy us. A man who takes it for granted that iron is a metal and who asks why iron conducts electricity—and not, say, wood—really means to ask why *any* metal conducts electricity, hence the answer "Because all metals conduct electricity" would provoke the rather impatient reaction "Of course, I know that, but I want to know *why* they all do it." For this reason the psychological situation would be more accurately rendered by the enthymeme" iron conducts electricity because it is a metal. (Suppressed premise: All metals conduct electricity.)" What the explanatory information "It is a metal" effects is an assimilation of a phenomenon that initially may have been surprising to already familiar phenomena. The question "Why does wood—but not, say, iron—float on water?" may be answered "Because wood is less dense than water" or "Because all solid bodies that are less dense than a given liquid float on the latter." The former answer would probably satisfy one who did not know that wood is less dense than water (in the sense that a cubic centimeter of wood weighs less than a cubic centimeter of water) but whose experience with, say, cork caused him to expect that a solid body that was less dense than water would float on it. If, on the other hand, he already knows, not only that wood floats on water but also that it is less dense than water, he may not be satisfied with the latter answer because he takes it for granted that similar objects exhibit similar behavior in similar circumstances. Insofar as he takes such uniformity for granted, the question why wood has this dispositional property is to him equivalent to the question why *anything* that is like wood in being less dense than water has it; hence the answer "Because *all* solid bodies . . . ," far from satisfying him, will only prompt him to repeat his question in generalized form.

These reflections, however, pertain to the psychology of explanation, not to the logic of explanation. For a complete subsumptive explanation of a confirmed law both premises, major and minor, are equally essential, and both must be confirmable. The *logical* gain that results from subsumptive explanation in terms of an independently confirmable broader law is increased inductive support—hence predictive reliability—of the explained law. Suppose that an inclusive class M contains S as a proper subclass along with S_1, S_2, and so on. Then the subsumption of "All S are P" under "All M are P" increases the inductive support for "All S are P" because all the evidence that confirms the coordinated generalizations "All S_1 are P," "All S_2 are P," and so on, confirms "All S are P" indirectly, by analogy. The discovery that not only wooden objects float on water, but also things made of cork and other things whose specific gravity is less than that of water, strengthens the justification for the belief that *any* wooden thing will float on water because this property is seen to depend only on a property that all wooden things have (not, for example, on the weight of the wooden thing, which, unlike the specific gravity, is variable). Clearly, the extensive evidence that confirms the major premise "All M are P" confirms the more restricted generalizations therein contained as special cases.

C. THEORETICAL EXPLANATION

A characteristic feature of subsumptive explanations is that the concepts occurring in the explanatory premises are of the same kind as those that occur in the explanandum. The "middle term" denotes a wider class than the subject-term of the explanandum, but it is still a class of more or less directly observable objects or events. Accordingly the major premise can be instantially confirmed just like the law to be explained. We will instantly hit upon the characteristic difference of theoretical explanation if we push on a little into elementary theoretical physics and examine the explanation for the law that solids float on liquids that exceed their density. We find the explanation already in one of the first treatises of theoretical physics in the history of science: Archimedes' treatise "On Floating Bodies." The law in question there appears as a theorem, derived by an indirect proof from a single postulate, of which we will state only that part which is used in the proof: "Let it be supposed that a fluid is of such a character that, its parts lying evenly and being continuous, that part which is *thrust* the less is driven along by that which is *thrust* the more . . . ."

The italized word "thrust" expresses a theoretical concept, since what it refers to is not directly observable but rather postulated for the sake of the explanation of observed uniformities of behavior of things. Archimedes needs only this postulate in order to prove the proposition "A solid lighter than (i.e., less dense than) a fluid will, if immersed in it, not be completely submerged but part of it will project above the surface." He argues simply that if, say, a block of wood were completely submerged in a liquid, then less pressure would be exerted on the part of the liquid directly below the block of wood than on the part of the liquid not directly below it; hence, according to the postulate, the former part of the liquid would be "driven along" by the latter, hence the liquid would not be at rest; it follows that the solid cannot, "in a condition of rest," be completely submerged. He proceeds to prove, again from the simple postulate characterizing a fluid in equilibrium as one in which the pressure is equal in all parts and in all directions, that proposition which comes closest to "Archimedes' principle" as formulated in contemporary text-books: "If a solid lighter than a fluid be forcibly immersed in it, the solid will be driven upwards by a force equal to the difference between its weight and the weight of the fluid displaced." But we need not repro-duce the latter proof. What matters for our concern is that the explana-tory postulate involves an unobservable, viz. pressure exerted by one part of a fluid on an another, and therefore is not directly confirmable the way the major premise of a subsumptive explanation is directly con-firmable. We cannot even conceive what it might be like to verify by direct observation of a liquid that is disturbed by immersion of a solid that some parts of it are subject to greater pressure than others. Such pressure is a "construct," as some philosophers of science say, which enables an explanation of several directly confirmable laws of hydrostatics, and to establish the truth of the postulate in which it occurs can only mean to confirm the laws that are derivable from it.

But the simplicity of Archimedes' hydrostatic theory should not de-ceive. A theoretical explanation of experimentally established laws usually involves several postulates in such a way that it is impossible to confirm them separately; though the postulates be logically distinguishable and even logically independent (in the sense that none is formally deducible from the others), they can be empirically confirmed only in each other's context. We propose to call this *contextual confirmation* of theoretical postulates. Let us illustrate this process in terms of a historical and method-ological analysis of the atomic theory in the form in which Dalton in-troduced it into chemistry. It asserts that chemical combination of ele-mentary substances consists in combination of fixed numbers of atoms. That is, when two elements X and Y unite chemically, the particles of the compound XY are formed by the combination of a fixed number of particles of X with a fixed number of particles of Y. As the very expres-sion "*The* atomic weight of X" indicates, the theory further assumes that all the atoms of a given element have the same weight. The latter assumption seemed plausible to Dalton because gases in a state of equilibrium are uniformly dense.[1] If these assumptions of not directly observable atoms and combinations of atoms are correct, one would expect not only the conservation of weight in chemical reactions (verified by Lavoisier) but also that the weight ratios of compounds to the combining elements are fixed. The latter law, experimentally confirmed by Dalton himself, is known as the "law of constant weight proportions." The atomic theory of chemical combinations further implies that the weights of an element X contained in compounds containing a greater amount of X be integral multiples of the weights of X in the compounds containing less of X: the law of multiple weight proportions. These laws, it should be noted, mention directly measurable quantities, such as weights and densities of gases; by contrast, the theory that purports to explain them postulates micro-objects and micro-processes.

The atomic theory, however, would have been of little value for chemistry if it had postulated atoms with constant weights without providing means for calculating those weights. Since the experimental data that provide the basis for such calculations are the densities of the chemical substances in their gaseous states, some assumption about the molecular structure of the compounds was required: the ratio of the densities of two substances indicates the ratio of the weights of their molecules, but in order to derive the weight of the atom of an element it must be known how many atoms of each element are contained in a molecule. Dalton made the natural assumption that if different compounds of the same elements differ in density, then they differ in molecular structure; in fact, this is not a new assumption but merely a consequence of the atomic theory. The law of multiple proportions can then be used to determine the molecular structures of the heavier compounds as a function of the assumed molecular structure of the lightest compound. Thus, if the molecule of the lightest compound of nitrogen and oxygen has the form NO, then the weight data prove that the molecules of the heavier compounds have the forms NO_2 and N_2O. But the form of the lightest molecule had to be guessed on the basis of a rule of simplicity: N_2O_2 would have been equally compatible with the relevant data available to Dalton, but his rule of simplicity led him to the formula NO. In the case of water the rule of simplicity actually misled him to the wrong formula HO, yielding as the atomic weight of oxygen—relative to the convention that the atomic weight of hydrogen is unity—7 instead of 14 (according to modern weight data, 8 instead of 16). But Dalton

1. The exact equality of the weights of the atoms of a given element is, of course, a simple assumption that is not entailed by this experimental fact. One might suppose that different numbers of atoms are contained in equal small volumes of a gas but that the volume containing fewer atoms contained the heavier ones; uniform density would then be a statistical uniformity consistent with differences in the weights of the individual atoms.

cannot be accused of methodological error. Without some postulate of simplicity no scientist can build a bridge from experimental data to a theory, as is especially evident from the method of deriving, inductively, a simple numerical law from the measurements of correlated variables. It later became possible to correct Dalton's formula for the molecule of water when the volume ratios of the combining elements in their gaseous states were determined. But if an element cannot be vaporized, then the methods of calculation of atomic and molecular weights from weight and volume data do not uniquely determine the atomic weight of the element. That is, if the molecular weight of an element X cannot be determined by obtaining the vapor density of X, then we do not know whether the lightest compound of X contains an atom or a molecule of X. Though chemists abandoned Dalton's rule of simplicity, they still had to make the simplifying assumption that the molecule of that compound of X which contains the smallest amount of X contains an atom rather than a molecule composed of several atoms of X.

The method of determining atomic weights we have discussed so far may be called the method of weight ratios. But disturbing inconsistency within chemical theory emerged in connection with the method of determining atomic weights on the basis of Avogadro's law: that equal volumes of gas, whether chemically alike or unlike, contain equal numbers of molecules under equal presure and temperature. Let W_1 and W_2 be the weights of equal volumes of two gases (simple or compound, chemically); then the ratio of W_1 to W_2 is equal to the respective densities. But $W_1 = n_1 \cdot w_1$, where w_1 is the atomic (or molecular) weight and n_1 the number of atoms (or molecules) composing the volume; similarly, $W_2 = n_2 \cdot w_2$. Therefore, since by Avogadro's assumption $n_1 = n_2$, $W_1/W_2 = w_1/w_2$. It should be noted that the distinction between an atom and a molecule of an element had not become clear at this stage of chemical theory.

But let us now combine the atomic theory with Avogadro's law, which, as we have seen, underlies the second method of determining relative atomic or molecular weights. Consider, for example, the chemical synthesis of nitrogen and oxygen into NO. Since the volume ratio is 1 : 1, Avogadro's law entails that the numbers of nitrogen and oxygen atoms are equal; and the atomic theory, conceptualizing the process of synthesis as a one-to-one coupling of oxygen and nitrogen atoms, entails that the number of formed compound molecules is equal to the number of nitrogen atoms, and to the number of oxygen atoms, in the combining volumes. Yet the volume of NO turns out to be twice that of each of the combining volumes, hence Avogadro's law entails that the number of compound molecules is twice the number of combining oxygen atoms and twice the number of combining nitrogen atoms. A plain contradiction! Dalton resolved the contradiction by abandoning Avogadro's law;

in this, however, he was inconsistent since he accepted the second method of determining relative atomic weights, which presupposes the rejected law. Avogadro saw a way out: he saw that the atomic theory could be reconciled with Gay-Lussac's laws of combining volumes by assuming that the molecules of nitrogen, oxygen, hydrogen, and other elements consist of two atoms that separate in the process of chemical synthesis. This assumption is reflected in the chemical symbolism still employed today. For example, the chemical equation

$$2H_2 + O_2 \longrightarrow 2H_2O$$

asserts that two diatomic hydrogen molecules combine with one diatomic oxygen molecule to form two water molecules. Clearly, in order for this to happen the oxygen molecule must split up. The ratio of the coefficients reflects the volume ratios, and the fact that the volume of the resulting steam is double the volume of the combining oxygen is consistent with the requirement of the atomic theory that the number of oxygen atoms should be equal to the number of steam molecules: for it is two oxygen atoms that, after the splitting of the oxygen molecule, combine with two hydrogen molecules to form two molecules of steam.

But a theory has explanatory value only if it is confirmable independently of the facts that suggested it in the first place; otherwise it is condemned as ad hoc. Like any theory, Avogadro's theory cannot, of course, be directly confirmed by somehow watching the molecules split up. But indirect confirmation is possible: the chemical equations that are derived with its help lead to molecular formulas for the compounds, and the latter can be checked by the method of calculating molecular weights from vapor densities. Theories, as we see from this illustration, are but contextually confirmable or disconfirmable. When a scientist says that such and such facts confirm a theory T, what he ought to say, accurately, is that they confirm T *relative* to assumptions T', T'', and so on. Similarly, disconfirming evidence disconfirms the system of theoretical assumptions as a whole; it never dictates which particular assumption to give up.

D. ARE THEORIES DESCRIPTIONS OF REALITY OR INSTRUMENTS OF PREDICTION?

There is a sense in which the objects, events, and forces postulated by physical theories are unobservable. You cannot observe an electron the way you can observe a grain of sand, you cannot observe the ether the way you can observe the movement of air, you cannot observe the gravitational attraction that is said to keep the planets revolving. It is a natural tendency of the human mind to think of physical reality as something that can be pictured, on the analogy of the objects of common-sense experience. As a result, physical theories are intuitively satisfactory only if they gain pictorial content through *models*. Where such models are lacking, as in the relativistic theory of geodesics in "curved" space and the quantum theory of probability waves, the feeling may arise that useful conceptual, mathematical constructions have replaced descriptions of physical reality.

What ought a scientific theory to be? Should it be a true description of reality or just an instrument for predicting what observable phenomena will follow observable conditions? Although this question is widely reputed to be a profound question of the philosophy of science, we bring it up here only in order to condemn it as a pseudoquestion that owes its longevity to pictorial thinking. Common sense takes it for granted that the statement "There is a table in the room," if true, describes reality, because a table can be seen and touched. But what if a philosopher said to the plain man, "Look here, all that you really see are visual sense-data of color, shape, and size, and all you really feel are tactual sense-data of hardness, temperature, shape, and size; the existence of a permanent table is only postulated by you as a hypothesis that allows you to predict conveniently that such and such sense-data will occur under such and such conditions of perception." It is unlikely that the plain man could prove the philosopher wrong. "You see," the philosopher may continue, "tables don't really exist, they are just conceptual constructions by means of which we order the manifold of sense-data." Except for the absurd denial of the existence of tables, the philosopher is not wrong; nor has the plain man been convicted of error. The philosopher has merely shown that "the table exists" is a hypothesis that is confirmable by the occurrence of certain kinds of sense-impressions and that could not conceivably be known to be true in any other way. The statements that "There is a table in the room" describes reality and that it is a hypothesis confirmable by the predictions it yields are perfectly compatible. Indeed, the latter statement explicates the meaning of the former. If one feels that the former means more than the latter, the feeling has the following psychological origin: when you think of the proposition that the table is in the room when nobody is there to perceive it, you yourself have in your mind an image of the table in the room, and this image is distinct from the purely hypothetical state of affairs that tablelike sense-data would occur *if* certain conditions were fulfilled. But any conceivable evidence for the existential proposition is evidence for the hypothetical proposition and conversely, since the propositions are logically equivalent, have the same factual content.

Similarly, the factual content, as distinct from the pictorial content, of a theory is exhausted by the sum-total of verifiable consequences— with the proviso, of course, that the theory has no factual content at all in isolation from other theories and interpretive sentences. To say that it describes reality can only mean that it is thus indirectly confirmable. If it seems to mean more, it is because we make mental pictures of the entities and events the theory postulates and feel that it does not, after all, follow from the fact that the theory is *in*directly verifiable that it is also directly verifiable, by some direct observation. But insofar as such "direct observation" is contrasted with predictive confirmation, it is meaningless. It is a common and proper use of "direct observation" to say that electrons are directly observed in the Wilson cloud chamber through the tracks they produce, and molecules through the Brownian motion which is attributed to their random agitations. But even here the theoretical entities are verfied through their observable effects, just as the table is verified through the sense-impressions to which it gives rise. A more direct observation of physical reality cannot even be conceived; hence theoretical entities are to be conceived as *defined* by the factual content of the theories that postulate them, and to ask whether they really exist is logically equivalent to asking whether the postulates of the theory are true. We cannot, of course, know that such postulates are true the way we can know that the observation statements in terms of which they are ultimately tested are true. But to doubt on this ground that they "describe reality" is absurd, since if they did describe reality the way observation statements do, they would not be postulates with an explanatory-predictive function.

Selected Readings

Bergmann, G., *Philosophy of Science* (Madison, Wis., 1957), chap. 2.

Birkhoff, G. D., "The Mathematical Nature of Some Physical Theories," in G. D. Birkhoff, *Collected Mathematical Papers* (New York, 1950), Vol. II.

Boltzmann, L., "Theories as Representations," in *Die Grundprinzipien und Grundgleichungen der Mechanik, 1* (Leipzig, 1905). [Reprinted in A. Danto and S. Morgenbesser (eds.), *Philosophy of Science*, trans. by R. Weingartner (New York, 1960).]

Braithwaite, R. B., *Scientific Explanation* (Cambridge, 1953), chap. 11, 12.

Campbell, N. R., *The Foundations of Experimental Science* (New York, 1957), chap. 5, 6.

Craig, W., "Replacement of Auxiliary Expressions," *Philosophical Review*, 1956.

Duhem, P., "Physical Theory and Experiment," in P. Duhem, *Aim and Structure of Physical Theory*, trans. by P. P. Wiener (Princeton, N.J., 1953). [Reprinted in H. Feigl and M. Brodbeck (eds.), *Readings in the Philosophy of Science* (New York, 1953).]

Fitch, F. B., and A. W. Burks, "Symposium: Justification in Science," in M. White (ed.), *Academic Freedom, Logic and Religion* (American Philosophical Association, Eastern Division, Vol. II, 1953).

Feigl, H., "Some Remarks on the Meaning of Scientific Explanation," in H. Feigl and W. Sellars, *Readings in Philosophical Analysis* (New York, 1949).

———, "Existential Hypotheses," *Philosophy of Science*, 1950.

Hempel, C. G., "The Function of General Laws in History," *Journal of Philosophy*, 1942. [Reprinted in H. Feigl and W. Sellars (eds.), *Readings in Philosophical Analysis* (New York, 1949); and in P. Gardiner (ed.), *Theories of History* (New York, 1959).]

———, "The Theoretician's Dilemma," in H. Feigl, M. Scriven, and G. Maxwell eds.), *Minnesota Studies in the Philosophy of Science* (Minneapolis, 1958), Vol. II.

——— and P. Oppenheim, "Studies in the Logic of Explanation," *Philosophy of Science*, 1948. [Reprinted in part in H. Feigl and M. Brodbeck (eds.), *Readings in the Philosophy of Science* (New York, 1953).]

Hesse, M. B., "Theories, Dictionaries, and Observation," *British Journal for the Philosophy of Science*, 1958.

Hospers, J., "On Explanation," *Journal of Philosophy*, 1946. [Reprinted in A. Flew (ed.), *Essays in Conceptual Analysis* (London, 1956).]

Hutten, E. H., "On Explanation in Psychology and in Physics," *British Journal for the Philosophy of Science*, 1956.

Kneale, W., *Probability and Induction* (Oxford, 1949), sec. 19–22.

———, "Induction, Explanation, and Transcendent Hypotheses," in H. Feigl and M. Brodbeck (eds.), *Readings in the Philosophy of Science* (New York, 1953).

Koerner, S. (ed.), *Observation and Interpretation* (New York, 1957).

Mach, E., "The Economy of Science," in E. Mach, *The Science of Mechanics: A Critical and Historical Account of its Development*, trans. by T. J. McCormack (La Salle, Ill., 1902). [Reprinted in P. P. Wiener (ed.), *Readings in Philosophy of Science* (New York, 1953).]

McNaughton, R., "Axiomatic Systems, Conceptual Schemes, and the Consistency of Mathematical Theories," *Philosophy of Science*, 1954.

Mehlberg, H., *The Reach of Science* (Toronto, 1958), part 2, chap. 3.

Mill, J. S., *A System of Logic* (London, 1893), Book II, chap. 3 sec. 3.

Miller, D. L., "Meaning of Explanation," *Psychological Review*, 1946.

Mises, R. von, *Positivism* (New York, 1951).

Nagel, E., "Science and Semantic Realism," *Philosophy of Science*, 1950.

———, *The Structure of Science* (New York, 1961), chap. 2, 3, 5–7, 14, 15.

Pap, A., *Elements of Analytic Philosophy* (New York, 1949), chap. 11.

Peirce, C. S., "What Is a Leading Principle?," in J. Buchler (ed.), *The Philosophy of Peirce* (New York, 1940), pp. 129–134.

Popper, K., "Philosophy of Science—a Personal Report," in C. Mace (ed.), *British Philosophy in Mid-Century* (New York, 1957).

Rescher, N., "On Prediction and Explanation," *British Journal for the Philosophy of Science*, 1958.

Ryle, G., *The Concept of Mind* (New York, 1949), chap. 5.

Scheffler, I., "Explanation, Prediction, and Abstraction," *British Journal for the Philosophy of Science*, 1957.

Schlick, M., "Description and Explanation," in M. Schlick, *Philosophy of Nature*, trans. by A. von Zeppelin (New York, 1949). [Reprinted in P. P. Wiener (ed.), *Readings in Philosophy of Science* (New York, 1953).]

——, "Positivismus und Realismus," *Erkenntnis*, 1933. [Reprinted in English translation as "Positivism and Realism" in A. J. Ayer (ed.), *Logical Positivism* (New York, 1959).]

Skarsgard, L., "Some Remarks on the Logic of Explanation," *Philosophy of Science*, 1958.

Smart, J. J. C., "Theory Construction," *Philosophy and Phenomenological Research* 1950–51. [Reprinted in A. Flew (ed.), *Logic and Language* (Oxford, 1955), Vol. II.]

Toulmin, S., *The Philosophy of Science* (London, 1953), chap. 2, 3.

Watson, W. H., "On Methods of Representation," in W. H. Watson, *On Understanding Physics*, (Cambridge, 1938). [Reprinted in part in A. Danto and S. Morgenbesser (eds.), *Philosophy of Science* (New York, 1960).]

Weingartner, R. H., "Explanations and Their Justifications," *Philosophy of Science*, 1961.

Yolton, J. W., "Explanation," *British Journal for the Philosophy of Science*, 1959.

CHAPTER 19

Teleology & Emergence

A. ARE TELEOLOGICAL EXPLANATIONS SCIENTIFIC?

Analytical philosophers of science have hitherto derived their models of scientific explanation mainly from the physical sciences. They have then held these models up as ideals of scientific explanation that any science must live up to in order to deserve to be called a science. The question arises, however, whether the imposition of a uniform pattern of explanation that has proved successful in physics upon biology, psychology, and the social sciences may not hinder, rather than further, the latter's development because the distinctive nature of life and conscious behavior calls for different modes of explanation. Specifically, our problem is whether explanation in terms of goals, functions, or purposes can be brought into the same logical form as explanation in terms of so-called efficient causes.

We have already argued (see Chapter 14, F) that explanation of human behavior in terms of the agent's purposes and beliefs raises no logical problems different from those of causal explanation in general. In particular, purposive behavior is not a case of the future exerting a mysterious causal influence on the present, since it is the mental anticipation of a goal, not the achievement of the goal, that causes the appropriate behavior. On the other hand, we find teleological explanations in biology that are definitely not explanations in terms of conscious purposes. It is this kind of explanation we wish to subject to logical analysis. What characterizes such explanation is that a certain process in, or a certain characteristic of, an organism is explained as one that serves a certain purpose, as either a necessary or a sufficient condition for the achievement of a goal without its being implied that there is any conscious striving toward that goal nor that the organism was constructed by an intelligent being so as to be capable of achieving that goal, in analogy to the human construction of machines.

In order to see the logical issues clearly, let us consider a very simple example of such explanation: the heart beats in order to circulate the blood, which circulation in turn is necessary for the organism's survival. The heart's activity is here explained in terms of the function it serves. Of course, to specify a function served by a process is merely to call attention to an effect of the process, unless one implies that the process was consciously instituted in order to produce that effect, as when we speak of the functions served by the various parts of a man-made machine. But the effects in terms of which characteristics of an organism are teleologically explained are specifically contributions to the self-maintenance or survival of the organism. The organism cannot survive unless the blood circulates, and the blood cannot circulate unless the heart beats: that's why the heart beats. It may be objected that such an explanation is anthropomorphic since it satisfies only because it is tacitly assumed that an intelligent being designed the organism in such a way that it is capable of maintaining itself. But even if this is a correct explanation of why teleological explanations are psychologically satisfying, it is easy to show that in respect of their logical form and empirical conditions of adequacy they do not differ from causal explanations. To assert that the beating of the heart is a necessary condition for blood circulation is equivalent to asserting that blood circulation is a sufficient condition for the beating of the heart. And this is to assert the confirmable lawlike generalization that if blood circulates in an organism, then the organism contains a beating heart. Add the verifiable premise that blood circulates in this organism and you get deductively the conclusion that this organism contains a beating heart.

Similarly, the presence of chlorophyll in a plant may be explained by saying that it is a necessary condition for the performance of photosynthesis, which in turn is necessary for the plant's self-maintenance. The same schema of causal explanation applies again: if a plant performs photosynthesis, then it contains chlorophyll; this plant performs photosynthesis; therefore it contains chlorophyll. Further, we can teleologically explain why the plant performs photosynthesis: organisms (and their parts) perform functions that are essential for their self-maintenance (the confirming evidence for this broad generalization is vast); photosynthesis is essential for the self-maintenance of a plant; therefore plants perform photosynthesis.

But, although teleological explanations have the same logical form as explanations in terms of efficient causes, it would be highly misleading to call them "causal." To say that there is a beating heart *in order* for blood circulation to occur is, indeed, equivalent to saying that blood circulation is a sufficient condition for the presence of a beating heart, if no imputation of conscious purpose is implied by that statement. But it would be odd to say that the blood circulation *causes* the beating of the heart, or that chlorophyll is *produced* by the process of photosynthesis. We must distinguish the proposition that A nomologically *determines* B, in the sense that B can be inferred from A on the basis of a confirmed law-like generalization, from the proposition that A is an efficient cause of B. In the terminology of Aristotelian philosophy, A is a *final cause*, but temporally an effect, of B if A *teleologically* determines B.

It must be noted, however, that teleological explanations are logically on a par with causal explanations only if the statement that a given process, or the presence of a given organ, serves a specific self-maintaining or adaptive or reproductive function means that the former is a *necessary* condition for the latter, not if it means that the former is a *sufficient* condition for the latter. Thus, if it were causally possible for the blood to circulate without the pumping activity of a heart, then one could not infer with certainty from an observation of blood circulation that the organism contained a pumping heart. At best the teleological explanation would be probabilistic, provided it could be shown to be highly improbable that the same end could be achieved without that particular mechanism.

A special case of teleological explanation is explanation in terms of "feed-back" mechanisms. A familiar example of such a mechanism is the thermostat. It is designed to maintain the room temperature at a certain desired level. There are two variables, which interact as follows: there is a certain value, T, of the room temperature (the temperature we desire to be maintained) such that if the room temperature falls below T, then the furnace goes on, and as a result of the operation of the furnace the room temperature rises to T, at which point the compensatory operation of the furnace stops. Here again we may say, if we wish, that the furnace went on *in order* to maintain T, meaning that unless heat is produced by the furnace T will not be maintained. There are similar feed-back mechanisms in the human body that keep the body temperature within the limits beyond which survival is impossible; that is, if the temperature of the environment is too low, the body develops compensatory heat, and if it is too high, sweating leads to evaporation of moisture which restores a favorable body temperature.

The example of the thermostat makes it clear that a teleological explanation is perfectly compatible with a *mechanical* explanation of the same event. Given two variables x and y that interact in such a way that a certain equilibrium state is maintained, we can teleologically explain a change in x in terms of a change in y: the change in x is a compensatory change made necessary (for maintenance of equilibrium) by a deviation of y from the equilibrium state. But such an explanation leaves us in the dark about the causal mechanism by which the change in one variable produces the compensatory change in the other variable. These mechanical explanations—or explanations of the mechanisms by which the various functions are performed—make use of physical and chemical laws. The "mechanists" insist that only the latter are genuine scientific explanations, that teleological explanations may have heuristic value but do not really further our understanding of organic nature. But the feud between mechanists and teleologists is unnecessary. Both types of explanation satisfy cognitively, in that they subsume diverse phenomena under constant laws: a teleological explanation subsumes the facts to be explained under the teleological law that organisms tend to have characteristics, both functional and structural, that have survival value, while a mechanical explanation exhibits them as instances of the operation of physicochemical laws.

B. IS BIOLOGY REDUCIBLE
TO PHYSICS AND CHEMISTRY?

The question whether teleological explanations can satisfy the logical and empirical criteria of scientific explanation should be distinguished from the question whether biology requires for the formulation of its laws special concepts, referring to irreducibly organismic or teleological traits of its subject-matter, that are not needed for the description and explanation of inorganic nature. As we have seen, it is not only possible but even desirable to supplement a functional description of organisms with a description of the causal mechanisms through which the functions are exercised. But is a description of causal mechanisms in terms of physics and chemistry even possible in principle? The answer is that if and only if the biological laws of growth, self-maintenance and reproduction are deducible from physicochemical laws concerning the underlying microprocesses, without invoking causal factors that are not mentioned in physics and chemistry, then biology ceases to be an autonomous science and is reducible to physics and chemistry. In order for such a reduction of laws to be possible, however, the concepts of biology must be definable in terms of the concepts of physics and chemistry, since there cannot occur in the conclusion of a valid explanatory deduction concepts that do not occur in the premises or are defined in terms of concepts occurring in the premises. The classical example of the reduction of thermodynamics to statistical mechanics illustrates the point: since the laws of thermodynamics involve the variable "temperature," which does not occur in the laws of mechanics, an assumption about the correlation of this macroscopic property of physical systems with microprocesses (molecular motions) must be made. This assumption is often referred to as a *definition* of temperature as the average kinetic energy of the constituent molecules, enabling the scientist to determine temperatures much higher than those that can be measured by ordinary thermometers. But if "definition" here meant a statement of synonymy, then the claim that one science has been reduced to another would be unwarranted; for in that case thermodynamics would have operated with the same concepts as mechanics from the very start. The meaning of "temperature" in the gas laws, then, would already have been "average kinetic energy of the constituent molecules," whereas in the context of experimental thermodynamics the term was but operationally defined, as something measurable by mercury thermometers.

Before one can significantly ask whether a science S is reducible to a science S', one must define the difference between S and S' by listing a set of primitive concepts that are distinctive of S and another set of primitive concepts that are distinctive of S'. Thus the distinctive primitive concepts of experimental thermodynamics are pressure, volume, and temperature; the distinctive primitive concepts of mechanics are length, mass, and time. But if a distinctive primitive concept of S were already, before the reduction of S to S', defined in terms of the primitive concepts of S', then it would not be a primitive concept of S at all, hence the question of reducibility could not arise. It is for this reason that the relevant assumptions that constitute a logical bridge from one science to another had better be called *composition laws*, which must first be empirically discovered, though after extensive confirmation the scientist is prone to call them "definitions." But they are definitions, not in the sense of notational abbreviation, but in the sense of a statement of a necessary and sufficient condition, in terms of microprocesses, for a macroscopic property of a physical system. That the combination of hydrogen and oxygen molecules in the volume proportion 2 : 1 produces a liquid with the sensible qualities of water was, of course, an empirical discovery, although *thereafter* the chemist "defines" water as the compound H_2O. Similarly, if biological processes have necessary and sufficient conditions that can be described in terms of physico-chemical concepts, they first have to be discovered empirically. Even after such a discovery has been made, there is no logical guarantee that the relevant biological laws are deducible from the fundamental laws of physics and chemistry.

But the important point is that reduction presupposes an empirical discovery of composition laws that connect distinguishable levels of natural existence. And the only way in which a composition law enabling reduction of S to S' could itself be deduced from the laws of S would be by its conversion, by redefinition, into an empty tautology—in which case it would be, of course, deducible from anything. When certain brain processes, caused by stimulation of a sense-organ and a subsequent process in the afferent nerves, occur, there arises, say, a distinctive kind of visual sense-impression. If you "define" that kind of sense-impression as that kind of brain process, then you cannot meaningfully ask for an explanation of that law: a tautology requires no explanation. But if the law is recognized as a contingent proposition, then it could not possibly be explained in terms of the laws governing the "lower" levels alone—in this example, the laws of neurophysiology. Similarly you cannot possibly deduce the mentioned composition law of chemistry from the laws of electrochemistry which do not mention perceivable sense-qualities. This simply follows from the principle that the conclusion of an explanatory deduction cannot contain a concept that is not contained in the premises or defined in terms of the concepts contained in the premises. If *physicalism* is the doctrine that all the laws of nature are deducible from the fundamental laws of physics, then it is untenable on logical grounds: the composition laws connecting the molecular physicochemical level with higher levels of organization can never be deduced from physicochemical laws alone. Even the simple law that hydrogen and oxygen combine to form a liquid with the sensible qualities connoted by "water" refutes such a physicalism.

C. EMERGENT LAWS AND EMERGENT QUALITIES

That permanent limits are set to the scientist's ability to predict by "the very nature of things" has been one of the inspiring themes of the doctrine of emergent evolution. The best-known emergent evolutionists in the English tradition are probably S. Alexander, the author of *Space, Time, and Deity,* and C. L. Morgan, the author of *Emergent Evolution* and, more recently, *The Emergence of Novelty.* Their central idea was that the process of evolution produces more and more complex "levels," such as the atomic level, the level of chemical compounds, the biological level, and so on, and that oneach level new qualities emerge that are absolutely unpredictable on the basis of the laws applying to the lower levels. Perhaps the best way to impress upon the reader the urgency of analyzing the meaning of the doctrine before either embracing or rejecting it is to present a sample or two of the language through which Alexander expresses his metaphysical insight:

The higher quality emerges from the lower level of existence and *has its roots therein*, but it emerges therefrom, and it does not belong to that lower level, but constitutes its possessor a new order of existent with its *special laws of behavior*. The existence of emergent qualities thus described is something to be noted, as some would say, under the compulsion of *brute empirical fact*, or, as I should prefer to say in less harsh terms, to be accepted with the "natural piety" of the investigator. *It admits no explanation.*[1]

. . . .

A being who knew only mechanical and chemical action *could not predict life;* he must wait till life emerged with the course of Time. A being who knew only life could not predict mind, though he might predict that combination of vital actions which has mind. . . . Now it is true, I understand, that, given the condition of the universe at a certain number of instants in terms of Space and Time, the whole future can be calculated in terms of Space and Time. But what it will be like, what qualities it shall have more than spatial and temporal ones, *he cannot know unless he knows already*, or until he lives to see.[2]

The italicized phrases are the ones to be clarified in the discussion that follows. The problem of emergence will be discussed semantically, but without further reference to Alexander. Instead, a similar view, expressed with more precision by C. D. Broad (in *The Mind and Its Place in Nature*, chap. 2) will serve as the basis of our analysis.

The old question of emergent qualities, which arose mainly in the context of the debate between vitalism and mechanism in the philosophy of biology, may be clarified by a semantic line of analysis that has been neglected by both parties. It is customary to discredit the belief in absolutely unpredictable qualities and laws on the ground that what scientific theories of today do not permit us to predict, scientific theories of tomorrow may well bring within the bounds of predictability. Thus there was a stage in chemistry when no general laws correlating molecular structure and macroscopic properties of compounds were known that would enable one to predict the macroscopic properties of a hitherto unobserved compound on the basis of its molecular structure; but such laws are now known.[3] To speak of absolute unpredictability, unpredictability once and for all, convicts one, in fact, of metaphysical obscurant-

1. S. Alexander, *Space, Time, and Deity* (London: Macmillan and Co., 1920), vol. 2, p. 46.
2. *Ibid.*, pp. 327–328.
3. For a precise statement of this "relativistic" theory of emergence see P. Henle, "The Status of Emergence," *Journal of Philosophy*, 1942, and, more recently, Hempel and Oppenheim, "Studies in the Logic of Explanation," sec. 5, *Philosophy of Science*, April 1948.

ism, motivated perhaps by a subconscious hostility against the faith in the omnipotence of science. Indeed, those who, following Alexander, recommend "natural piety" in the face of absolute novelty may have no clear idea as to what they mean by such "absolute novelty." Nevertheless, this vague notion of absolute emergence can, with the help of semantical concepts, be explicated in such a way that whether a quality or law is emergent does not depend on the stage of scientific knowledge but rather on the question whether certain predicates are only ostensively definable. Specifically, a law correlating a quality Q with causal conditions of its occurrence can, without obscurantism, be argued to be *a priori unpredictable* if the predicate designating Q is only ostensively definable. The concept of a priori predictability will be defined presently.

Broad makes a distinction between an emergent (or "ultimate") law and a nonemergent (or "reducible") law. An example illustrating his notion of emergent law is the law connecting the properties of silver chloride with those of silver and of chlorine and with the molecular structure of the compound:

> . . . if we want to know the chemical (and many of the physical) properties of a chemical compound such as silver-chloride, it is absolutely necessary to study samples of *that particular compound*. It would of course (on any view) be useless merely to study silver in isolation and chlorine in isolation; for that would tell us nothing about the law of their conjoint action. . . . The essential point is that it would also be useless to study chemical compounds in general and to compare their properties with those of their elements in the hope of discovering a *general* law of composition by which the properties of *any* chemical compound could be foretold when the properties of its separate elements were known.[4]

According to the definition of an emergent law, implicit in the quoted passage, at least a necessary condition (but perhaps likewise a sufficient condition) of the emergent character of a law of the form "If $C_1, \ldots,$ C_n, then R" (where the antecedent refers to a set of interacting components, and the consequent to a result of this interaction) is that instances of R would have to be observed before the law could be known with some probability. More exactly, if L is an emergent law in Broad's sense, then it cannot be confirmed *indirectly*, by deduction from more general laws, *before* direct confirming evidence is at hand. For short, let us say that an emergent law is *deducible only a posteriori*, or *a priori unpredictable*. The meaning of this statement will become clear by considering Broad's illustration of a reducible law, i.e., a law that could be, theoretically, predicted with the help of a general composition law before any direct observational evidence was available.

4. C. D. Broad, *The Mind and Its Place in Nature* (New York: Humanities Press, Inc.), p. 64.

Consider the law of projectiles according to which the trajectory of a projectile is, under ideal conditions, a parabola. It is true that direct observational evidence for this law was at hand before Galileo deduced it with the help of the parallelogram law of forces (Broad's model of a *general* composition law) from the law of freely falling bodies and the law of inertia. But it is clearly conceivable that the law might have been reached by deduction from those premises concerning the effects of gravity and of inertia before instantial evidence was obtained (in fact, this was the case with respect to a special case of the law, viz. the flight of high-speed cannon balls). This is what Broad would call a reducible law: it is a priori predictable in the sense that it is capable of prior confirmation through deduction from antecedently confirmed laws with the help of a general composition law before any confirming instances are observed. For the present purpose we may be satisfied with a denotative definition of "general composition law" as the kind of deductively fertile composition law illustrated by the parallelogram law. It is not, of course, the general composition law that is claimed to be a priori predictable; rather, it is claimed to make special composition laws, such as the law of projectiles, a priori predictable.

But how could it ever be shown that a given law is absolutely irreducible? In order to show this, one would have to prove that no general composition law could conceivably have been known that would have enabled a skilled scientist to predict the law. Broad himself seems to recognize the relativity of such irreducibility to the stage of scientific knowledge at least in the case of chemistry, for the quoted passage concerning the properties of silver chloride is followed by the statement "*so far as we know*, there is no general law of this kind." Indeed, it is easily describable what such a general composition law of chemistry might be like: if a metal combines with an acid in solution, there results a salt and free hydrogen. This law may have been inductively derived by observing interactions of metals M, M', M'', with acids A, A', A'', and may then be used to predict that if M''' should react with A''' a salt would result of which no instances have yet been observed.

Broad admits that "mechanistic" progress in chemistry is possible to the extent that a deduction of R from $C_1, \ldots, C_n$ with the help of general composition laws might be accomplished if R is a *physical* disposition of compounds, such as ready solubility in water. But he holds such deduction to be in principle impossible if R is a secondary quality, i.e., a disposition to produce a sensation of a certain kind, such as a pungent smell.[5] Although Broad is inconsistent with his own definition of emergence in claiming absolute emergence for laws correlating secondary qualities with microscopic physical conditions, he nevertheless comes

5. *Op. cit.*, p. 71.

close to making a valid point overlooked by the "relativists." Broad claims that not even the "mathematical archangel" could predict what NH_3 would smell like unless someone—not necessarily himself—had smelled it before. If Broad denies the possibility of theoretically certain prediction, his assertion is true but trivial: even the probability that is conferred on a special law of dynamics by deduction from the parallelogram law falls short of the maximum, since the parallelogram law itself is still falsifiable as long as not all of its deductive consequences have been tested. But if he denies the possibility of prediction in the only sense in which prediction is ever possible, he is clearly wrong. Just suppose that chemists had evidence suggesting the generalization "Whenever two gases combine chemically in the volume proportion $1 : 3$, the resulting compound has the smell S." If the original evidence for this (hypothetical) general composition law does not include observations of the formation and properties of ammonia, the special composition law "NH_3 has smell S" could well have been a priori predicted by someone less eminent than a mathematical archangel before anybody had smelled that gas. We must not, of course, confuse the proposition just shown to be false with the true but irrelevant proposition that "This gas has smell S" cannot be logically deduced from the premise "This gas has such a molecular structure" alone, without an additional premise asserting the correlation between structure and secondary quality.

There is, however, a logical difference between our hypothetical general composition law of chemistry and the parallelogram law, which will prove crucial for the problem of emergence. The deduction of a special law from the former took simply the form of deriving a substitution-instance, and the predicate referring to the predicted quality was explicitly contained in the general premise. But the parallelogram law does not contain the concept of a specific type of compound motion, such as circular motion or motion along a parabola; it only contains the concept of a specific form of functional dependence of the direction and magnitude of a resultant vector on the directions and magnitudes of the component vectors. A simple way of putting the difference is this: One could understand the parallelogram law without thinking of the specific form of motion it may be used to predict, and therefore without having witnessed an instance of that form of motion. But since the law correlating microprocesses with sensations of quality Q contains the very same concept of Q as the derived substitution-instance, and Q is a simple quality of which, in Hume's language, one cannot have an "idea" without "antecedent impression," the law cannot even be understood unless an instance of the predicted quality has been perceived. In this sense the deduction made from such a law does not lead to "novelty." Suppose, on the other hand, that the parallelogram law had first been inductively derived from observations of rectilinear motions only, and was then tested by the prediction that if a body in uniform rectilinear motion is acted on by a central force, it will describe a circle around the center of attraction. In that case a new form of motion, one not previously observed, would have been predicted. The unpredictable secondary quality, then, is "emergent," the predictable quality of motion not. The law "If C_1, . . . , C_n, then Q" is emergent if it must be directly confirmed, by perception of instances of Q, before it can be deduced from a general composition law.

Let us clarify the issue by considering a law correlating wave motions of the air with sound phenomena. One may be inclined to think that a general law correlating frequencies and pitches could easily be formulated that would enable a priori prediction of hitherto unheard sounds in just the way the parallelogram law could, in principle, predict so far unobserved forms of motion. Thus, let X be the highest pitch so far heard, but not the highest audible pitch, and suppose that comparisons of various pitches led to the law "The higher the frequency, the higher the pitch." With the help of this simple law we can easily predict that the pitch corresponding to a frequency higher than the frequency corresponding to X will be higher than X, and we can make this prediction before ever having heard such a pitch. If now the question should be raised whether this deduction is just like the discussed case of deduction by simple substitution, i.e., a prediction of a quality that must already have been observed if the general premise is to be intelligible, the answer will have to be somewhat qualified. Strictly speaking, the quality which is being predicted is "higher in pitch than X," which quality is not explicitly mentioned in the general premise and hence need not have been perceived in order for that general premise to be understood. This, then, must be admitted to be an instance of a novel (that is, so far unperceived) quality that is not unpredictable. Yet, the reason why such prediction is possible is that the predicate designating the quality is complex and made up of parts whose meanings are understood through ostensive definition; the meaning of "higher pitch" is understood because some, though not all, instances of this relation have been experienced, and the meaning of the proper name "pitch X" is understood—let us suppose—because X has been heard. Generalizing from this example, we lay down the following principle: If a novel (that is, so far unperceived) quality is to admit of a priori prediction, then it must be complex in the sense that the expression describing it contains simpler predicates and/or proper names that, being understood through ostensive definition only, designate old qualities. It follows that if there are qualities that admit of a priori prediction, there must also be qualities, less complex ones, that do not admit of a priori prediction. In terms of our illustration: one would, indeed, make a perfectly defensible claim if one said, like Broad, that no amount of physical and physiological information could enable one to predict that a frequency increase would produce a sensation of rising pitch, if "rising pitch" were only ostensively definable, since in that case *one would not know what quality one was predicting* and the deduced statement would acquire its meaning only after verification, which is absurd.

Unpredictability of qualities, as here analyzed, hinges on the assumption that certain descriptive predicates admit only of ostensive, not of verbal, definition. Accordingly we must examine in each case whether the relevant predicate is ostensively or verbally defined. Take, for example, the question whether it could be a priori predicted that a definite frequency would produce that definite pitch named X. According to the present analysis, this question reduces to the question whether the meaning of X could be understood—in other words, whether the designated quality could be imagined—by someone who had never perceived the quality. Conceivably the pitch might be described in terms of interval relations to already heard pitches—say, as the pitch one-third higher than pitch Y, where "one-third higher" would itself be defined as meaning "such that if Y and X occur simultaneously, the interval named 'third' is heard." If such a relational description enabled one to anticipate imaginatively, or at least to recognize on presentation, the as yet unheard pitch, one would know what one was predicting, hence the quality would not be emergent.

It may seem that the relativists' critique of emergentism remains valid after all, since it is always conceivable that a given descriptive predicate be understood before being applied to a sense perception. Indeed, whether a given proper name is but ostensively definable or verbally definable by means of a synonymous description is not a logically decidable question but a question of psychology, specifically concerning possibilities of imagination or identification of qualities that have not previously been perceived. Just as in one logical calculus the logical constants C_1 and C_2 may be primitives and C_3, C_4, C_5 defined, while in another calculus C_4 and C_1 are taken as primitives and the rest defined; so in a descriptive language, such as the language describing sound phenomena, the set of ostensively defined proper names is not uniquely determined. Thus, using "C" as all ostensively defined proper name and "higher pitch" (or "lower pitch") and "third" as ostensively defined relational predicates, we could introduce the proper names "E," "G," "B" by verbal definition (for simplicity's sake, the C-major scale is here taken as the field of the relation so as to neglect the distinction between augmented and diminished intervals). This procedure assumes the psychological possibility of imagining or identifying an as yet unsensed quality in the field of a relation some instances of which have been sensed, on the basis of sensed qualities in the same field. If we further provide an ostensive definition for the relational predicate "equidistant (pitches)," we might even be able to introduce the names of all the remaining pitches in the C-major scale by description. But an alternative construction of the language is clearly conceivable: we might take "second" and "higher pitch" as ostensively defined relational predicates, "G" as ostensively defined proper name, and then all the other proper names and interval-designations might be introduced by description without the use of "equidistant." It may perhaps be doubted whether the description, "The complex pitch resulting if a pitch a second higher than the pitch a second higher than G is sounded simultaneously with G," would enable one to get an auditory image of a third if one had never heard a third before; but this is a psychological question of fact.

If we call our first model of a language of sound experience *L* and our second model *L'*, we can make the following assertions: A law correlating the pitch G with a frequency is a priori unpredictable in *L'*, and so is the law correlating a definite frequency ratio with the interval called "second"; but those same laws are a priori predictable in *L*, if we assume that the meanings of verbally defined expressions in *L* are intelligible in the sense that the verbal definition conveys a concept of the quality or relation defined, independently of any previous experience of the latter. In this sense emergence is relative to a system of semantic rules, and in this respect it is analogous to indefinability of concepts and indemonstrability of propositions.

Is the relativist, then, wrong in denying the existence of absolutely emergent qualities? He is wrong if he denies the semantic truism that some descriptive terms must be given meaning by ostensive definition if any descriptive terms are to be given meaning by verbal definition. Perhaps he is right, on the other hand, in his claim that no descriptive term is, by some obscure kind of necessity, definable by ostentation only. Even Hume, whose principle that every simple idea must be preceded by a corresponding impression is equivalent to the semantic principle that predicates designating simple qualities can become meaningful only through ostentation, allowed for the famous exception, the missing shade of blue—in fact, this was probably meant as just one example of an unlimited class of exceptions. Nevertheless, it seems that for every sense-field there is an ordering relation, instances of which could not possibly be imagined before being sensed: the relation *higher pitch* for the auditory sense-field, the relation *brighter color* for the visual sense-field, and analogous transitive and asymmetrical relations for other sense-fields or other dimensions of the same sense-fields. When a term designating an element in the field of such an ordering relation *R* is verbally defined, the relational predicate *R* is itself used in the definiens, together with one or more names of other elements in the field. Thus Hume's missing shade of blue, which has not been seen yet, would be verbally defined as the shade equidistant from, say, b_4 and b_6, where these are separated by a larger "distance" than the other consecutive elements in the series of increasingly dark shades. To say that b_5 (the missing shade) is equidistant from b_4 and b_6 evidently means that it is just as much darker than b_4 as b_6 is darker than it. But then the meaning of "darker" must be understood by ostentation and, on pain of circularity, the method by which b_5 was verbally defined is unavailable. Indeed, it is difficult to imagine what an *analysis* of such a simple relational concept could be like. If so, then a law correlating quantitative changes in physical conditions with such changes in sensed qualities as are expressed by "darker," "louder," "higher in pitch," and the like is absolutely emergent after all. And limits are set to the possibility of a priori prediction, not by the stage of scientific progress, but by the limits of semantic analysis.

Selected Readings

Alexander, P., "Theory-Construction and Theory-Testing," *British Journal for the Philosophy of Science*, 1958.

Bergmann, G., "Outline of an Empiricist Philosophy of Physics," in H. Fiegl and M. Brodbeck (eds.), *Readings in the Philosophy of Science* (New York, 1953).

——, *Philosophy of Science* (Madison, Wis., 1957), chap. 3.

Birkhoff, G. D., "The Mathematical Nature of Some Physical Theories," in G. D. Birkhoff, *Collected Mathematical Papers* (New York, 1950), Vol. II.

Boltzmann, L., "Theories as Representations," in *Die Grundprinzipien und Grundgleichungen der Mechanik, I* (Leipzig, 1905). [Reprinted in A. Danto and S. Morgenbesser (eds.), *Philosophy of Science*, trans. by R. Weingartner (New York, 1960).]

Bondi, H., *Cosmology* (Cambridge, 1952), pp. 3–19.

Braithwaite, R. B., *Scientific Explanation* (Cambridge, 1953), chap. 10.

——, "Axiomatizing of a Scientific Theory by Axioms in the Form of Identifications," in L. Henken, P. Suppes, and A. Tarski (eds.), *The Axiomatic Method* (Amsterdam, 1959).

Broad, C. D., "Mechanical Explanation and Its Alternatives," *Aristotelian Society Proceedings*, 1918–19.

Brown, R., "Dispositional and Teleological Statements," *Philosophical Studies*, 1952.

Campbell, N. R., "The Structure of Theories," in N. R. Campbell, *Physics: The Elements* (Cambridge, 1920). [Reprinted in H. Feigl and M. Brodbeck (eds.), *Readings in the Philosophy of Science* (New York, 1953).]

——, *The Foundations of Experimental Science* (New York 1957). chap. 5, 6.

Destouches-Fevrier, P., "The Logical Structure of Physical Theories," in L. Henken, P. Suppes, and A. Tarski (eds.), *The Axiomatic Method* (Amsterdam, 1959).

Deutsch, K., "Mechanism, Teleology and Mind," *Philosophy and Phenomenological Research*, 1951.

Dewey, J., *The Quest for Certainty* (New York, 1929), chap. 8.

——, *Logic, the Theory of Inquiry* (New York, 1939), chap. 14.

Ducasse, C. J., "Explanation, Mechanism, and Teleology," in H. Feigl and W. Sellars (eds.), *Readings in Philosophical Analysis* (New York, 1949).

Duhem, P., *The Aim and Structure of Physical Theory* (Princeton, N.J., 1954), part 1.

Feigl, H., "Some Remarks on the Meaning of Scientific Explanation," in H. Feigl and W. Sellars (eds.), *Readings in Philosophical Analysis* (New York, 1949).

——, "Existential Hypotheses," *Philosophy of Science*, 1950.

Fitch, F. B., and A. W. Burks, "Symposium: Justification in Science," in M. White (ed.), *Academic Freedom, Logic and Religion* (American Philosophical Association, Eastern Division, Vol. II, 1953).

Frank, P., "Comments on Realistic versus Phenomenalistic Interpretations," *Philosophy of Science*, 1950.

Henle, P., "The Status of Emergence," *Journal of Philosophy*, 1942.

Kemeny, J. G., and P. Oppenheim, "On Reduction," *Philosophical Studies*, 1956.

Lovejoy, A. O., "The Meanings of 'Emergence' and Its Modes," *Proceedings of the Sixth International Congress of Philosophy*, 1926. [Reprinted in P. P. Wiener (ed.), *Readings in Philosophy of Science* (New York, 1953).]

Mace, C. A., "Mechanical and Teleological Causation," in H. Feigl and W. Sellars (eds.), *Readings in Philosophical Analysis* (New York, 1949).

Madden, E. H., "The Nature of Psychological Explanation," *Methodos*, 1957.

Meehl, R. E., and W. Sellars, "The Concept of Emergence," in H. Feigl and M. Scriven (eds.), *Minnesota Studies in the Philosophy of Science* (Minneapolis, 1956), vol. I.

Nagel, E., "Reduction in the Natural Sciences," in R. C. Stauffer (ed.), *Science and Civilization* (Madison, Wis., 1949). [Reprinted in P. P. Wiener (ed.), *Readings in Philosophy of Science* (New York, 1953).]

——, "Mechanical Explanation and Organismic Biology," *Philosophy and Phenomenological Research*, 1950–51.

——, "Wholes, Sums, and Organic Unities," *Philosophical Studies*, 1952.

——, "Teleological Explanation and Teleological Systems," in H. Feigl and M. Brodbeck (eds.), *Readings in the Philosophy of Science* (New York, 1953).

——, *The Structure of Science* (New York, 1961), chap. 11, 12.

Putnam, H., and P. Oppenheim, "Unity of Science as a Working Hypothesis," in H. Feigl, M. Scriven, and G. Maxwell (eds.), *Minnesota Studies in the Philosophy of Science* (Minneapolis, 1958), vol. II.

Rosenblueth, A., N. Wiener, and J. Bigelow, "Behavior, Purpose and Teleology," *Philosophy of Science*, 1943.

Scheffler, I., "Thoughts on Teleology," *British Journal for the Philosophy of Science*, 1959.

Schlick, M., "Philosophy of organic life," in Dessoir (ed.), *Die Philosophie in ihren Einzelgebieten* (Berlin, 1925). [Trans. by H. Feigl and M. Brodbeck and reprinted in H. Feigl and M. Brodbeck (eds.), *Readings in the Philosophy of Science*, New York, 1953).]

Stout, G. F., "Mechanical and Teleological Causation," *Aristotelian Society Proceedings*, supp. vol. 14 (1935).

Woodger, J., *Biological Principles* (New York, 1929).

CHAPTER 20

Mind & Behaviorism

A. THE SUBJECT-MATTER
OF PSYCHOLOGY

Psychology used to be conceived as the science of mind or consciousness. Its subject-matter different from that of the natural sciences in lacking public accessibility, in being directly observable by introspection only. German introspectionist psychology, however, has been largely repudiated in the United States where Watson initiated the behaviorist revolution. The inspiration for this revolution was largely methodological. Scientific propositions must be intersubjectively verifiable; the verdicts of introspection, however, are not intersubjectively testable; therefore a science based on introspection is not really a science. Some ardent behaviorists did not confine themselves to the adoption of natural science methodology in psychology: the point of view that psychology should study human and animal behavior without hypothesizing "private" mental states behind the publicly observable stimuli and responses. They felt impelled to justify this change not only by methodological considerations, but also by the flat denial that such a "private" subject-matter of psychology exists at all. This form of behaviorism, *reductive* behaviorism, is old materialism pure and simple: there is no such thing as consciousness, there is but behavior, dispositions to respond in specific ways to specific stimuli, and neurophysiological processes within the human and animal body. They did not, of course, deny that there is a difference corresponding to the verbal difference between "mental" and "physical." But they held that processes and states called mental are special kinds of physical processes and states.

Thus the very question concerning the subject-matter of psychology verges into the old philosophical question of the difference between the physical and the mental. This question is usually called a "metaphysical" one, but a clarifying discussion of it is possible only by focusing on the *meanings* of psychological and physical statements. And since questions of meaning are, as shown in Part I, closely connected with questions of evidence and verification, the metaphysical question is not, after all, separable from questions of methodology and epistemology.

Let us, then, attempt a clarification of the old problem of "dualism" versus "monism" by asking whether psychological statements are translatable into physical language. That they must be so translatable if a science of psychology is to be possible, was a dogma of the early physicalists, led by Carnap; they regarded this thesis of translatability as an obvious corollary of their principle that a scientifically meaningful statement must be intersubjectively verifiable. It is as such a consequence of the positivist theory of meaning that physicalism must be understood. In isolation from that theory, the thesis of translatability seems so obviously absurd that it is hard to understand how it could have been maintained by acute philosophers. Is it not evidently conceivable without self-contradiction that a given mental state occurs without being accompanied by its usual "symptoms"? How could the statement "I am now imagining a pretty girl" be synonymous with a statement describing manifest behavior, considering that such an image may be completely unexpressed so that only the imagining subject knows of its occurrence? And how could it be synonymous with a description of a brain process, considering that we don't know which specific brain process corresponds to that mental state and how it differs from that corresponding to a mental image of a handsome boy? But the relevant question to ask in evaluating physicalism, in the sense defined, is whether such translation into physical language is indeed required by the postulate of intersubjective verifiability of scientific statements. Yes, said the physicalists, *you* may know that you suffer toothache without looking at your face, hearing yourself groan, or even examining your teeth. But how is anyone else to know this? On the basis of analogical inference? But analogical inference, they maintained at that time, is a genuine inference only if its conclusion is intersubjectively verifiable; if not, as in the case of analogical inference to another mind, then it is a "pseudo-inference."

As we have already argued in Part I (Chapter 4, C), any physicalist who, in the footsteps of Carnap's later *Testability and Meaning*, properly distinguishes between conclusive verification and confirmation, must recant this condemnation of analogical inference to other minds. On the basis of analogical inference hypotheses about other minds are *confirmable* in terms of publicly observable stimuli and responses though untranslatable into physical language. Indeed, in the spirit of *Testability and Meaning*, contemporary physicalists affirm only the *reducibility* of psychological terms to the terms of the "thing language," i.e., the language of everyday life that describes material objects. But let us be clear about the real reason why the thesis of translatability had to be abandoned. According to the original program of physicalism, statements about other minds were to be construed as conjunctions of implications of the form "If stimulus S acts on O, then response R occurs"; e.g., a partial physicalistic analysis of "O sees red" would be "If O is asked, 'What color do you see?' O replies, 'I see red.'" But since Carnap and his associates required the language of science to be extensional, they had to construe these implications as material. And since, just as in the case of disposition predicates, they could not allow that the mere absence of the relevant stimulation insured the truth of the psychological statement, they had to abandon the thesis of translatability. Yet, how would it be if in the physicalistic translation the causal "if-then" (in the sense of Chapter 15) were substituted for the material "if-then"? Obviously, the translation would still be inadequate, since it is by no means self-contradictory to suppose that O sees red but does not reply "I see red" to the question "What color do you see?"—perhaps because he is dishonest, perhaps because he does not know the meaning of "red," perhaps because he just does not want to betray the secret. The point is that a statement of the form "If O is in mental state M, then, if S acts on O, then R results" is in general *synthetic*. This seems to be admitted by Carnap himself in *Logical Foundations of the Unity of Science*, where he writes that "angry" cannot at the present time be *defined* in the physical language since we do not know any physical state of an organism that is a strictly necessary and sufficient condition for such a mental state. Surely this entails that any equivalence of the form "O is angry if and only if O is in the physically observable state P" that might be established by behaviorists or physiologists at some future time is synthetic. If so, it is hard to see why the thesis of the reducibility of intersubjectively meaningful psychological terms to terms of the thing language should be incompatible with a dualism that is not committed to the belief in substantial and immortal minds.

There are, however, monists who admit that consciousness is not identical with behavior nor with physiological processes in the sense that psychophysical correlations can be established by meaning analysis, without empirical investigation. Still, they maintain, there is a *factual* or *contingent* identity. They point out that many accepted identity statements—in fact all informative identity statements outside of mathematics and logic—have to be empirically established, such as the identity of the morning star and the evening star, or the identity of the author of

Macbeth and the author of *Hamlet*. The prima-facie objection to this form of identity thesis is that if $x = y$, then, regardless of whether the identity hold analytically or empirically, every predicate that is true of x must be true of y, and a fortiori, whatever can be *meaningfully* said about x can be meaningfully said about y. But whereas it makes sense to say that one sees a spatially localized event or object, such as a brain process, such statements as "I now see the dream image he is describing" or "I just saw a suicidal thought" seem to be altogether senseless. Further, though there are forms of consciousness that have phenomenologically spatial attributes, such as pains and organic sensations, there are others, especially the "higher" or "spiritual" ones, to which spatial attributes cannot be ascribed. Consider thoughts, decisions, memories, intellectual desires. We surely cannot say that these mental events occur "in" the brain in the same spatial sense in which a flow of blood corpuscles occurs in the brain. Rather such localizations of thoughts in the brain must be interpreted as localizations of their physical correlates. A pain that phenomenologically is in the leg is, of course, correlated with a brain event; and so is every thought, according to scientific hypothesis, though thoughts have phenomenologically no spatial location at all (except, perhaps, if they give rise to headaches). But even if it be held that all mental events are located somewhere in an organism, the assertion of psychophysical identity still seems vulnerable: we cannot be *directly aware* of what happens in our brains the way we are directly aware of our pains, feelings, thoughts, and the like. Does it not follow that something is true of mental events that is not true of physiological events?

But such a semantical argument against monism may be answered by another semantical argument. It has been tacitly presupposed that to different kinds of observation, such as introspection and looking, there correspond as observed objects of different types. Now, looking is a mode of observation that is just as different from smelling, touching, and listening as from introspecting. Accordingly we should in consistency deny that something that can significantly be said to be smelled could significantly be said to be seen. This would lead us to regard visual sense-data as seen objects, smells as smelled objects, tactual sense-data as touched objects, and so on. Relative to such stipulations it is just as senseless to say that I smell something blue as to say that I see something bitter. But such stipulations conflict with ordinary language. After all, we say that the *same* thing that looks blue smells sweet, that the same thing that looks round feels smooth, and so on. Why, then, should it amount to a violation of semantic rules were one to say that the same event of which one person is introspectively aware might be visually observed, through a cerebroscope, by someone else—or through an autocerebroscope by the very same person? The latter would have the same sort of evidence for the assertion of psychophysical identity that the simultaneous and contiguous perception of a visual and a tactual quality gives for asserting that the same thing is being seen and touched.

Although this rejoinder is perfectly valid, it does not amount to a proof of monism and a disproof of dualism, but rather reveals the *verbal* nature of the whole issue. For what is our reason for saying that an *identical* thing has diverse sensory qualities? After Berkeley's critique of material substance the answer "Because such diverse qualities are regularly found to coexist" has almost the status of a truism. If visual sphericalness were at one time associated with the tactual quality we call by the same name, at another time, at the same place, with the tactual quality of cubicalness, at still another time, at the same place, with the tactual quality of a cone, we would not speak of a sphere that has both visual and tactual qualities. The notion of thinghood is rooted in constant associations of diverse qualities. Now, if psychophysics discovered more and more one-one correlations between mental and physiological events, one could with just the same linguistic propriety—or impropriety—speak of identical events that have mental as well as physical attributes. This is strictly a matter of linguistic convention. Surely we could employ different names for visual and tactual spheres, and instead of speaking in the realistic subject-predicate idiom of an identical thing that is both visually and tactually spherical, we might say "phenomenalistically" that under certain "normal" conditions visual sphericalness is compresent with tactual sphericalness. But even if we prefer, in speculative anticipation of ever more empirical discoveries of psychophysical correlations, to speak of identical events with both physical and mental attributes, we would still have to recognize the same empirically given duality that impresses the dualist—just as we recognize the irreducible difference between visual and tactual roundness in spite of our verbal identification of the data.

We must, then, recognize the difference between mental and physical events even if we prefer to speak, "monistically," of irreducibly different *aspects* of certain central events in the human, and probably animal, organism. We are thus led to the difficult problem of clarifying the dualistic concept of a mental event. The usual definition is in terms of *logical privacy:* if and only if *E* is a mental event, then it is logically impossible that more than one organism should observe *E* directly; if *O* can observe *E* directly, then any organism other than *O* can know about the occurrence of *E* only by inference. A familiar type of objection to this analysis is Gilbert Ryle's (see *The Concept of Mind*, chap. 7): to speak of observing one's sensations, he holds, is nonsense; one *has* a sensation when one observes something, but one does not observe one's sensation. But Ryle's argument from "proper usage" is far from convincing. When the doctor asks you "Where do you feel pain?" you observe your pain in trying to localize it, and in trying to answer the question what kind of pain it is, sharp or diffuse, pulsating or continuous, and so on. Similarly, when you try to test the assertion that a penny that is perceived as round really produces, under oblique perspective, an elliptical image on the retina, you focus attention on your visual impression, not on the physical object. And in a case of hallucination, the experience of attending to what appears is intrinsically just like the experience of attending to the properties of a physical object; yet, since my attention then does not have a physical object, what am I attending to if not my own sensations or images?

Although Ryle's arguments against the privacy theory of the mental are not convincing, the latter is nonetheless in need of clarification because it rests on a distinction between direct awareness and inference that is dubious. If these terms have psychological meanings, then there is but a difference of degree. Thus it cannot be denied that the penny's circular shape is directly seen though the angle of vision is oblique, if this only means that no conscious inference occurs—say, the inference that the penny will feel circular when contacted. In just this sense—no conscious inference takes place—one may be directly aware that someone else is angry or puzzled or disappointed. The theory that beliefs about other minds are nevertheless arrived at by *unconscious* analogical inference really amounts to a substitution of the *epistemological* concept of hypothesis for the *psychological* concept of inference: it must be understood to mean that such statements as "He is now angry," just like statements about objective properties of things ("the coin *is* circular though it appears elliptical"), are but *hypotheses* that are confirmable in terms of their consequences, in contrast to so-called *basic propositions* ("I am angry," "I see red") which the assertor knows to be true with a kind of certainty to which propositions referring beyond immediate experience can never attain. The term "direct awareness" seems to have this epistemological meaning in Bertrand Russell's writings when he says—as recently as 1958[1]—that the mental is that of which direct awareness, in contrast to inferential knowledge, is possible. If so, then the ontological mental-physical dualism reduces to an epistemological dualism that has been much discussed in analytic philosophy during the last three decades or so.

A basic proposition is distinguished from one that refers to "objective reality" by being a pure report of an experience, sensory or otherwise, without any predictive or postdictive content. If on the basis of a visual impression I say "That's salt," I implicitly predict a certain taste sensation, certain chemical reactions, and so on, and if any of these predictions

1. "What Is Mind?" *Journal of Philosophy*, 1958.

should be falsified my assertion would be disconfirmed (at least proba-
bilistically, if not conclusively). But the basic proposition "That looks like
salt to me (I see a saltlike sense-datum)" would not be disconfirmed.
Those who believe in basic propositions admit, of course, that one might
make a *verbal* mistake in descriptions of immediate experience, also that
one might be lying, but they quite properly distinguish this sort of
falsehood from a subsequently discovered falsehood of one's judgment,
of the proposition one intended to assert. If owing either to a slip of the
tongue or to ignorance of the language I said, "That's sugar," intending to
assert the proposition that is correctly expressed by the words "That's
salt," then subsequent experience of a salty taste would not, of course,
refute my judgment. Again, if I honestly report, "I see a blue patch,"
and use the word "blue" correctly, then what I say must be true and no
observations that other people might make at the same time—e.g., a
physiologist observing my brain and noting that the brain event that
then occurs is one that is normally correlated with seeing red—could
invalidate my assertion.

A classical objection to this theory of basic propositions is that in
describing the seen patch as blue I judge its color to be sufficiently similar
to the color of patches I have seen in the past and that I was taught to
call "blue," and this memory judgment might be mistaken. It may, however, be countered by distinguishing between the *meaning* of the statement "That's blue" and the facts of resemblance that justify application
of "blue" to the given patch. If my relevant memory should be mistaken,
then I would, after all, have made a verbal mistake, since what I would
have forgotten is just the semantic rule governing "blue" (if that rule is
"Apply 'blue' to patches, and only such, whose color closely resembles
the color of patches *a, b, c*, at least as closely as the colors of *a, b, c*,
resemble each other," then remembering the rule entails remembering the
color of *a, b, c*). But what I am asserting in saying "That's blue" is not
"That resembles patches I was taught to call 'blue' sufficiently to be itself
properly called 'blue.'" That this is not what I am asserting follows from
the plausible principle[2] that it is logically possible for a class defined by
an ostensive predicate—such as the class of blue patches—to have just
one member. It seems intelligible to suppose the given patch to be the
only blue patch in the universe, but if to say that it is blue were to say
that it resembled other blue patches, then that supposition would be
self-contradictory. Indeed, the process of learning the meaning of "blue"
is such that it is most unlikely, perhaps impossible, that there would be a
word designating the color blue in our hypothetical universe containing
a solitary blue patch. But it is one thing to describe the conditions pre-

2. See A. J. Ayer, "Basic Propositions," in M. Black, ed., *Philosophical Analysis*
(Ithaca: Cornell University Press, 1950).

supposed by the *semantic* fact that "*x* is blue" means what it means, a different thing to analyze its meaning; indeed, its meaning does not seem to be analyzable at all, as we have reached a so-called "atomic" statement.

Again, the notion of absolutely certain basic propositions may be objected to on the ground that we are sometimes uncertain about the specific nature of a sense experience and that such uncertainty is different from uncertainty about the conventionally correct description of it. Thus we may not be sure whether a ticklish sensation is pleasant or painful. Such uncertainty is, of course, different from a foreigner's uncertainty as to whether "pain" or "pawn" is the word used by English-speaking people to designate that kind of sensation. And we can easily decide whether it is such a purely linguistic uncertainty by asking the foreigner to describe the sensation in his native language. Nevertheless, uncertainty about the intrinsic quality of the phenomenally given cannot be anything else than uncertainty about the applicability of a *vague* predicate. Is the ticklish sensation sufficiently like sensations I have been conditioned to call "pleasant" or sufficiently like those I have learned to call "painful"? Well, very likely it is a borderline case. We are not uncertain about the truth-value of a precise proposition but about the meaning of a vague ostensive predicate. In fact, to suppose that "painful" had a *precise* meaning for a given person would be to suppose that for every sensation of his he would *know* whether or not it was painful.

Finally, the conception that the mental subject-matter of psychology can be described by absolutely certain basic propositions has been criticized on the ground that one cannot properly speak of "knowledge" of such basic facts, hence cannot claim such basic facts to be disclosed by scientific observation. To say that *A* knows that *p*, so goes the argument, is to say that *p* is true, that *A* believes *p* to be true and moreover has good reasons for believing *p* to be true; but "*A* believes that he sees red (or that he has a headache) and has good reasons for believing this" does not make sense. This is, like Ryle's argument we criticized above, an argument from proper usage, and it is no more cogent. One difficulty with it is that it may depend on the tense of a sentence whether it can be said to express a proposition that the assertor knows to be true. Suppose you are about to get an injection. It is surely proper for you to say, silently or aloud, "I believe that I will feel pain shortly," and of course you may have excellent inductive reasons for your belief. It would seem that the proposition you subsequently verify—as directly as nobody else can verify it—by just feeling pain while remembering your prediction is just the proposition you properly claimed to believe before the injection. But how can we consistently say that the utterance "I will feel pain" expresses a proposition the speaker knows to be true, the utterance "I now feel pain," made by the same speaker a little later, expresses just the same proposition, but that no knowledge is expressed by the latter utterance? Rather than swallow this contradiction, we should question whether "*A* know that *p*" entails in all contexts "*A* believes that *p*" in the sense in which belief implies the possibility of doubt—and therewith the linguistic argument against knowledge of basic propositions.

At any rate, the analysis of "basic proposition" to be presented avoids the problem of the proper uses of "to know" and "to believe" by using instead the verb "to assert." An assertion of a basic proposition is certain, indubitable, in the sense that, provided the speaker is honest and makes no verbal mistake, the fact that verifies his assertion is a necessary causal condition of his making the assertion. That is, if these two conditions are fulfilled, the assertion would not be made if it were false. If I am not lying, nor using the wrong word to say what I intend to say, then I cannot assert that I have a headache unless I have one; whereas a person without intent to deceive and able to express himself by conventionally correct language might, of course, make mistaken assertions about physical objects, about the past and the future, and about other minds. This analysis seems to accord with the common-sense attitude of accepting a person's report of immediate experience without question or further investigation unless one has reason to suspect dishonesty or a linguistic handicap.

If this analysis of basic assertions is correct, then we may define the *primary* mental subject-matter of psychology—specifically of introspectionist psychology—as that which can be described in basic assertions. It is certainly a weak argument against the reliability of introspection that the very act of introspection interferes with the object of introspection so as to distort it. There is no reason why the state of introspection cannot be a complex the objective element of which—that which is introspected—has the same nature as part of the complex as it would have if it were not introspected. But even if it be held that the introspective act is a supervenient mental state that supplants the mental state that is its object, the fact that the phenomenal present is "specious" rather than mathematically instantaneous allows for perfect reliability of the memory involved in introspection.

The secondary subject-matter of psychology consists in whatever actions and reactions—including dispositions to such—are causally connected with introspectable experiences. Behavioristic psychology has been very fruitful in uncovering causal and statistical laws of human and animal behavior, but its neglect of the introspectively disclosed phenomenal states of organisms as determiners of overt behavior is neither methodologically nor philosophically justified.

"This is True"

B. INTERVENING VARIABLES

American behavior theory has been methodologically influenced to a considerable extent by positivist and operationist strictures against explanations in terms of unobservables. At the same time it was clear from the very beginning that the responses of animal and human organisms are not uniquely determined by the external stimuli. Commonsensically one would suppose that human behavior also has mental determinants, such factors as memories, expectations, desires, perceptions, beliefs. But since these "intervening variables" were supposed to be inaccessible to scientific investigation, the tendency developed to interpret them as certain *dispositions* to overt behavior. No doubt behaviorists tried to imitate the physicists: what does the physicist mean if he explains the observable response of an electroscope in terms of an electrical force acting on it? Is not the electrical force just a symbol for a regularity of behavior, viz. whenever, during a certain time, an electroscope is brought into that position, then its leaves diverge? Just so, they attempted to interpret intervening variables as dispositional states of organisms. That it is *possible* to develop a predictively fertile theory of behavior without postulating private, subjective states such as the observer can introspectively detect within himself, will not be disputed here. But we will question the *necessity* of such abstinence.

Symptomatic of the underlying confusion about methodology in this area is a certain inconsistency, on the part of leading behavior theorists, in their interpretation of intervening variables. We will choose as the basis of our analysis an older article by Tolman,[3] in which he introduces the concept of intervening variables. He illustrates it in terms of "demands for positive goal-objects" and "demands against negative goal-objects," which phrases translate into ordinary language as "desires for experiences expected to be pleasant" and "desires to avoid experiences expected to be unpleasant." A question immediately prompted by the very terminology "intervening *variables*" is whether the values of these variables are used to describe *states* of an organism, and whether these variables are accordingly comparable to physical state variables, such as pressure, temperature, and volume in the case of gas theory. This interpretation is suggested by the equational schema $B = f_2(I_a, I_b, \ldots, I_n)$ (where the function B represents a variable response and the arguments are the intervening variables) which Tolman puts down in the

3. E. C. Tolman, "Psychology versus Immediate Experience," *Philosophy of Science*, July, 1935. [Reprinted in *Collected Papers in Psychology* by E. C. Tolman (University of California Press, Berkeley: 1951), pp. 94–114.]

context of explaining that functional equations connecting response-variables and stimulus-variables can be obtained but indirectly, by studying first the causal connections between the observables and the I's. Furthermore, Tolman speaks of the I's definitely as of *causal factors* determining the responses of the organism, just as the pressures and amounts of heat applied to a gas determine its behavior (the crucial expressions are italicized):

Under the heading *demands for positive goal-objects* I conceive a set of variables (i.e., behavior-readinesses) such that when any one of them is *operative* it will act to *produce* a specific positive consummatory response, if the appropriate goal-object be present. It will also operate, if this goal-object be absent, to *produce persistent exploratory activity* until an instance of this appropriate type of goal-object has been found.[4]

Now, if the I's really represented dispositional properties of organisms, the way "elasticity," "solubility," and "thermal conductivity" represent dispositional properties of physical systems, then they could not be state variables, and the above equation schema would not make sense. Consider a simple functional equation of physics, such as "Strain $= k \cdot$ stress," applicable to such simple physical systems as wires. Here it is the constant of proportionality, not the variables, that represents a dispositional property of the system, in this case the degree of elasticity of the wire. For a given system, whose states are described in terms of the successive values of the variables in the equation, this disposition is not a variable at all.[5] The same holds for other quantified physical dispositions, such as thermal conductivity, represented by a constant of proportionality in an equation relating rate of heat flow to temperature difference. It is true that we could, and do, say that the behavior of a physical system is *determined* by these constants as well as by the "initial conditions," i.e., the instantaneous values of the state variables. But it is clear that we cannot regard the dispositions, represented by the constants, as causal factors *coordinated with* the initial conditions, as though they were, like the latter, momentary states of the system. For in stating a constant for a given system, the physicist states the law of correlation of the variables that enables him to predict the value of the dependent variable from the values of the independent variables.

Now, when Tolman and other behaviorists causally explain observed responses of organisms, such as choosing food in preference to a mate, in terms of the operation of demands or motivations, their explanation is analogous to the explanation of the elongation of a wire by the stress it was subjected to, or the explanation of why a specified amount of heat

4. *Ibid.*, p. 367 [*Collected Papers*, p. 103].
5. But see the reservation below, p. 390.

was transmitted by a conductor during a specified time by the temperature differential of the conductor. The statement that the organism was motivated by such and such a demand is not a statement of a stimulus-response *law* about the organism. If it were, then the equational schema $B = f_2(I_a, I_b, \ldots, I_n)$ could not be meaningfully applied to a given organism, since for a given organism the I's would be constant (at least approximately). There is no explicit endorsement of demands or motivations as dispositions in Tolman's article, except that such an interpretation is suggested by the use of the word "tendency": ". . . demands for short routes would be my name for the tendencies which appear in behavior to select, after learning, short paths rather than long ones to positive goal-locales and from negative goal-locales."[6] But the word "tendency" is ambiguous. If I say of a man that he has a tendency to fall in love with slim, blue-eyed blondes, I state nothing but the vague statistical law that most of the women he falls in love with are of the specified physical type. For this reason it would be no explanation at all if I "explained" his falling in love with a woman of that type in terms of his "tendency" to react that way, as though the tendency were itself a causal factor, something like an introspectively observable *urge*. The same usage of "tendency" is illustrated by the statement "I have a strong tendency to forget the names of the people I dislike," and should be distinguished from the usage in which the word is intended as the name of a mental state, an urge, as in "Whenever I see that man, I feel (not "have") a strong tendency to give him the fist." It follows that if Tolman's explanations in terms of intervening variables are genuinely causal, then "tendency" must be used by him to name causally efficacious *drives*, not statistical uniformities.

There is also a tendency among behaviorists to construe the concept of *motivation* as a disposition concept. But motivations in the sense of efficacious demands are not dispositions. What has led some to assimilate motivations to dispositions is their insight into the impossibility of *explicitly defining* motivation concepts in terms of test operations and test results, coupled with the erroneous opinion that whatever empirical concept resists such explicit definition must be a disposition concept (Carnap's *Testability and Meaning* may have been influential here). They correctly notice that no given *symptom* of a desire for food is a necessary condition for the occurrence of the desire. In other words, the desire does not necessarily manifest itself by just the behavior by which it manifests itself in a given situation. If the hungry but sexually indifferent rat had not been exposed to those stimuli by which the experimenter hoped to catch a glimpse of its momentary motivation, it still would have

6. *Op. cit.*, p. 368 [*Collected Papers*, p. 104].

been hungry and sexually indifferent at that time. In the case of such comparatively unsophisticated organisms as rats a certain kind of preferential behavior may, perhaps, be regarded as a *sufficient* condition for the occurrence of the motivation in question, but not even this could be said of organisms like humans, that are capable of simulating motivations. Thus what psychologists loosely call "operational definitions" of motivation concepts are more accurately characterized as reduction sentences, describing tests in specific situations but leaving the concepts "open" for further experimental tests not yet explored. But this openness of motivation concepts does not entail their dispositional character. Electrical current is similarly an open concept of theoretical physics, but it would be odd to conclude that the physicist ascribes a disposition to a wire when he says that there is an electrical current of specified intensity in it.

The term "intervening variable" is usually employed in behavior theory as a synonym for "theoretical construct," but either term is used ambiguously. It sometimes refers to *states*, either mental or physiological, of an organism that the variability of responses to identical stimuli leads one to infer and that are *causally* connected with the stimuli on the one hand and with the responses on the other hand. And sometimes it refers to *dispositions*, like Hull's "habit strength" or "reaction potential," which are explicitly defined, as shorthand concepts, in terms of the directly measurable stimuli and responses. This ambiguity may be encountered even within one and the same methodological paper. Thus Hull[7] illustrates the use of intervening variables of "symbolic constructs" (synonyms in Hull's usage) in terms of such writers as Carnap, Brunswik, Tolman, and himself, without indicating any awareness of the vast difference in the types of "constructs" used by Carnap, Brunswik, and Tolman on the one hand, and Hull himself on the other hand. For anger (Carnap), perceptions (Brunswik), expectations and needs (Tolman) are states, whether mental or physiological, of an organism that literally "intervene" between stimulus and response events. They are postulated events, from the point of view of the experimenting psychologist (though not from the point of view of the subject investigated), in the same sense—to use an analogy from chemistry—in which the decomposition of air molecules into nitrogen and oxygen molecules is a postulated "intervening" even between the heating of solid mercury and the formation of mercuric oxide. But Hull's concepts "habit strength" and "reaction potential" are of a different logical type. They are disposition concepts, comparable to such concepts of physics as "breaking strength," "heat of combustion," and "mechanical advantage," that refer to constant properties of systems going through a succession of states; and their logical relation to the so-

7. C. L. Hull, "The Problem of Intervening Variables in Molar Behavior Theory," *Psychological Review,* 1943.

called observables is the straightforward relation of explicit definability, so one cannot speak of causal connections between the referents of such constructs and stimulus and response events. When we ascribe a given breaking strength to a given rope we enunciate the law that the rope would break if a tension exceeding a specified amount—the value of the breaking strength—were produced in it; "tension" is here the state variable representing states of the rope, and it is these states, not the disposition "breaking strength," that can be significantly said to be caused by and in turn to cause such and such events. Thus, when a physical equation is formulated for a given physical system it is the (nonarbitrary) constants of proportionality, not the variables of the equation, that represent these dispositions.

When we ascribe a given habit strength, in Hull's sense, to an organism we are not describing a present state of the organism but are making a conditional prediction. To ascribe, for example, a specific strength to a rat's habit of pulling that lever with which reward, in the form of food, is associated, is to predict that extinction of the acquired habit would occur after a specified number of disappointments ("negative reinforcements").[8] As we might put it, no "existential hypothesis" is involved in the introduction of a construct such as habit strength. The latter, it seems, is not even a concept introduced by reduction sentences, for whatever can be said in terms of it can, according to Hull, be said *synonymously* in terms of such observables as "number of past reinforcements," "delay of reinforcements," and so on.[9] Thus it seems to be a construct introduced

8. It is true that Hull's explicit definition is given rather in terms of a variable representing the past of the organism that now possesses the habit: the number of positive reinforcements that were necessary to produce the present habit, i.e. to insure invariability of the rewarded response. But this is a historical rather than an operational definition.

9. One might nevertheless argue that, Hull's statement notwithstanding, habit strength rather functions as an open concept. There is, as it were, a double anchorage in observables: a historic measure, viz. number of past reinforcements that produced the habit strength, and a response measure, viz. the number of unrewarded responses that is necessary and sufficient to extinguish the habit. Now, what would Hull have said if, having determined a habit strength by means of the historic measure, he found a significant discrepancy between the actual and the predicted number of negative reinforcements required to extinguish the habit, the prediction being based on the historic measure of the habit strength. Would he necessarily have concluded that the law expressing the number of negative reinforcements required for extinction as a function of habit strength had been refuted? Or might he have said that the historic measure of habit strength is not a reliable one? It would, at any rate, not be unreasonable to draw the latter conclusion. This is the reason that it is misleading to say that habit strength is explicitly defined in a sense in which this implies that it is an eliminable shorthand expression. It suggests an artificial dichotomy of analytic and synthetic statements about the construct that does not correspond to scientific procedure.

by explicit definition on the basis of observables, just for the sake of a simpler formulation of laws. In that case it is not comparable to such physical constructs as "electron" or "field strength" or even "mass" but to such shorthand concepts as kinetic energy (explicitly defined in terms of mass and velocity) and power (explicitly defined in terms of force, displacement, and time).

In psychology . . . the number of variables entering into even the simplest behavior situation that can be experimentally produced is so great and the structure of their interrelationship is so complex that we are unable to make even a first guess as to the mathematical form of the equations directly from the empirical data without some auxiliary theoretical device. *The terms defined by Hull's postulates provide just such a device.* They attempt to bridge the gap between the two sets of variables, those manipulated by the experimenter and those measuring the observed responses. Technically, they aim at providing the means for ascertaining a rational fit to the empirical curve.[10]

The last statement is particularly clarifying. To give a simple analogy of such "theoretical devices" enabling "ascertainment of a rational fit to the empirical curve" from elementary physics: suppose that the only available quantitative concepts for describing the motions of bodies on inclined planes were "displacement," "time," and "angle of inclination." And suppose we wanted to discover some law regulating the motions of bodies on (nearly frictionless) inclined planes of varying steepness. We would find it a rather complicated affair to obtain an equation in those underived variables. But by the introduction of the derived variables "acceleration" and "sine of an angle" we arrive at the simple relationship "acceleration $= k \cdot \sin \theta$." The function and method of introduction of Hull's disposition concepts, then, seems to resemble closely the function and method of introduction of such a physical construct as acceleration.

Although this interpretation of Hull's "intervening variables" is undoubtedly supported by some of Hull's own statements, Hull also makes another statement that suggests that the use of "habit strength" reflects an existential hypothesis after all:

While it is perfectly possible to put into a single equation the values of events which occur at very different times, it is hard to believe that an event such as a stimulation in a remote learning situation can be causally active long after it has ceased to act on the receptors. I fully agree with Lewin that all the factors alleged to be causally influential in the determination of any other event must be in existence at the time of such causal action. I believe that it is some such consideration as this which has led to the universal common sense use of the concept of habit; in my system $_sH_R$ is merely a quantitative repre-

10. G. Bergmann and K. Spence, "Operationism and Theory in Psychology," *Psychological Review*, 1941, p. 10.

sentation of the perseverative after-effects of the no-longer-existent compound events represented by S (stimulus energy) . . . , G (nature of the past re-inforcements), and N (number of past reinforcements).[11]

Hull here embraces, in agreement with Lewin, the postulate of contiguous causation according to which action at a temporal distance is just as impossible as, according to some physicists, action at a spatial distance: the sum total of severally necessary and pointly sufficient causal conditions of an effect must exist immediately before the effect occurs; in other words, it should be possible to predict a given effect from a complete survey of the *presently existing* causal conditions, without having to know anything about the past of the system whose behavior is to be predicted (cf. Chapter 14, G). In the chapter "Traces and Dispositions" of his *The Mind and Its Place in Nature*, Broad has shown with great finesse how the postulate of contiguous causation leads to the repudiation of "mnemic" causation, i.e., the direct agency of past experience to produce, usually in conjunction with a present stimulus, external or internal, a memory that in turn modifies the organism's response to the present stimuli, and instead suggests the persistence of brain traces. These brain traces, the brain's storage provisions, as it were, for latent memories that may be activated at any moment by a stimulus with proper associative power, evidently correspond to what Hull calls "the perseverative after-effects of the no-longer-existent" past causal conditions.

The argument based on the theory of brain traces runs as follows: If we confined ourselves to causal explanation of an organism's behavior in terms of molar observables, then we could only state (*a*) the stimulus conditions of the organism's responses, (*b*) the organism's disposition to respond differently to the same kind of stimulus S if S has in the past perceptual environment of the organism been associated with some other kind of stimulus S'. But (*b*) is not a causal condition in the sense in which (*a*) is a causal condition; it is not a *state* of the system whose behavior is to be predicted. Indeed, in stating (*b*), we are just saying that if we confine ourselves to molar description of the states of an organism, to the use of molar state variables, we cannot arrive at *unique* predictions. Thus the postulate of determinism (all events are uniquely predictable—if only we knew the initial values of enough state variables), jointly with the postulate of contiguous causation (we don't need to know the past of a system in order to predict its future uniquely) leads to the existential hypothesis of brain traces that codetermine the organism's responses. The assumption of a brain trace may in fact be said to *explain* the disposition or law described under (*b*) in the following straightforward

11. Hull, *op. cit.*, p. 285.

sense: From the assumption that the perceived association of S with S' produced a brain trace B, together with the assumption that if a present instance of S is accompanied by an excitation of B then the organism's response will be different from what it would have been before B was formed, it follows that through the perceived association with S', S will acquire the power to produce a different response from the response it produced before conditioning took place—which is precisely the organism's disposition or law of behavior (b) that was to be explained.

As we seem to be now on the track of the main reason behind the confusing shift of meaning of "intervening variable" from "shorthand concept, expressing a disposition" to "constructs such as are involved in theories postulating microentities and microevents" (existential hypotheses), the analogy of physical theory may shed light on the issue. Consider again the simple example of a physical system with the corresponding theory used to predict its behavior: a wire whose deformations are described by Hooke's law. The molar state variables used are stress and strain; i.e., we could alternatively describe the successive states of a wire subject to stretching forces in terms of the successive values of stress or in terms of the successive values of strain. But could we predict the future behavior of a wire from a description of the stress alone? The well-known answer is negative: the same stress may produce different strains in different wires, and it may produce a reversible elongation of one wire, and irreversible elongation of another wire (i.e., exceed its "elastic limit"), and it may even lead to breaking of a third wire. The physicist describes these differential responses to the same stimulus (to adopt the behaviorist terminology with a generalized meaning) in terms of disposition concepts: coefficient of elasticity, elastic limit, breaking strength. These physical constants, as they are usually called, represent dispositions because in ascribing them to a given wire we are not ascribing an instantaneous *state* to the wire but are asserting a *law* about the wire: to say, for example, that the coefficient of elasticity of a steel wire at t equals x is to say that for any stress A and corresponding strain B, if A is applied to the wire at t, then $A/B = x$.

The above law was deliberately stated in terms of the time variable in order to indicate that the degree of such a quantitative disposition as elasticity may vary, not only from system to system, but also for a given system from time to time. Elasticity is known to vary, for example, with temperature. It follows that, since the very law of variation of stress with strain does not necessarily remain constant for a fixed wire (in other words, the "constant" is itself a function of another variable— strictly speaking it is a constant only in a statistical sense), the postulate of determinism or unique predictability would not be satisfied by molar state descriptions in terms of the sole variable "stress." That postulate thus leads the physicist to postulate *microstates* correlated with variations of the wire's elasticity, i.e., molecular arrangements (cohesive forces of molecules determined by the relative positions of molecules) that are postulated to vary with temperature fluctuations so as to explain the variations of elasticity. There is a striking analogy here between the variations of elasticity due to temperature changes and the variations of the behavior dispositions called "habits" due to conditioning on the one hand, and between the postulated variations of molecular structure and the postulated variations of brain structure on the other hand.[12]

A serious confusion about the implications of scientific method for the concept of intervening variables appears in Tolman's presidential address "The Determiners of Behavior at a Choice Point."[13] When he introduces his list of intervening variables, such as demand, appetite, hypotheses (i.e., anticipations, guesses), he seems to feel impelled to make apologies to "honest behaviorists" for their "subjective" flavor. His apology takes the form of the claim, which he then proceeds to make good, "that each of them is nonetheless capable of perfectly objective definition and measurements."[14] Thus he gives an operational definition (also called "defining experiment") of "demand" in terms of a graph: if we keep all variables relevant to food demand constant except the so-called "maintenance schedule (M)," i.e., hours elapsed since the last feeding, we obtain a curve expressing demand as an increasing function of M, and this functional relation is to serve as the very definition of "demand." If Tolman were asked how it is that an experiment is required in order to define an intervening variable, he would probably reply that he is using "definition" just the way the physicist uses the term when he speaks of a definition of temperature in terms of the mercury thermometer: there too the form of the functional dependence of the defined variable on the defining variable has to be found out by experiment. But if this is to be an experimental question, unlike a question such as "How does the kinetic energy of a body vary with its velocity?", there must be some *independent* way of testing statements about the defined variable, such as whether it has increased or not. In the case of temperature such independent tests are provided by *sensations* of temperature differences and temperature equalities. What corresponds to

12. On theoretical explanation of dispositions in terms of microstructure, see Broad's *The Mind and Its Place in Nature* (New York: Humanities Press, Inc., 1929), chap. 10, pp. 430–440. For a clarifying resolution of the ambiguity of "intervening variables" as meaning sometimes a disposition and sometimes a postulated central state, see Meehl and MacCorquodale, "On the Distinction between Intervening Variables and Hypothetical Constructs," reprinted in H. Feigl and M. Brodbeck, eds., *Readings in the Philosophy of Science* (New York: Appleton-Century-Crofts, Inc., 1953).

13. *Psychological Review*, January 1938.

14. *Loc. cit.*, p. 16.

such tests in the case of "demand"? It evidently cannot be the same kind of test, since there can be no such thing as a sense impression of a rat's demand. The true answer is implicit in what Tolman later confesses, with disarming frankness, to be the method of guessing the form of the functional relations between the intervening variables and the response variables:

> . . . There seems to me every advantage in *beginning* by conceiving the situation loosely and anthropomorphically. I might never have arrived at this point of view of accepting anthropomorphism as a perfectly proper heuristic procedure all by myself. . . . But, in any case, I in my future work intend to go ahead imagining how, *if I were a rat,* I would behave as a result of such and such a demand combined with such and such an appetite and such and such a degree of differentiation; and so on. And then, on the basis of such imaginings, I shall try to figure out some sort of f_3 rules or equations [read: equations connecting the *I*'s *with response variables*].

This is equivalent to saying that such laws are guessed by extrapolating psychophysical laws confirmed through introspection of such mental states as desires, anticipations, and the like to the behavior of rats. However, what Tolman calls an "advantage," as though the inquirer had a choice between more or less fruitful methods of discovery, is rather a methodological necessity requiring no apology whatever. It is wholly inconceivable how a physicist could arrive at a nonarbitrary quantitative operational definition of temperature in terms of already measurable properties correlated with temperature, unless comparative judgments about temperature (such as "This object is now warmer that it was a while ago") could be made to begin with on the basis of sensation. Analogously, the establishment of functional relations between a variable such as "intensity of food demand (hunger)" and measurable physical variables such as the time elapsed since the animal's last feeding presupposes verification in terms of immediate experience of such comparative judgments as "x is now hungrier than an hour ago," and "immediate experience" can here mean only introspective awareness. Tolman's designation of this method of analogical extrapolation as a "heuristic procedure" is unfortunate because it suggests that the analogical inferences do not enter into the logical validation of the eventually formulated equations. But this suggestion is just as untrue as would be the claim that perceptual judgments of warmer and colder have nothing to do with the verification of the equation relating temperature to length. It would be tantamount to a lack of understanding of the epistemological foundations of a quantitative science. Furthermore, the bad conscience with which Tolman confesses "anthropomorphism" is entirely out of place. It would be at least as appropriate to use the word "egomorphism" here, for so human are rats, or so ratlike are humans, that the same intervening variables would have to be used by the psychologist in order to explain the less sophisticated aspects of the behavior of fellow humans. If I infer, without feeling guilty of primitivist habits of explanation, that *you* are propelled in your behavior by appetites and anticipations such as I occasionally experience myself, I need not feel ashamed to display the same egomorphism towards rats. The methodological problem would not be different if one of the rats experimented with in the laboratory turned out to be capable of verbal responses, so that the psychologist could test his hypothesis by asking, "Dear rat, do you now, after so many rewards followed your turning left at the choice point, expect more strongly that your response will be rewarded than you did at the beginning?" For when we explain a human organism's affirmative response to a question about his experience by the hypothesis that the experience did occur, we assume that the questioned subject both understood our question and was not lying—which is again to assume intervening variables.

C. THE UNCONSCIOUS

Psychoanalysis competes with relativity theory and the quantum theory for the title of the most dramatic intellectual revolution of this century. What the concept of space-time interval is to relativity theory and the concept of probability waves to quantum theory, the concept of unconscious wishes and repressions is to psychoanalytic theory. But whereas the physicists are, at least for practical purposes, sufficiently clear about their conceptual foundations to be able to get on quite well without the philosophers' assistance, the same could not be said of psychoanalytic theory. The meaning of "unconscious" still awaits clarification, though psychoanalytic jargon has become part and parcel of everyday speech.

We are fortunate to be able to build on the clarifying survey of different senses of "unconscious" by the Cambridge philosopher C. D. Broad.[16] Broad begins by distinguishing various "nonliteral" senses of the word, the most important of which is a sense in which an unconscious mental "event" is no event at all but a mental disposition—if, indeed, what is referred to is something mental at all and not a brain trace. Thus the content of the mysterious Unconscious is often described as a mass of latent memories. But a latent memory, in contrast to an actual

16. *The Mind and Its Place in Nature,* sec. C.

memory, a sudden flash of remembering, is no mental event or process at all, as Broad rightly points out. The expression that such memories are "stored up" in unconscious form is of the same dispositional kind as the physicist's expression that potential energy is stored up in the resting stone. Another nonliteral use of the expression "unconscious experience," which is also a dispositional use, is that in the sense of an *unrecognized need*. Thus, to borrow Broad's own example, a man might consciously desire wealth, but it turns out that the wealth he eventually acquires does not satisfy him and that his unrest and self-dissatisfaction persists until he acquires fame—whether by means of his wealth or by means of different accomplishments. Some people would then say that he unconsciously desired fame. This state of affairs, as Broad points out, would be more accurately expressed by saying that the man *needed* fame though he did not recognize this, instead of suggesting a mysterious undercurrent of unconscious desire. This is again a dispositional use of "unconscious," since to say "*A* needed *X*, though he (consciously) desired *Y*" is to make the prediction that *A* would be satisfied if he acquired *X* and would remain dissatisfied if he acquired *Y*; which analysis reveals that the only *events* referred to are the physical event of reaching a goal and the *conscious* experiences of satisfaction and dissatisfaction.

As may be surmised from Broad's dismissal of the dispositional uses as "nonliteral," there is according to him an important literal use in which it is mental events, not dispositions, that are characterized as unconscious, and this use is alleged to be the typically psychoanalytic one. He defines a literally unconscious mental event as a mental event that could not have been introspectively discriminated while it happened. This definition cries out for elucidation. To begin with, why is such introspection supposed to be impossible, why is not the unconscious mental event simply a mental event that the subject *actually* is not aware of? But this question is easily and plausibly answered by Broad: since with most people introspection is the exception, not the rule, such a definition would turn the vast majority of experiences that are normally called "conscious" into unconscious ones, and thus the definition would make the existence of unconscious mental events uncontroversial. Since the distinguishing mark of the literal use of "unconscious" is just that there may be reasonable controversy concerning the existence of the unconscious in that sense, an adequate definition of this concept must leave it an open question whether it applies to anything at all. But secondly, what is the sense of the implied suggestion that an event that was not introspectively discriminated while it happened may be thus discriminated later? Evidently Broad inserts this suggestion into his definition in order to allow for the psychoanalytic technique of making the patient conscious of the unconscious wishes that allegedly caused his abnormality. That is, "unconscious" is supplied with a temporal index, so that the same experience that was unconscious at one time may become conscious at a later time. The allegedly unconscious experience may be a persistent process, like the repression of a libidinal impulse, such that it could be asserted without contradiction that earlier phases of the process were unobserved and later phases observed. Or the unconscious experience may be a short-lived event, but saying that this same event later is apprehended means that it is consciously remembered.

But the evidence for the occurrence of such unconscious mental events that Broad adduces is far from convincing. It amounts to an argument from conscious memories of experiences that were not conscious states of the mind now remembering them. Thus a man is reported to have searched unsuccessfully for his glasses in the drawer of his desk, and to have subsequently remembered having perceived them there; but had he consciously perceived them, he would have found them, since he was looking for them; therefore he must have *unconsciously* perceived them. Broad agrees that this argument is inconclusive since the whole curious incident could be described as a *memory hallucination*: an optical stimulus such as undoubtedly occurred when the man searched his drawer and affected his visual nerve normally produces the state of consciousness called "visual perception"; the perception is believed, by all psychologists except those who accept mnemic causation, to leave a brain trace; a subsequent excitation of the brain trace then produces a memory of the perception that left the trace. If we eliminate from this causal sequence the perception, we have a memory hallucination: just as a drunkard who seems to see a pink rat that is not there is said to be in a state of perceptual hallucination, so a person might be said to have a memory hallucination when he seems to remember an experience that he never had. If we describe the situation by saying "He remembers having seen the glasses but he did not see them," we use, of course, paradoxical language that will make it difficult to accept the concept of memory hallucination. How can one remember an experience one never had? But it should be obvious that the same paradox, which can easily be obviated by substituting for "remembering" "seeming to remember," would make it equally difficult to accept the concept of perceptual hallucination.

Strangely, Broad seems to be inconsistent in his attitude toward memory hallucinations. For while he accepts this hypothesis as a way of avoiding the postulation of unconscious perceptions, he does not, apparently, think of using it when he examines the evidence for unconscious mental processes such as calculations unconsciously performed under hypnosis:

. . . A patient under hypnosis is told to perform a certain act at a certain number of minutes (which may run into hundreds or thousands) after he has been awakened. It is found that certain patients perform the suggested action automatically at or very near to the suggested time. This seems to imply that the time which was given in minutes has been reduced to days and hours by some process of mental arithmetic, and that a watch has been kept for the arrival of the calculated moment. Yet the patient cannot discover this process of calculation and of watching by introspection.[17]

Broad then considers the possibility that under subsequent hypnosis the same patient actually remembers having performed the calculation, and maintains that if this happened it would be conclusive evidence for the hypothesis that under hypnosis a process of calculation occurred that was literally unconscious relative to the mind normally controlling the patient's body (distinguished from the mind controlling the patient's body while under hypnosis). But if the concept of memory hallucination is applicable to the drawer incident it is equally applicable to this story. Whatever process occurs in the brain when a person calculates may, under the special conditions of hypnotism, fail to be accompanied by the conscious process we call "calculating" and yet leave the sort of brain trace that makes subsequent memory possible.

That Broad's concept of a literally unconscious mental event has any application becomes further doubtful once the question is raised in just what sense it is supposed to be *impossible* to be introspectively aware of a given mental event. Broad makes an analogy between physical and psychoanalytic theory: the eventual observation by astronomers of a planet that had not been sighted at the time its existence was postulated in order to account for the deflection from its predicted orbit of a known planet, he compares with the eventual emergence into consciousness, with the help of psychoanalytic therapy, of an unconscious wish that had been postulated to account for abnormal behavior. But this comparison is hardly illuminating unless one can argue that the planet was, not just unobserv*ed*, but unobserv*able*, at the time its existence was postulated. Let us see whether Broad's actual use of this concept of impossibility of introspective awareness will shed light on the matter. The man looking for his glasses failed to perceive them consciously, though the physical and physiological conditions (illumination, sufficiently acute vision—even without glasses) were such that a visual perception could normally be expected. Later, he remembered even the exact location of the glasses. Broad argues that the only way the nonoccurrence of a conscious perception could be explained without recourse to the unconscious would be in terms of the absence of conditions that were clearly fulfilled: physical and physiological conditions were favorable, and inattention

17. *Ibid.*, p. 427.

cannot be the explanation since the man was intent on finding his glasses. But according to Broad's definition of "unconscious mental event" the explanation of the subsequent memory in terms of unconscious perception is hardly intelligible: the memory of a perception that did not occur is explained as the result of a perception that it was impossible to be aware of! The very qualification that it was impossible to be aware of the perception while it occurred makes the explanation circular, since the only evidence for the hypothesis is the memory, which is just the explanandum!

Having found Broad's concept of an unconscious mental *event* unintelligible, we propose in the following a *dispositional* analysis of "unconscious desire" and "unconscious wish." As we have seen in Chapter 15, dispositional talk is characteristic of the *pretheoretical* stage of a science, since to ascribe dispositions is, to borrow a suggestive metaphor from Herbert Feigl, to issue promissory notes. One "promises" future discovery of a generalization that will, together with relevant singular statements, explain an observed regularity; but this is not equivalent to explaining the latter. The law that anything with a structural microproperty K dissolves in aqua regia, together with the premise that these objects have K, explains the observed regularity that these and similar objects (pieces of gold) dissolve when immersed in aqua regia. But the dispositional statement that objects with these surface characteristics are soluble in aqua regia does not explain it; it says only that the explanation that it is hoped will be discovered is one in terms of (at the time of the dispositional assertion unknown) *intrinsic* properties of the objects, not one in terms of a fortuitous collocation of circumstances. The same holds for the "explanation" of observed regularities in terms of instincts. The statement that the observed regularity is due to some kind of instinct is not an empty tautology, but it is not an explanation either (except the negative one, that learning is not the explanation); it may, however, be construed as a promise of a forthcoming explanation. To give a dispositional analysis of the typically psychoanalytic meaning of "unconscious," therefore, is to suggest that psychoanalysis so far is to a large extent a pretheoretical science.

If to ascribe an unconscious desire or wish to an organism is to ascribe to it a dispositional state, then unconscious desires are not causal antecedents of overt behavior, and it is a mistake to suppose that an item or pattern of overt behavior has been causally explained when one says that it expresses such and such an unconscious desire. Suppose that a person A regularly acts with respect to person B as though he disliked B; that is, *if* A disliked B he could be expected to act with respect to B just the way he is observed to act with respect to B. We say to A, "Obviously you dislike B," but A in apparent sincerity denies this. Now, what does it mean to say that, nevertheless, *A unconsciously* dislikes *B*? If it meant "*A* acts as if he consciously disliked *B* but he does not consciously dislike *B*," our explanation of *A*'s actions would have the curious form: *q*, because (if *p*, then *q*) and not *p*. According to the dispositional analysis of "unconscious dislike," however, this means that *A*'s apparently unfriendly or discriminatory actions towards *B* are not just the result of an accidental collocation of circumstances that are independent of *A*'s relevant attitudes, but depend on some intrinsic property of *A*: *A* has some intrinsic property such that any person with the same intrinsic property would probably react similarly in similar circumstances. It may be, for example, *A*'s belief that *B* threatens his professional position. Once such a property is discovered, a genuine causal explanation is at hand, but the word "unconscious" will have disappeared. In many cases no immediate causal antecedents can be detected on the molar level in terms of which observed responses, mental or physical, could be uniquely explained. In that case the intrinsic property to be discovered consists in certain aspects of the person's past experience (problem of *mnemic* laws in biology and psychology) or—at a utopian state of physiological psychology that fills the daydreams of physicalists—in brain modifications resulting from such past experience. Thus psychoanalysts often claim to have traced neurotic adult behavior to certain kinds of traumatic experience in childhood. Also Freud's famous case of the bride's disappointment during her wedding night leading to a strange form of compulsive behavior falls into this category. Here we have genetic laws—of an imperfect probabilistic character, indeed, and so far wholly unexplained in terms of a general theory of psychopathic behavior, but they can legitimately be used for probabilistic and in principle confirmable explanations of abnormal behavior patterns. The point is that the word "unconscious" cannot appear in any genuine causal explanation, whether rigorously deterministic or probabilistic, whether in terms of the postulates of a rigorous theory of human behavior or, more modestly, in terms of pragmatically reliable empirical generalizations, because its function is only to *mark*, not to *solve*, a problem of explanation.

It is often said that Freud and his followers are concerned with explanations of pathological behavior in terms of *motives*, specifically *unconscious* motives, hence not with causal explanations. Freud reports that his patient did not know why she performed that ritual every morning (shedding red ink on her bed sheet) until he made its "meaning" clear to her: it was a substitute fulfillment of her (unconscious) wish that her husband might have proved potent during that traumatic night. Now, let us first see what is meant by "motive" in an uncomplicated context such as "What motivated him to marry the unattractive old widow was the desire to inherit her considerable fortune." Ryle is surely wrong in contending that such an explanation of behavior is "analogous to the explanation of reactions and actions by reflexes and habits, or to the explanation of the fracture of the glass by reference to its brittleness."[18] To say that a person is in the habit of doing such and such in circumstances X is, indeed, to assert a hypothetical lawlike proposition, but the statement that he desired to inherit her fortune is not of this sort. It is true that a state of desiring something is not "occurrent" like a state of seeing, hearing, or smelling something. One can desire, or intend, something at a time when one is not actually aware of such a desire or intention, while one cannot, in the same sense, smell a foul smell without being aware of it or see a red patch without being aware of it. But given some stimulus occasioning an introspective act—such as the question "Why do you marry that woman?"—the man will become aware of (*a*) desiring to inherit her fortune and (*b*) being impelled to marry her in order to satisfy that desire, in a sense in which one cannot be aware of a hypothetical fact expressed by a subjunctive conditional. Motives of the familiar sort, then, are desires, intentions, purposes that causally determine human behavior and of which the agent becomes aware when certain normal conditions of self-examination are fulfilled.

But it is a mistake to regard unconscious motives as just a different kind of causal antecedents of human, especially neurotic behavior that are like motives of the familiar kind except that, owing to repression, they cannot under normal conditions become objects of the agent's awareness. If to ascribe an unconscious wish to the patient is to predict that under therapy he will eventually become aware of such a wish (provided certain essential conditions, such as cooperation with the analyst, and so on, are fulfilled) and acquire the beneficial belief—whatever it may mean—that his neurotic symptoms served the purpose of its "substitute fulfillment,[19] then an unconscious wish is a dispositional state of a person. In that case the "explanation" of neurotic symptoms in terms of an unconscious wish is, to borrow Ryle's example for use in a more appropriate context, like explaining the breaking of an object in terms of its brittleness and unlike explaining it in terms of the antecedent event of its being released. To ascribe the fracture to brittleness is to assert that the observed event is to be explained in terms of some intrinsic property of the object; that is, we express the belief that the antecedent event (release) would

18. Gilbert Ryle, *The Concept of Mind* (New York, Barnes & Noble, 1950), p. 90.

19. The question of the relevance or irrelevance of therapeutic success to validation of psychoanalytic theory is beyond the scope of this discussion. It should be noted, however, that the fact that the patient's neurotic behavior disappears after the analyst gets him to believe that it served such and such unconscious purposes has no bearing on he question whether the analyst's "explanation" is correct. In the same way religious beliefs may be psychologically beneficial without having a clear cognitive meaning according to scientific standards of cognitive significance.

be followed by the same effect (fracture) under a wide variety of circumstances *provided* the object involved resembled the given one in certain—as yet unspecified—intrinsic properties. Similarly, the explanation in terms of the patient's unconscious wish is of this "promissory" sort: similar traumatic experiences will result in a similar neurosis provided the person who suffers them is in certain as yet undiscovered respects (perhaps physiological, perhaps psychological) like the present patient. The language of unconscious motives, therefore, has a heuristic rather than an explanatory function.

D. INTERACTIONISM AND EPIPHENOMENALISM

The age-old question whether there is mind-body interaction has already been answered in the affirmative by us when we defined the subject-matter of psychology as consisting of mental events and their causal connections with physical stimuli, responses, and actions. But since there are not only philosophers but also psychologists who hold the belief in mind-body interaction to be scientifically inadmissible, something ought to be said to defend interactionism against their objections.

Historically, interactionism is associated with a dualism of substances, the dualism, in Cartesian terms, of "thinking" and "extended" substances. Indeed, the very expression "The mind acts on the body" suggests such a dualism. In order to make it clear that the interactionism here defended is not committed to the belief in the existence of substantial minds, we shall first show that in fact the motion of a substantial mind is fraught with such serious difficulties that it is not clear just what is asserted by the proposition that there are such things, and that they might survive the death of the body. It is perfectly possible, we shall argue, to be a "naturalist" insofar as one rejects the mind-body dualism of Christian theology, and nevertheless accept the obvious fact that human organisms go through mental as well as physical states and that there are causal relations between them. Why a naturalist must reject the notion of a substantial mind is not a very simple story, but we shall tell it as simply as possible.

To begin with, the question whether disembodied minds are possible is ambiguous in that logical or causal possibility may be meant. Whether the extinction of consciousness with the destruction of the cerebro-nervous system is logically necessary depends on the analysis of statements about one's self, such as "I am now angry," "I am now thinking about the proof of the Pythagorean theorem." Such extinction would, indeed, be logically necessary if the following, *materialistic,* analysis of the concept of selfhood were correct: "I am in mental state $M = M$ occurs and its immediate cause is a process in my brain." This analysis, to be sure, is materialistic only if the word "my" can be eliminated from the context "my brain" and replaced by a purely physical description of a definite physical object. The analysis must, however, be rejected for two reasons: first, it entails that it is logically impossible for an experience of mine to be directly caused by processes in some other body than the one I am accustomed to call mine or even by states of some other mind. But such causality is surely conceivable. We can easily imagine, for example, that a congenitally blind person is caused to have visual perceptions by optical stimulation of some other organism. And telepathy, defined as direct causation of certain states of one mind by states of another mind, without physical mediation, cannot be rejected as logically absurd, whatever the alleged empirical evidence for it may be deemed to prove. Secondly, this analysis seems to be circular, since the concept "my body" (and therewith "my brain") already involves the concept of selfhood. That is, by "my" body I seem to mean that body B such that the direct causes and the direct effects of *my* experiences, specifically, of my sensations and volitions, are changes in B.[20] (Note how interaction is involved in the very definition of "my body.") Not that we have a fixed criterion for the use of "my body." Suppose that one morning, on awakening, I discover a sixth finger on my left hand. Is that limb part of my body or not? Suppose it turns out to be insensitive and completely inaccessible to volitional control. I might say that for this very reason it is not really part of my body, and this conclusion would no doubt be reinforced if it turned out to contain a bone and a liquid quite unlike human bones and blood. On the other hand, the criterion of spatial continuity with the object already well established as "my" body by the causal criterion might lead me to say that my body now has a part that is causally disconnected with both my sentient and my volitional life. But whatever the linguistic decision, the important fact remains that the causal criterion is one of the criteria of identification of my body; and since this criterion cannot be formulated without using "my" again in connection with sensations and volitions, the analyst remains confronted with the task of clarifying the concept of selfhood.

This reflection, coupled with the feeling that it makes perfectly good sense to suppose that one day one discovers that the body hitherto called one's own has mysteriously vanished, suggests the Humean theory of the self as a series of mental events whose unity consists in contingent relations between its members. To make this conception of the self as a "logical construction" out of mental events precise is to analyze asser-

20. This definition is due to C. J. Ducasse. See his *Nature, Mind, and Death* (La Salle, Ill.: Open Court Publishing Co., 1951), chap. 18.

tions of mind-ownership ("There now occurs a pain, and a color sensation, that is *mine*") as assertions of class membership. But how are the relevant classes of mental events to be defined? Which relation between two successive mental events is the necessary and sufficient condition for their being states of the same mind? We all know the vague answer that the self's unity is constituted by memory. Hume himself clearly saw that a strict constructive definition of the self in terms of mnemic relations between logically independent experiences is not possible, for, even if "*x* is a memory of *y*" were a sufficient condition for "*x* and *y* are states of the same mind," it surely is not a necessary condition. It is not self-contradictory to suppose that I have no memory of many past perceptions and feelings *of mine*. One may now try to improve the definition by substituting dispositional memory for occurrent memory: if *y* is a past state of my mind then I must at least be capable of remembering *y*. But this will not do either. To begin with, we can hardly claim to have constructed the self out of mental events if we have to bring in capacities. Secondly, exactly what is meant by saying that, though I do not now actually think of my feelings this mornnig, I *could* remember them? Suppose it means that if I tried hard enough to remember them, I would. But what is the criterion of having tried hard enough? Clearly, it must, on pain of tautology, be independent of the actual success. But the vast majority of our past experiences we cannot remember no matter how hard we try, hence the assertion that we are capable of remembering them is either false or else reduces to the innocuous proposition that if *x* is a state of mind *M* and *y* a later state of *M*, then it is logically possible that *y* be a memory of *x*. It may be replied that there is empirical evidence for a mnemic continuity of present consciousness with past consciousness that extends far beyond what is revealed in normal circumstances in our actual memories, since under abnormal conditions of hypnosis or psychoanalytic treatment or artificial excitation of brain traces people often remember events of their remote childhood. But if it is admitted to be a question of fact whether under such conditions a subject will consciously remember its dreams or its waking experiences of a long time ago, then dispositional memory even in this extended sense cannot be the whole or part of the *meaning* of "personal identity."

If this difficulty in the analysis of selfhood remains unsolved, the concept of a substantial mind remains obscure and even the practically inconsequential question of the *logical* possibility of personal survival lacks a sufficiently clear meaning to be answered one way or the other. It is not clear just how much of its former embodied life a disembodied spirit would have to remember in order to count as still the same person divested of a body (or at any rate of its former body). In the case of embodied spirits, gaps in mnemic continuity are compensated by biological continuity; we can conveniently say that we are still the same person as the one who looked and behaved thus and so twenty years ago though we remember very little of our former conscious life, because we can use the criterion of bodily identity. The latter is obviously not a sufficient criterion of personal identity, otherwise we could not consistently speak of split personalities. But we would not speak of continuing persons to the extent that we do if we did not heavily rely on the criterion of biological continuity. It is not clear, therefore, in just what sense a surviving mind would be identical with a once embodied mind. My dreams usually do not include memories of my waking life, and most of my dream images I cannot remember on awakening. The words "my" and "I," therefore, must in this very statement refer to a continuing body if I should survive the death of my body in some form of dream life, it would not be *I* who survived unless this dream life included a great, great many more memories of my bodily life than my this-worldly dreams ever do, because there is, *ex hypothesi*, no bodily continuity that could fill the gaps of mnemic continuity.

But once interactionism is purged of the notion of substantial minds and merely asserts two-sided interaction between mental and bodily states of an organism, it can stand up against all the usual philosophical arguments. The latter arise mainly from inadequate conceptions of causality, as has been pointed out by several writers.[21] Thus epiphenomenalists maintain that mental events, such as volitions and sensations, are "epiphenomenal," i.e., by-products of brain events that are not themselves links in the causal chain of events. The muscular contraction, for example, that precedes my making a fist is supposed to be caused by a brain event, not by the conscious volition that accompanies the brain event. The first logical point to be made here is that if the epiphenomenalist assumes a strict parallelism between brain events and conscious states—while denying both that conscious states have physical effects and even that there are causal relations between conscious states—then he could not possibly put his thesis to a test. For how would he refute a philosopher who maintained, on the contrary, that the volition causes the brain event, not the other way around? He would have to show that the brain event can occur without any volition at all and will be followed by just the same bodily movements as those that follow an introspectable volition. But this demonstration is precluded by the assumption that the brain event and the volition always occur together. Suppose, however, he holds that although no volition can occur without a corresponding brain event, the brain event may under special conditions occur without its usual conscious accompaniment. Supposing that under those conditions exactly the same chain of physical effects were observed, would this amount to an empirical proof of epiphenomenalism? If the reader remembers our analysis of causation, he will see that the answer

21. See especially C. D. Broad, *The Mind and Its Place in Nature*, chap. 3.

is negative: to say that a specific instance *e* of a repeatable kind of effect *E* was caused by a specific instance *c* of a repeatable kind of cause *C* is *not* to assert that every instance of *E* must be preceded by an instance of *C*; therefore the refutation of that universal proposition is consistent with the truth of the singular causal proposition. If the situation in which the movement of my arm is supposedly preceded by a specific brain event but not by the volition that is its usual concomitant differed from the normal situation *solely* in the absence of the volition, then the epiphenomenalist's conclusion would be justified at least for the case of volition, though he would still be far from having established his *general* thesis, which denies causal efficacy also to perceptions, beliefs, feelings, acts of interpretation, and so on. But at any rate it is hard to conceive how such an ideal application of the method of single difference would be feasible.

A more fruitful approach to the problem, perhaps, is to distinguish the causal language by which we describe regularities in common-sense experience from the language of theoretical explanation. Volitional causation, "making things happen," is the very paradigm case of the common-sense concept of causation; to deny, therefore, that what appears like causal efficacy of the will is *really* a case of causation is semantically as absurd as to say that blood is not really red, or that headaches are not really pains. If physiologists should succeed in perfecting a physiological theory that enabled them to "define" specific sorts of mental states in physiological terms so as to be able to predict all human behavior from purely physical premises, they still would not have shown that volitional causality is a mere illusion, any more than the kinetic theory of heat has refuted the common-sense belief that increase of sensed temperature causes the butter to melt and substituted the scientific truth that it is "really" molecular motions that cause the butter to melt. Finally, we should remember that insofar as epiphenomenalism is inspired by the belief that "everything" must be capable of explanation in terms of physics alone, it is based on a simple confusion, for the occurrence of the "epiphenomenal" concomitants of brain events certainly could not be explained by the laws of physics.

E. COULD A MACHINE BE CONSCIOUS?

According to the Cartesian view, the possession of a soul distinguishes man not only from whatever machines were available in the age of Descartes but even from animals: men alone were held to be "thinking substances," capable of deliberately controlling their actions. In the nineteenth century

T. H. Huxley, the biologist who stood up in defense of Darwin as Galileo had stood up in defense of Copernicus, elevated animals to the dignity of "conscious automata" but at the same time degraded man to that same level. Experimental physiology had disclosed the dependence of the sort of rational, goal-directed behavior we take as evidence of consciousness on brain functions. Huxley wrote: ". . . To the best of my judgment, the argument which applies to brutes holds equally good of men; and, therefore, . . . all states of consciousness in us, as in them, are immediately caused by molecular changes of the brain-substance." Today, in the age of cybernetics (the theory of self-directive mechanisms), the dignity of man seems to be threatened still more. Machines have been constructed that are so manlike and intelligent in their behavior—if not in appearance—that the question has been raised whether it is not in principle possible to construct a machine as complex as the human brain —and if so, whether one would have any better reason for denying consciousness to it than for denying it to fellow human beings. For example, do we have a right to say that an electronic brain, which within minutes performs calculations and deductions it would take a human brain many years to perform, "thinks" in the sense in which a person thinks?

Now, to say that a machine thinks, remembers, anticipates (a move by the chess partner), intends to reach a goal, and so on, would not be paradoxical at all if these terms designated just certain forms of behavior. According to behavioristic definitions of psychological terms it would obviously make good sense to ascribe mental attributes to a machine. For example, the following behavioristic definition of goal-directed (purposive, teleological) behavior could obviously be satisfied by a machine as well as by a living organism:

> . . . a sequence of movements which (i) is evoked by a negative condition E' and is such that the introduction of a contrasting condition, E, at any time in the sequence would terminate the process in question, (ii) is such that with repetition of the process constituent actions which favor E tend to be stabilized while actions which are adverse to E tend to be eliminated, with the result that the process as a whole approximates to a form in which it consists of a set of component actions performed in a certain order which (a) performed in that order are sufficient to produce E and (b) are such that the omission of any action would prevent the occurrence of E.[22]

Again, if to say that an organized system of parts "remembers" means that its responses to stimuli are determined not only by the nature of the stimuli but also by its past states, machines might remember and learn from experience.

22. C. A. Mace, "Mechanical and Teleological Causation," reprinted in H. Feigl and W. Sellars, *Readings in Philosophical Analysis* (New York: Appleton-Century-Crofts, Inc., 1949).

But does it make sense to apply such psychological terms to machines when they are taken in the mentalistic sense in which we apply them to ourselves? The answer is that, unless one precludes applicability of mentalistic predicates to a machine by the very definition of machine (so that "conscious machine" is stipulated to be self-contradictory), our justification for ascribing forms of consciousness to a machine is *in principle* the same argument from analogy as that by which we justify beliefs about other human minds. The only question is whether in any given case the analogy is sufficiently strong, the machine structurally and functionally sufficiently similar to a human being to warrant such an inference. So far the existence of such machines is, of course, merely a subject of science fiction. But one cannot maintain *a priori* that being an artifact is logically incompatible with being conscious, nor that "*x* is conscious" entails "*x* is made of biochemical materials." As to the first point: If biochemists should succeed in synthesizing sperms that in turn were used to fertilize a woman artificially, the resulting human being would be partly an artifact, yet it is doubtful that we would for that reason deny consciousness to it. Would we have good reasons for the belief that natural generation is a necessary condition for consciousness if an artifact were constructed that exhibited all the behavioral signs of consciousness—including an electronic brain comparable in complexity to the brains of higher animals? This leads to the second point: We associate consciousness with certain complex physical objects made of organic substance because these objects are strikingly similar in appearance and behavior to ourselves. But just because analogy is a vague concept, we have no fixed rule that dictates what we should say if, say, on another planet we encountered robots made of inorganic materials that behaved like intelligent beings and even communicated with us. Would we regard them as conscious beings or as machines that behave as though they were conscious? The former alternative is more likely, but neither alternative is *entailed* by the rule governing "conscious," simply because that rule is a vague rule of analogy.

A final a priori argument against conscious machines is the argument from free will. Human beings are certainly distinguished from other physical systems by the ability to falsify deliberately a prediction of their behavior. But as we have seen (Chapter 17, F), such "spontaneity" is compatible with determinism. It is, therefore, fallacious to urge that a machine cannot be conscious because, by definition of "machine," it is in principle predictable. A man's desire to falsify a prediction of his action is simply a further antecedent condition that determines his action. That we are free means, roughly, that our behavior is partly determined by our own desires and decisions (for subtler qualifications, cf. Chapter 17, F). It follows that to argue that machines cannot be conscious *because* they lack "free will" is (*a*) to confuse freedom with indeterminacy, (*b*) to beg the question.

Selected Readings

Bain, A., *Mind and Body* (London, 1873).

Bawden, H. H., "The Presuppositions of a Behaviorist Psychology," *Psychological Review*, 1918.

Beck, M., "Proper Object of Psychology," *Philosophy and Phenomenological Research*, 1953.

Bergmann, G., "An Empiricist Schema of the Psychophysical Problem," *Philosophy of Science*, 1942.

———, "Psychoanalysis and Experimental Psychology," *Mind*, 1944.

———, "On Some Methodological Problems of Psychology," *Philosophy of Science*, 1940. [Reprinted in H. Feigl and M. Brodbeck (eds.), *Readings in the Philosophy of Science* (New York, 1953).]

———, "The Logic of Psychological Concepts," *Philosophy of Science*, 1951.

———, "Theoretical Psychology," *Annual Review of Psychology*, 1953.

——— and K. W. Spence, "Operationism and Theory in Psychology," *Psychological Review*, 1941.

Bills, A. G., "Psychology as Science," *Psychological Review*, 1938.

Blanshard, B., "Behaviorism and the Theory of Knowledge," *Philosophical Review*, 1928.

Boring, E. G., "Mind and Mechanism," *American Journal of Psychology*, 1946.

———, "The Role of Theory in Experimental Psychology," *American Journal of Psychology*, 1953.

Broad, C. D., *The Mind and Its Place in Nature* (New York, 1929), sec. C.

Brunswick, E., "Psychology as Science of Objective Relations," *Philosophy of Science*, 1937.

———, *The Conceptual Framework of Psychology* (International Encyclopedia of Unified Science, I, no. 10, Chicago, 1939).

Buck, R. C., "On the Logic of General Behavior Systems Theory," in H. Feigl and M. Scriven (eds.), *Minnesota Studies in the Philosophy of Science* (Minneapolis, 1956), vol. I.

Bunge, M., "Do Computers Think?," *British Journal for the Philosophy of Science*, 1956.

Cronbach, L. J., and P. E. Meehl, "Construct Validity in Psychological Tests," in H. Feigl and M. Scriven (eds.), *Minnesota Studies in the Philosophy of Science* (Minneapolis, 1956), vol. I.

Ducasse, C. J., *Nature, Mind, and Death* (La Salle, Ill., 1951), parts 3, 4.

Feigl, H., "Logical Analysis of the Psychophysical Problem," *Philosophy of Science*, 1934.

———, "Principles and Problems of Theory Construction in Psychology," in W. Dennes (ed.), *Current Trends of Psychological Theory* (Pittsburgh, 1951).

———, "The Mind-Body Problem in the Development of Logical Empiricism," in H. Feigl and M. Brodbeck (eds.), *Readings in the Philosophy of Science* (New York, 1953).

Feigl, H., "The Mental and the Physical," in H. Feigl, M. Scriven, and G. Maxwell (eds.), *Minnesota Studies in the Philosophy of Science* (Minneapolis, 1958), vol. II.

Freud, S., "The Unconscious," in *Collected Papers* (London, 1924), vol. VI.

——, "A Note on the Unconscious in Psychoanalysis," in J. Rickman (ed.), *A General Selection from the Works of Sigmund Freud* (London, 1937).

Geldard, F. A., "Explanatory Principles in Psychology," *Psychological Review*, 1939.

Ginsberg, A., "Hypothetical Constructs and Intervening Variables," *Psychological Review*, 1954.

Guthrie, E. R., "Psychological Explanations," *Psychological Review*, 1933.

Hardie, W. F. R., "Explanation of Human Conduct," *Analysis*, 1950.

Hempel, C. G., "The Logical Analysis of Psychology," in H. Feigl and W. Sellars (eds.), *Readings in Philosophical Analysis* (New York, 1949).

——, "A Note on Semantic Realism," *Philosophy of Science*, 1950.

Hook, S. (ed.), *Philosophy, Psychoanalysis and Scientific Method* (New York, 1959).

Hull, C. L., "Mind, Mechanism and Adaptive Behavior," *Psychological Review*, 1937.

——, "The Problem of Intervening Variables in Molar Behavior Theory," *Psychological Review*, 1943.

Laird, J., *Our Minds and Their Bodies* (London, 1925).

Lashley, K. S., "Behavioristic Interpretation of Consciousness," *Psychological Review*, 1923.

Lewis, C. I., "Some Logical Considerations Concerning the Mental," *Journal of Philosophy*, 1941. [Reprinted in H. Feigl and W. Sellars (eds.), *Readings in Philosophical Analysis* (New York, 1949).]

Mace, C. A., "Some Implications of Analytical Behaviorism," *Proceedings of the Aristotelian Society*, 1948–49.

MacIntyre, A. C., *The Unconscious* (London, 1958).

MacKay, D. M., "Mindlike Behavior in Artifacts," *British Journal for the Philosophy of Science*, 1951.

Maher, M., *Psychology* (London, 1940).

Mandelbaum, M., "Professor Ryle and Psychology," *Philosophical Review*, 1958.

Marx, M. H., "Hypothesis and Construct," in M. H. Marx, *Psychological Theory* (New York, 1951).

——, "Intervening Variable or Hypothetical Construct," *Psychological Review*, 1951.

Mays, W., "Can Machines Think?," *Philosophy*, 1952.

Meehl, P., and K. MacCorquodale, "On the Distinction between Intervening Variables and Hypothetical Constructs," *Psychological Review*, 1948. [Reprinted in H. Feigl and M. Brodbeck (eds.), *Readings in the Philosophy of Science* (New York, 1953).]

Money-Kyrle, R. E., "The World of the Unconscious and the World of Commonsense," *British Journal for the Philosophy of Science*, 1956.

Pap, A., "Semantic Analysis and Psycho-physical Dualism," *Mind*, 1952.

Pratt, C. C., *The Logic of Modern Psychology* (New York, 1939).

Reichenbach, H., *Experience and Prediction* (Chicago, 1938), chap. 4, sec. 26.

Rozeboom, W., "Mediation Variables in Scientific Theory," *Psychological Review*, 1956.

Russell, B., *The Analysis of Mind* (London, 1921).

——, "What is Mind?," *Journal of Philosophy*, 1958.

Ryle, G. *The Concept of Mind* (London, 1949).

Schlick, M., "On the Relation between Psychological and Physical Concepts," *Revue de Synthèse*, 1935. [Reprinted in H. Feigl and W. Sellars (eds.), *Readings in Philosophical Analysis* (New York, 1949).]

Scriven, M., "The Mechanical Concept of Mind," *Mind*, 1953.

———, "A Possible Distinction between Traditional Scientific Disciplines and the Study of Human Behavior," in H. Feigl and M. Scriven (eds.), *Minnesota Studies in the Philosophy of Science* (Minneapolis, 1956), vol. I.

———, "A Study of Radical Behaviorism," *ibid.*

Shoben, E. J., Jr., "Psychological Theory Construction and the Psychologist," *Journal of General Psychology*, 1955.

Sellars, R. W., "The Double Knowledge Approach to the Mind-Body Problem," *Aristotelian Society Proceedings*, 1922.

———, "An Analytic Approach to the Mind-Body Problem," *Philosophical Review*, 1939.

Sellars, W., "A Semantical Solution of the Mind-Body Problem," *Methodos*, 1953.

Singer, E. A., *Mind as Behavior* (Columbus, Ohio, 1924).

Skinner, B. F., "The Operational Analysis of Psychological Terms," *Psychological Review*, 1945. [Reprinted in H. Feigl and M. Brodbeck, *Readings in the Philosophy of Science* (New York, 1953).]

———, "Are Theories of Learning Necessary?," *Psychological Review*, 1950.

———, *Science and Human Behavior* (New York, 1953).

Snygg, D., "Scientific Method in Psychology," *Journal of General Psychology*, 1955.

Spence, K. W., "The Postulates and Methods of 'Behaviorism,'" *Psychological Review*, 1948. [Reprinted in H. Feigl and M. Brodbeck (eds.), *Readings in the Philosophy of Science* (New York, 1953).]

———, "Historical and Modern Conceptions of Psychology," in K. W. Spence, *Behavior Theory and Conditioning* (New Haven, Conn., 1956). [Reprinted in E. H. Madden (ed.), *The Structure of Scientific Thought* (Boston, 1960).]

———, "The Empirical Basis and Theoretical Structure of Psychology," *Philosophy of Science*, 1957.

Spilsbury, R. T., and R. T. MacKay, "Mentality in Machines," *Aristotelian Society Proceedings*, supp. vol. 26 (1952).

Taylor, R., "Comments on a Mechanistic Conception of Purposefulness," *Philosophy of Science*, 1950.

Tolman, E. C., "The Determiners of Behavior at a Choice Point," *Psychological Review*, 1938.

Turing, A. M., "Can a Machine Think?," in J. R. Newman (ed.), *The World of Mathematics* (New York, 1956), vol. IV.

Watson, J., "Psychology as the Behaviorist Views It," *Psychological Review*, 1913.

———, *Behaviorism* (New York, 1924).

Wisdom, J., *Problems of Mind and Matter* (Cambridge, 1934).

Wisdom, J. O., "Can Epiphenomenalism Be Refuted?," *Proceedings of the Second International Congress of the International Union for the Philosophy of Science*, Zurich, 1954.

———, "Mentality in Machines," *Aristotelian Society Proceedings*, supp. vol. 26 (1952).

Zener, K., "The Significance of Experience of the Individual for the Science of Psychology," in H. Feigl, M. Scriven, and G. Maxwell (eds.), *Minnesota Studies in the Philosophy of Science* (Minneapolis, 1958), vol. II.

CHAPTER 21

The Analysis
of Value Judgments

A. IS NORMATIVE SCIENCE
POSSIBLE?

The social sciences have so far been mentioned in this book only by way of illustrations of general principles of methodology. This procedure would be justified if the social sciences had no peculiar methodological problems, problems that do not arise in the logical analysis of the natural sciences. Such a "unity of science" may, however, be disputed on the ground that the social sciences have the unique task of solving questions of *value*, which raises special logical and methodological difficulties. The ultimate task of the social sciences, it may be held, is to *improve* human society, hence social scientists waste their skill on aimless descriptions and statistics unless there are standards of value to guide their activity.

The simple and definitive answer to this is that the scientist qua scientist makes no value judgments whether his subject-matter be social or natural. This point of view was expressed by the famous German sociologist Max Weber by the dictum that social science must be "value free." The positing of ends, he held, is an activity outside of science which the scientist must presuppose before he can even formulate a question he can answer qua scientist: if you tell me your aims, I will tell you what is the best means for achieving the aim. Social science cannot establish what ends human beings *ought* to pursue; it can only tell them the best procedure for securing their actual ends. In this way alone is science relevant to human values.

We must beware, however, of misleading formulations of this essentially correct insight. It is sometimes said that there can be no science of ends but only of means, and this provokes the retort that surely there must be a scientific way of distinguishing between *good* and *bad* ends. This is an entirely futile dispute which arises from oversight of the *relative* character of the terms "end" and "means." Clearly anything that is an end in one context is a means in another context. The end for which the Western Allies were negotiating with the Russians in 1961 was to keep West Berlin within the Western fold; but this end was in turn a means to preserve capitalism in the face of communist expansion, and if a capitalist were asked how he justified fighting for capitalism he would probably say that capitalism is an indispensable means to human freedom and happiness. On the other side, the Russians would justify their conflicting proximate ends, by just the same method, with reference to remoter ends—and in fact their professed ultimate end has been *verbally* identical with that professed by the capitalists: peace, freedom, and happiness. The correct formulation of the conception of value-free social science, then, is: there is no science of ends *qua ends*. And this is an analytic proposition, just like the proposition "No axiom is provable qua axiom": by definition, to justify an end is to show that it is a good, or even indispensable *means* to some ulterior end.

If by normative science is meant a deductive system in which specific normative propositions are deduced from general normative propositions conjointly with factual premises, then of course normative science is possible. Thus, the premises "You ought to keep your promises" and "You promised to pay back the loan" entail the conclusion "You ought to pay back the loan" by the same principle of syllogistic reasoning with which we are already familiar. Let us refer to such arguments as *practical syllogisms*. Now, since the terms that occur in the conclusion of a valid syllogism must also occur in one premise, specifically the major term (the predicate of the conclusion) in the major premise, we see at once that a conclusion with a normative predicate can follow only from a *normative* major premise. It is this simple point of logic that is expressed by the dictum "You cannot deduce what *ought to be* from what *is*." But this does not mean that factual investigations are irrelevant to normative conclusions, for a nontrivial normative conclusion can be derived from a normative major premise only with the help of a factual premise ("You promised to pay back the loan," in our illustration). We might say that insofar as normative science is logically possible, it is a deductive systematization of normative propositions by means of relevant factual propositions. But to strive for a normative science that spins normative conclusions out of purely factual, descriptive premises is to strive to produce a rabbit out of a silk hat.

But how can a normative major premise, such as "It is your (prima-facie) duty to keep your promises," be justified? Is there any way of *justifying* the major premise of a practical syllogism the way an empirical scientist can explain a major premise by deduction from an independently confirmable more general law or theory? The approach of traditional ethics has been to provide such a justification by deduction from an ethical principle. Perhaps the best known and the one most relevant to the concerns of social science is the *utilitarian* principle of Bentham and Mill: a form of behavior is morally justified to the extent that it tends to maximize the amount and distribution of human happiness as compared with alternative forms of behavior. Let us call this property of actions that, according to utilitarianism, confers moral value on an action the "happiness-maximizing" property. Then the justification of the moral rule "You ought to keep your promises" would be the argument: you ought to perform happiness-maximizing actions, keeping your promises is a happiness-maximizing form of conduct, therefore you ought to keep your promises.

Since we are not here concerned with the problems of substantive ethics, i.e., which forms of behavior are morally justified and which is the true standard of morality, the utilitarian or the Kantian or some other, we will not analyze the utilitarian principle or any other ethical principle in detail. We are here concerned exclusively with the *logic* of moral justification. Clearly we are driven to ask how any proposed ethical principle can in turn be validated. Here the analogy with theoretical explanation in science breaks down: the acceptance of an explanatory theory is justified by showing that the theory explains laws that can be inductively confirmed independently of the theory. But the major premises of practical syllogisms cannot be inductively established: we either accept them without justification, as rules we have been brought up to obey, or else we justify them by deduction from an ethical principle; hence it would be circular to justify the ethical principle by showing that it entails the rules of moral behavior that are to be justified. How, then, is an ethical principle justifiable at all?

This fundamental question has forced philosophers concerned with ethics into *metaethics* since G. E. Moore's *Principia Ethica*. That is, they were forced to ask what sort of statements ethical statements are— empirical or a priori, analytic or synthetic, or perhaps pseudostatements that, though grammatically declarative, are really imperatives in function. Unless one is clear on this question, deductive systematization of ethical statements does not provide a justification for any ethical belief.

B. METAETHICAL THEORIES

An exhaustive classification of pure metaethical theories can be obtained as follows. An ethical statement is either like a scientific statement in being true or false, or it is not. In the latter case it is an expression of attitude or emotion or desire and an attempt to influence attitudes, emotions, or desires. The theory that so construes ethical statements is called *emotivism*. Nonemotivist theories, on the other hand, may be called *cognitivist* because they hold that ethical statements express cognitive claims, whether true or false. But a cognitivist may be either a *naturalist* or an *intuitionist*.

A naturalist subscribes to the epistemology of logical empiricism according to which every cognitively significant statement is either analytic or empirically testable, whereas an intuitionist holds that some ethical propositions are synthetic a priori truths. The naturalist construes an ethical principle, such as the utilitarian principle, as an analytic (nonarbitrary) definition of an ethical predicate in terms of descriptive predicates. Such a definition is to be derived inductively, according to him, by examining instances of actual application of the ethical predicate and noting a common property that is the actual criterion of application. Once the definition is agreed upon, synthetic ethical statements that apply the defined ethical predicate to specific situations and forms of conduct become empirically testable.

The intuitionist holds that ethical predicates stand for "nonnatural" qualities or relations, i.e., qualities or relations that are not given in sense perception nor in introspection nor are definable in terms of such. Any statement, therefore, that connects an ethical predicate with a descriptive predicate (such as "If an action is a fulfillment of a promise, then it is prima facie right," or "If an act is an act of wanton cruelty, then it is evil") is held to be synthetic by intuitionists. It may seem that intuitionists must hold any such statement to express a self-evident a priori truth, since by hypothesis ethical predicates designate nonnatural, hence not empirically observable, qualities or relations. But it is surely implausible to suppose that in all cases of ethical disagreement one party simply fails to grasp an a priori truth because he fails to grasp the relevant ethical concept. As a matter of fact, the intuitionist is not committed to this implausible position, as reflection on the practical syllogism will show. When we argue, "You ought to pay back the loan because you promised to do so and it is your prima-facie duty to keep promises," we adduce in support of the ethical conclusion an empirical fact, namely, "You promised to pay back the loan." Now, a statement expresses an a priori truth only if no empirical fact is relevant to its truth or falsehood. Therefore the conclusions of practical syllogisms cannot, even on the intuitionist's conception, express a priori truths. It is only the major premise that, if true and if not further justifiable via an empirical premise by an ethical principle, expresses an a priori truth according to intuitionism. And, of course, whatever ethical principle is proclaimed by an intuitionist is proclaimed as a self-evident a priori truth.

The chief varieties of ethical naturalism are (1) hedonistic utilitarianism,

(2) relativism, (3) the dispositional approval theory. The hedonistic utilitarian holds that the rightness or wrongness of an action that we must decide whether or not to perform depends on its consequences for human happiness. The application of this criterion is not always clear-cut. Apart from the difficulty of forecasting the likely consequences, there may arise the dilemma that of two alternative actions one is likely to maximize the amount of happiness and the other the distribution of happiness. Nevertheless, in spite of its vagueness, this would seem to be the criterion that is most relevant to the decisions of legislators and policy-makers. Note that from the point of view of metaethics, the adoption of this criterion of rightness is not sufficient to mark a person as a hedonistic utilitarian. An intuitionist could adopt just the same criterion, but whereas the hedonistic utilitarian *as naturalist* conceives of it as an analytic definition of rightness, the intuitionist holds rightness to be a nonnatural quality of actions that is synthetically and necessarily connected with the utilitarian quality. Clearly, the basic metaethical question here is whether, and in what sense, an ethical predicate can be *synonymous* with a descriptive predicate. We shall face it below, in connection with a discussion of what G. E. Moore called "the naturalistic fallacy."

Relativism is popularly, loosely, and confusedly expressed by the dictum that things are good or evil, right or wrong, because "we think them so"—in somewhat the same sense that a painting is beautiful because we find it beautiful. As an *analysis* of the meaning of "right" this is, of course, nonsense. If "x is right" means "People think that x is right," then it means "People think that people think that people think . . ."—an infinite regress generated by obviously circular definition. The precise intent of relativism can, however, be clarified by saying that according to relativism "right" has a variable egocentric meaning, i.e. when A says "x is right" he asserts that A approves of x, when B says "x is right" he asserts that B approves of x. Since thus different speakers who assign the same ethical predicate to the same action do not assert the same proposition, they never either agree or disagree *in belief* about the ethical quality of an action. In particular, if A asserts that legalized birth control is right and B verbally contradicts him, A and B nevertheless assert compatible propositions though they express conflicting attitudes.

Now, it happens all the time that a person approves of an action or a situation but *would* disapprove of it if he were more enlightened about the relevant facts, such as consequences or motivations. Or a person who disapproves of a state of affairs *would*, under the same conditions of enlightment, approve of it. If the words "right" and "wrong" had such dispositional meanings, then we could say without contradiction that what is approved, either by a particular individual or by the society to which he belongs, may nevertheless be wrong, and *mutatis mutandis* for

the case of disapproval. And since such statements are in fact not contradictory, there is a prima-facie case for the dispositional approval
theory. It may be further made plausible by analogy with the distinction
between apparent and objective qualities of physical objects. There is no
contradiction in saying of an objectively red thing that, under special
conditions, it does not look red, for to say that it is objectively red is to
say that it *would* look red if the normal conditions were fulfilled. At the
same time this analogy reveals where the dispositional approval theory
is most vulnerable: in the specification of *normal* conditions. If the
criterion of moral normalcy of a person making ethical judgments is
that under conditions of perfect enlightenment about relevant facts he
would approve of right and only right states of affairs, then we are
caught in a vicious circle. And if that criterion is not thus question-
begging, it would seem that in laying it down we are making just the
sort of *value* judgment of which we want to provide a naturalistic
analysis. If, for example, we stipulate as a necessary condition of
normalcy that the person should not love cruelty, have we not made the
value judgment that cruelty is bad?

C. THE "NATURALISTIC FALLACY" AND THE QUESTION OF SYNONYMY

It appears from the foregoing analysis that the different metaethical
theories are really different assertions concerning the synonymy or non-
synonymy of expressions. The intuitionist denies that there can be a
synonymy relation between an ethical predicate and a descriptive predicate, the naturalist affirms this. The emotivist denies it, not on the ground
that ethical predicates stand for properties that are not empirically verifiable, but on the ground that they do not stand for properties at all,
that they have only emotive meaning, not the sort of *semantical* meaning
that entitles an application of the predicate to be considered true or false.

Both intuitionists and emotivists commonly accept G. E. Moore's
"open question argument" (developed in his *Principia Ethica*) as proving
that any naturalistic analysis of an ethical predicate must be wrong.
Suppose, for example, that "*x* is right" were synonymous with "*x*
maximizes happiness." Then, said Moore, the question whether an action
that maximizes happiness is really right, or whether an action that
is right really maximizes happiness, would be as silly as the question
whether right actions are really right. But the question is not silly;
no matter what empirical property you propose as criterion of moral

value, it is never *self-contradictory* to suppose that something that has that property lacks moral value or that something that has moral value lacks that property. To conclude that the ethical property is *identical* with the empirical property from the premise—which may be true—that whatever has one property has the other is to commit the naturalistic fallacy.

But if Moore's argument were valid, it would prove that *any* meaning analysis is either trivial—or, rather, no analysis at all—or else incorrect. Suppose, for example, that the word "uncle" were declared synonymous with "man who has the same parents as some other man who is a parent." Although I am perfectly familiar with the word "uncle," i.e., can use it correctly, as well as with the words composing the definiens, I may ask myself, in testing the assertion of synonymy, whether indeed an uncle is necessarily a man who has the same parents as some other man who is a parent. It will quickly occur to me that this need not be the case, that a man could be an uncle because he is married to a woman who has the same parents as someone else, or because he has the same parents as some woman who is a parent. I then formulate the correct analysis: an uncle is a man who either has the same parents as someone else who is a parent or who is married to a woman who has the same parents as someone else. But surely this analysis, though correct, is sufficiently complex to make one a little hesitant about the assertion of synonymy. Before convincing myself that definiendum and definiens are really synonymous, I might well ask myself whether something that satisfies the definiendum necessarily satisfies the definiens, and conversely, though I am perfectly familiar with the uses of all the expressions entering into the analysis. It is only if the definiens is fairly simple, so that it is self-evident whether or not it is synonymous with the definiendum, that Moore's "open question" appears silly. At any rate, it follows that Moore has not formulated an argument against ethical naturalism that is not equally an argument against all nontrivial assertions of analytic synonymy.

There is, however, a special reason why even in the case of very simple naturalistic definitions of ethical predicates Moore's question always remains open. This is that ethical predicates always have an *emotive* meaning that cannot be duplicated in neutral descriptive language. An ascription of an ethical predicate to something always involves a commitment. In saying of an action A that it is right, I commit myself to preferring A to non-A; in other words, if my judgment is sincere, then I will feel *motivated* to prefer A to non-A, I will feel that I *ought* to prefer A to non-A. But reflection on this motivational aspect of ethical language easily explains why one who recognizes the *cognitive* synonymy of, say, "x is right" and "x maximizes happiness," i.e., their being true under the same conditions, may nevertheless raise the open question. He may not feel sure that when faced with a choice between an action that he believes to maximize happiness and its alternatives, he would feel sufficiently motivated to decide on the former.

That ethical predicates have such a double function, descriptive and motivational, is explicitly recognized by a metaethical theory that is a hybrid of emotivism and naturalism and that is at the present time more widely held than any of the "pure" theories. Let us call it *emotive naturalism.* Of course, that ethical terms have an emotive/motivational meaning that purely descriptive terms lack is so obvious that it can hardly have been overlooked by intuitionists and naturalists. But what is original about emotive naturalism is the thesis that the descriptive meaning of an ethical term, i.e., the empirical truth-condition of statements applying the term, is a function of the attitudes of the persons using the term. It is possible for two people to agree in their ethical evaluation of a certain state of affairs and yet to have different empirical bases for their evaluation. A says that legalization of birth control is good and B agrees with him. But A's reason for approval is that such a measure would weaken the Catholic church, B's reason is that such a measure would improve the lot of poor families. The emotive naturalist identifies these reasons with the descriptive meanings of the value judgments. Whether the value judgment *as intended* by A is true depends on whether the consequence he deems desirable comes about, and whether the same judgment as intended by B is true depends on whether the different consequence B deems desirable will follow. And it is because A and B approve of different consequences, that their judgments, though identical in emotive/motivational meaning, differ in their empirical truth-conditions. Similarly, how do I know whether what A is asserting by "Jones is a good man" is true or false? It is not enough that I know what sort of a person Jones is. I have to know what dispositions or habits of a man A approves of. That is, it is equally important to know what sort of a person A is. If, for example, A is generous and kind, it is likely that he appreciates the same qualities in other people, hence I can infer with high probability from his calling Jones a good man that he believes him to be generous and kind. If in fact Jones is generous and kind, the value judgment A made about him is true as A intended it. The point of emotive naturalism, then, is this: though ethical terms are like descriptive terms in that there are empirical truth-conditions for their applications in different contexts, they do not differ from descriptive terms *just* in having in addition emotive/motivational meaning. The decisive difference is that the descriptive meaning of an ethical term in any given application must be inferred from the attitudes of its user. In this sense ethical judgments remain intimately wedded to people's attitudes and desires in spite of having empirical truth-conditions.

D. EMOTIVISM OR EMOTIVE NATURALISM?

Undoubtedly the predicates "true" and "false" are properly applicable to value judgments whereas they are not properly applicable to imperatives. Since emotive naturalism concedes that value judgments are true or false, while emphasizing that the truth-conditions vary with people's attitudes, it seems to be more consonant with actual practice than emotivism. It has always been held against emotivism, the revolutionary metaethics of logical positivism and Russell, that, after all, we constantly argue in support of our value judgments, and if value judgments were neither true nor false it would be senseless to argue about them. But actually emotivism can easily survive this objection, and we will argue that the *practical* difference between emotivism and emotive naturalism is nil.

To begin with, it does not follow from the fact that it is possible to adduce reasons in support of a value judgment that the latter expresses a true-or-false proposition, for if so, then we would be driven to the conclusion that even imperatives or commands express true-or-false propositions. An instructor may issue to his students the command to deliver their term papers two weeks before the close of the term, and give as a reason that he must leave town right after the term closes and is expected to turn in the course grades before he leaves but requires about two weeks to examine their papers with care. This is a reasonable argument, but it does not follow that in issuing the order he made a true assertion. What his argument amounts to is that he imparted to his students beliefs that would dispose them to comply with his order. Generally speaking, suppose you favor a state of affairs S and you want to get someone who is either indifferent to S or against it to favor it also. You can accomplish this aim by getting him to believe that S has certain consequences that he favors and that cannot be brought about without S, and that S does not have other consequences that are so undesirable as to outweigh the advantages. Instead of saying, therefore, that an argument has been constructed that establishes the truth of the value judgment "S is good," we could say that we have succeeded in getting our friend to share our favorable attitude towards S by getting him to believe certain causal propositions that are relevant to that attitude, i.e., belief in which is causally connected with that attitude. The emotivist admits the possibility of arguing in support of a value judgment, but he regards the argument not as a proof of a truth either of the same kind as an empirical, scientific truth or of the same kind as an a priori truth, but as an attempt to change or reinforce attitudes by changing or imparting causally related beliefs. Insofar as "true" is associated either with an empirical decision procedure that is objective in not depending on people's volitional attitudes or with a priori insight, which is likewise independent of such subjective factors, it may, indeed, be advisable to withhold "true" from value judgments though this abstinence would not accord with ordinary usage. There is, however, a still stronger argument for the emotivist position.

The emotive naturalist, as we have seen, identifies the empirical evidence in terms of which a value judgment is supported with the truth-condition of that judgment as intended by the particular person. Returning to our earlier example, A's judgment that legalization of birth control is good is true if and only if such a measure weakens the Catholic church. But clearly we can then ask A why he thinks it is a good thing to weaken the Catholic church. And he may give as a reason that the Catholic church spreads bigotry and undermines the respect for scientific truth, and this, according to emotive naturalism, explicates the meaning of "good" in this new context. But of course A would not have given this reason unless he believed that respect for scientific truth is a good thing. And what does that mean? It must again mean something else, according to the metaethics under discussion—say, that respect for scientific truth will in the long run produce more happiness for mankind. Finally we have arrived at the ultimate value judgment that the happiness of mankind is good, indeed *intrinsically* good. But since, ex hypothesi, no further justification of the value judgment is now possible, the emotive naturalist must consistently hold that nothing is asserted by "The happiness of mankind is good," that this judgment has no truth-condition at all. But this is an incongruous position. For it would appear that, according to this analysis, the ultimate reason that supports the proximate reasons *as reasons* is not a reason at all, in the sense in which a reason is a *proposition* adduced in support of another proposition. By contrast, the emotivist is not caught in such an incongruity. He allows for just the same process of reasoning in support of the initial value judgment, but interprets it as an attempt to produce a certain derivative attitude by causally relating it through believed propositions about consequences to an ultimate attitude—such as the ultimate attitude expressed by "Human happiness is intrinsically good."

It is not only the difference between emotivism and emotive naturalism that is practically inconsequential. All metaethical differences, although they constitute semantical and logical problems of intrinsic interest, have little if any bearing on practical questions of value. The plain truth is that, no matter whether we call value judgments true or false, and if so, a priori or empirically true, *practical* ethical agreement presupposes a common human nature, i.e., a set of volitional attitudes that all human beings have in common, such as the desire for material welfare, for peace, for political freedom, for scientific progress, and last but not least, the desire to share these values with others. To the extent that this presupposition is fulfilled—to the extent that common ends are posited—the social sciences in cooperation with the natural sciences can attempt to point the best way towards fulfillment of those desires. To the extent that the presupposition fails, no amount of ever so sophisticated rational argument will make any progress towards practical ethical agreement. Science by its very nature is "value free," as Max Weber said. It can only support hypothetical imperatives, not categorical imperatives. It cannot say "You ought to do *A*" but only "If you want *B*, then you ought to do *A*."

Selected Readings

Ayer, A. J., "On the Analysis of Moral Judgments," in A. J. Ayer, *Philosophical Essays* (London, 1954).

Black, M., "Some Questions about Emotive Meaning," *Philosophical Review*, 1948.

Brandt, R., "The Emotive Theory of Ethics," *Philosophical Review*, 1950.

——, "The Definition of an 'Ideal Observer' in Ethics," *Philosophy and Phenomenological Research*, 1955.

Broad, C. D., "Some of the Main Problems of Ethics," *Philosophy*, 1946, no. 21. [Reprinted in H. Feigl and W. Sellars (eds.), *Readings in Philosophical Analysis* (New York, 1949).]

Edwards, P., *The Logic of Moral Discourse* (New York, 1955).

Findlay, J. N., "Morality by Convention," *Mind*, 1944.

Firth, R., "Ethical Absolutism and the Ideal Observer," *Philosophy and Phenomenological Research*, 1952.

Hare R. M., *The Language of Morals* (Oxford, 1952).

Hospers, J., *Introduction to Philosophical Analysis* (New York, 1953), chap. 7.

——, *Human Conduct* (New York, 1961).

Kaplan, A., "Are Ethical Judgments Assertions?," *Philosophical Review*, 1942.

Pap, A., *Elements of Analytic Philosophy* (New York, 1949), chap. 2.

Reichenbach, H., *The Rise of Scientific Philosophy* (Berkeley, Calif., 1951), chap. 17.

Russell, B., *Religion and Science* (Oxford, 1935), chap. 9. [Reprinted in P. Edwards and A. Pap (eds.), *A Modern Introduction to Philosophy* (New York, 1957).]

Sellars, W., and J. Hospers, *Readings in Ethical Theory* (New York, 1952), parts 2–5.

Stevenson, C. L., *Ethics and Language* (New Haven, Conn., 1944).

Storer, T., "The Logic of Value Propositions," *Philosophy of Science*, 1946.

Weber, M., *The Methodology of the Social Sciences*, trans. by E. A. Shils and H. A. Finch (New York, 1949).

Glossary

Ad hoc hypothesis—assumption made in order to save a theory that is apparently refuted by the facts, the assumption not being independently testable

Analogical inference—conclusion from the fact that a set of objects are similar in certain respects that they are probably similar in some further respect

Analytic, broadly—true by virtue of the meanings of constituent terms
        strictly—substitution instance of a logical truth (logically true), or translatable into such a statement with the help of adequate analytic definitions

Antecedent—if-clause of a conditional statement

A posteriori knowledge—knowledge based on experience

A priori knowledge—knowledge that is independent of experience

A priori truth—possible object of a priori knowledge

Atomic statement—singular statement that contains no statements as components

Circular definition—definition in which the definiendum occurs in the definiens, or a part of the definiens is defined in terms of the definiendum

Circular explanation—explanation of a fact in terms of assumptions that are not testable independently of the fact they purport to explain

Conditional statement—statement of the form "If *p*, then *q*"

Confirmation, direct—confirmation, e.g., of a generalization of the form "All *A* are *B*" by observation of *A*'s that are *B*'s
        indirect—confirmation of generalization by direct confirmation of a more comprehensive generalization from which it follows

Conjunction—statement of the form "*p and q*"

Connotation—a predicate is said to connote (logically) those properties which a thing must have in order for the predicate to be applicable to it.

Consequent—*then*-clause of a conditional statement

Contingent proposition—*p* is contingent if *p* as well as not-*p* is logically possible.

Contradictory—The contradictory of *p* is that proposition which must be false if *p* is true and must be true if *p* is false.

Contrary—*p* and *q* are contraries if they cannot both be true but may both be false.

Deductive inference—an inference whose conclusion is claimed to follow necessarily from the premises (In other words, it is claimed to be contradictory to conjoin the premises with the denial of the conclusion.)

Definiendum—expression that is defined

Definiens—complex expression by which the definiendum is defined

Definition analytic—analysis of the meaning of the definiedum

   conditional—the same as a reduction sentence

   contextual—rule for translating sentences containing the definiendum into synonymous sentences that do not contain it; although permitting elimination of the definiendum, it is not an explicit definition (e.g., "*x* is a brother of *y*" may be contextually defined as "*x* is a male and has the same parents as *y*")

   explicit—definition such that the definiendum can simply be replaced by the definiens in any sentence without changing the remainder of the sentence (e.g., "father" defined as "male parent")

   implicit (postulational)—A set of postulats (axioms) is said to define implicitly the primitive terms in it; i.e., it delimits the possible interpretation of the primitive terms

   operational—definition in terms of experimental operations required to determine whether the definiendum applies in a given case (or to determine the numerical value of a defined functor)

   ostensive—explaining the meaning of a term by pointing at, or including experience of, instances denoted by it

   recursive—rule for eliminating definiendum in a finite number of symbolic transformations from expressions in which it occurs together with constant arguments (e.g., "+" from "3 + 2")

Descriptive predicate—word designating a sensory quality or relation, or a characteristic whose presence can be inferred from what is observed

Disjunction—statement of the form "*p or q*"

Disposition predicate—predicate designating a tendency to react in a certain way to a certain kind of stimulus (in a generalized sense of "stimulus")

Empirical statement—statement whose truth or falsehood must be discovered by experience (contrasted with *a priori* statement)

Enthymeme—argument with a "suppressed" (tacitly assumed) premise or conclusion

Equivalence, logical—Two statements are logically equivalent if to suppose one true and the other false amounts to a contradiction.

   material—Two statements are materially equivalent if they are both true or both false.

Essential occurrence of a term—A term occurs essentially in a sentence if the truth-value of the sentence may change when the term is replaced by another that is grammatically admissible in the context (contrasted with *vacuous* occurrence, q.v.).

Existential quantifier—the expression "There is an *x*" or its idiomatic equivalents "something," "somebody" or the like

Existential statement—statement asserting that something (one or more) has a specified property, without saying which thing it is (they are)

Explanandum—fact to be explained

Explanans—assumptions in terms of which a fact is explained

Explicandum—concept to be explicated (analyzed)

Explicatum—more articulate or precise concept by which explicandum is replaced

Extension of a predicate—class of objects of which the predicate is true

Extensional language—language whose molecular statements, i.e., statements containing parts that are themselves statements, are truth-functions and whose nonmolecular statements have a truth-value that depends only on the extensions, not the meanings, of the predicates they contain (excludes, for example, sentences of the forms "It is necessary that *p*" and "*A* believes that *p*")

Factual consequence—follows by virtue of empirical laws, not by sole virtue of logical laws

Factual proposition—emperical proposition; i.e., the truth-value of the proposition depends on an empirical fact (synonymous with *contingent proposition*)

Formal derivation—derivation without attention to the meanings of nonlogical constants

Formal implication—statement of the form "For every *x*, if *x* is *F*, then *x* is *G*" meaning that *there is no x* that is *F* but not *G* (not that this is impossible)

Formal truth—statement that is true by virtue of its form alone, i.e., by virtue of the meanings of logical constants (synonymous with "logical truth")

Functor—expression designating a magnitude, mathematical or physical (e.g., "sum," "length")

Inductive inference—inference from empirical premises that such and such an hypothesis is *probably* true (without strictly following from the premises)

Instantial evidence—*A*'s that are *B*'s constitute instantial evidence for the generalization "All *A* are *B*."

Language system—language defined by an explicit listing of primitive (undefined) vocabulary, both logical and descriptive, and by the following kinds of rule: rules of sentence formation, rules of deduction, semantic rules (contrasted with *natural language*)

Lawlike generalization—generalization in the form of a subjunctive conditional, applying to an unlimited number of possible cases

Logical consequence—*q* is a logical consequence of *p* if "If *p*, then *q*" expresses a logical truth.

Logical constant—term such as "and," "or," "not," "if-then," and parentheses, determining the *form* of a sentence

Logical construction—an entity *A* is said to be a logical construction out of a specified set of entities *S* if the expression "*A*" that denotes *A* is contextually definable by reference to members of *S*.

Logical independence—Two propositions are logically independent if they are compatible and neither is a logical consequence of the other; in a derivative sense, predicates are said to be logically independent.

Logical necessity—p is logically necessary if not-*p* is logically impossible.

Logical possibility—state of affairs that is conceivable without self-contradiction

Logical truth—statement that is true solely by virtue of the meanings of logical constants

Major premise—that premise of a syllogism which contains the predicate of the conclusion

Minor term—subject of the conclusion of a syllogism

Middle term—that term which occurs in both premises of a syllogism

Minor premise—that premise of a syllogism which contains the subject of the conclusion

Minor term—subject of the conclusion of a syllogism

Material implication—*p* materially implies *q* if either *p* is false or *q* is true—though *p* and *q* may be wholly unrelated in meaning.

Meaning, pragmatic—mental states causally connected with the use and interpretation of signs but irrelevant to the question of truth or falsehood

    semantic—that aspect of the meaning of a sign which is relevant to the question of truth or felsehood (e.g., the property logically connoted by a predicate; the state of affairs described by a declarative sentence)

    syntactic—formal relations between signs, in abstraction from their possible applications

Metalanguage—language used to talk about a language

Natural language—(contrasted with *language systems*) The rules of a natural language are implicit in the use of the expressions, but most of the rules are not explicitly formulated; further, a natural language is characterized by ambiguity and vagueness.

Necessary condition—Property *P* is a necessary condition for property *Q* if nothing can have *Q* without having *P*.

Nomological implication—implication expressing a logical or causal connection, unlike material or formal implications

Object-language—correlative to metalanguage; (q.v.); the language about which—not "in" which—one speaks; in a more restricted sense, language in which one speaks about extralinguistic objects

Observable predictate—predicate designating an observable quality or relation

Observation language—language used to describe actual or possible observations; contrasted with *theoretical language*

Observation statement—statement in the observation language

One-one correspondence—Two classes *A* and *B* are in (or can be set into) one-one correspondence if there is a one-one relation *R* by which every member of *A* is related to just one member of *R* and every member of *B* to just one member of *A*.

One-one relation—relation *R* such that at most one element has *R* to a specified element and a specified element has *R* to at most one element

Primitive concept (*term*)—undefined concept (term)

Probability implication—obtains from *p* to *q* if *q* has a certain probability relative to *p*

Propositional calculus—that part of deductive logic in which nonmolecular propositions are treated as units, without being further analyzed (In traditional terminology, only relations between propositions, not between terms, are dealt with.)

Propositional function—expression containing one or more variables such that a true-or-false statement results when suitable constants are substituted for the variables

Quantifier—expression such as "some," "all," "for every," by means of which general statements are constructed

Question of fact—a question that can be answered only through empirical investigation; contrasted with both *verbal* and *logical* questions

Reduction sentence—sentence describing a test procedure for a not directly observable property but, unlike explicit and contextual definitions, not having the form of an equivalence; usually a postulate connecting a disposition predicate with observable predicates

Reference class—the class by reference to which a probability is assigned to an event

Relation, asymmetrical—For all *x* and *y*, if *xRy*, then not-*yRx*.

> *symmetrical*—For all *x* and *y*, if *xRy*, then *yRx*.

> *converse*—The co...verse of *R* is the relation *S* such that *xRy* if and only if *ySx*.

> *reflexive*—a relation that anything has to itself provided it has it to something

> *irreflexive*—a relation that nothing has to itself

> *transitive*—For all *x*, *y*, *z*, if *xRy* and *yRz*, then *xRz*.

> *intransitive*—for all *x*, *y*, *z*, if *xRy* and *yRz*, then not-*xRz*.

Self-contradictory—affirming and denying one and the same proposition

Singular statement—statement containing no quantifiers

Statement form—schema containing statement variables ("*p* or *q*"); sometimes used in the more general sense of *propositional function*

Substitution instance—statement derivable from a universal statement by substituting the same constant for each occurrence of a variable bound by the same universal quantifier ("for every x," "(x)"); also statement derived by substitution from a propositional function

Sufficient condition—Property P is a sufficient condition for property Q if everything that has P has Q.

Syllogism (categorical)—deductive argument consisting of two premises (major and minor) and a conclusion, each of which has one of the following forms: all A are B, some A are B, some A are not B, no A are B

Syntactic—referring to linguistic forms, not to meanings

Synthetic—a statement that is neither analytic nor self-contradictory

Tautology—sense 1: compound statement that is true no matter what the truth-values of its component statements may be

    sense 2: propositional function (or statement form) all of whose substitution instances are tautologies in sense 1

    sense 3: logical truth

Truth-condition—state of affairs whose existence is the necessary and sufficient condition for the truth of a statement (i.e., the statement is true if and only if that state of affairs exists)

Truth-function—propositional function constructed by means of connectives ("or," "not," "and,") in such a way that the truth-value of its substitution instances is uniquely determined by the truth-values of the atomic propositions; or substitution instance of a truth-function in this sense

Truth table—table constructed in order to define a connective in terms of truth-yielding combinations of truth-values of the component statements, or in order to decide on the basis of such tables whether a given truth-function is a tautology, a contradiction, or neither

Theoretical construct—concept referring to something that is postulated in order to explain the observed but that is not directly observable (e.g., electron, gravitational potential, unconscious wish)

Theoretical language—the language in which the scientist speaks about theoretical constructs; contrasted with *observation language* (*q.v.*)

Universal proposition—proposition about all the members of a class, i.e., of the form "All A are B"

Vacuous occurrence (of a term)—inessential occurrence (of a term)

EPILOGUE

A Memoir

by Brand Blanshard

ARTHUR PAP was one of the ablest younger philosophers of his generation. In a life of thirty-eight years he accomplished more than most of his colleagues are able to do in twice that time. In this last book of his, published posthumously, it seems fitting that a few words should be said about him personally. I cannot claim to have known him intimately; few even of his acquaintances did, for without being a recluse or unsociable, he was singularly impersonal in his interests and would always rather talk about philosophy than about other persons or about himself. But he was a man of striking individuality, who challenged notice in any company; and after working in the same department with him for four years, and collaborating with him in an undergraduate course, I came to know at least enough about him to admire him greatly.

Pap was born and brought up in Zürich, where his father was a successful businessman, and until he was nineteen years old the language he spoke was German. The family were of Jewish extraction, and in 1941, when a Nazi invasion of German Switzerland seemed imminent, they uprooted themselves, made their way through unoccupied France, Spain, and Portugal to the United States, and settled in New York.

Arthur's beginning in this country was hardly characteristic. To those who knew him later it will seem strange to hear that this most single-minded of men suffered for a time from a mind that was painfully divided. He had a passion for music: he had been a promising student of piano under Walther Frey in Switzerland and had thoughts of becoming a concert pianist. In New York he entered the Juilliard School and practiced assiduously for eight hours a day. But he also enrolled for extension classes at Columbia University, where a rival interest developed that before long pushed music into the shadow. This new interest was in philosophy. To be sure, it was not quite new. Already as a gymnasium student in Zürich he had cut his teeth on Hegel, and the first impression he made on his philosophy teachers in this country was that of a rather belligerent Hegelian. But dicussions with such fellow students as John Hospers, Martin Lean, and Morton White instilled doubts in his mind. After obtaining his bachelor's degree at Columbia, he was still interested enough in speculative philosophy to be drawn by Cassirer to Yale, where he proceeded to a master's degree. But by this time the empiricist antibodies were working strongly in his blood; his budding interest in analytic philosophy was encouraged by Charles Stevenson, and he found that Cassirer's metaphysical speculation held little appeal for him. He returned to Columbia to write a doctoral dissertation under Ernest Nagel on "The A Priori in Physical Theory." This was an acute and competent essay, which won him the Wood-bridge prize for the best philosophical thesis of 1946.

Then came a series of difficult years. Pap had to support himself, and he secured a modest appointment as teacher in one of the Columbia extension courses he had known as a student. Among his pupils was a young lady whose friendship with him soon ripened into an engage-ment and marriage and whose enduring confidence in him was a source of much strength. Fortunately for the two young people, the war had just ended, and the universities were looking for instructors to help them handle the tides of returning servicemen. Pap was offered and accepted an instructorship at Chicago. It was an important step in his intellectual life, for here he came for the first time under the direct influence of Rudolf Carnap, who was to affect his thought profoundly. But Carnap was in the graduate school and Pap's own assignment was in the undergraduate college, where the educational views of Hutchins and Adler were being put to the test. Departmental barriers were disregarded, and Pap was asked to teach both chemistry and philosophy. As a natural specialist, he did not like it; he felt that such diffusion of interest was bad for both teacher and taught. With characteristic outspokenness he said so, and at the end of the year he was again a needy philosopher without a job.

A minor post cropped up at City College, and for two years Pap returned to New York. Then an assistant professorship came in view on the opposite side of the continent, and he went for four years to the University of Oregon. His work there was brought to an end by another surprising invitation from a distance. Putting to use his knowledge of German, he had translated Professor Kraft's history of the Vienna Circle. On Kraft's recommendation he was appointed a Fulbright lecturer at the University of Vienna for 1953–54. It was an exciting year: he lectured in German at the University; he went with his wife to see old friends

in Switzerland; he took a trip to Italy; by reason of his special competence in analytic philosophy and the rapidly increasing interest in it, he
was asked to lecture at Uppsala and Copenhagen, Oxford and Cambridge.
I recall a paper of his at the Congress of Philosophy in Brussels. His
Vienna lectures appeared in revised and expanded form in German under
the title *Analytische Erkenntnistheorie.*

On his return he did not go back to Oregon, but accepted a tempo-
rary post at Lehigh University in Pennsylvania and before the year was
out was looking anxiously round again for some suitable opening. As it
happened, the eye of the Yale philosophy department was at that moment
roving the horizon for a philosopher of science, and this eye fell specu-
latively on Pap, whose production and reputation had by now shot up
impressively. To his delight, Yale asked him to come. The new assignment was not exactly a bed of roses. Yale was a stronghold of metaphysics; Pap was notoriously hostile to metaphysics. Still that was a main
reason that Yale wanted him; it has long prided itself on the diversity
of its philosophic points of view, each of which is submitted to the frank-
est criticism by the others. Pap set out with pleasure to meet the demands
upon him. He gave courses and seminars in logic, in probability and
induction, in the philosophy of Russell, and in various phases of analytic
philosophy. The Yale University Press published his book on *Semantics
and Necessary Truth,* which is the most thorough treatment of the topic
in English, and articles and reviews flowed ceaselessly from his little
office in Linsly Hall. He had a growing family—three sons and a daugh-
ter—to whom he was devoted. The future looked bright.

Suddenly fate struck at him with a brutal lack of warning. He had not
been feeling up to the mark and in March, 1959, went round to the university hospital for a casual check-up. It was clear to the examining
physicians when tests were made that he was suffering from a kind of
nephritis for which there is no known remedy. They did not betray their
hopelessness, and he returned to his classes. Work became increasingly
difficult, however, and, puzzled and impatient, he had to return re-
currently to his hospital bed. Through the summer he was manifestly
getting weaker, though with an indomitable buoyancy he talked to the
end about resuming his classes with the opening of the fall term. It was
not to be. He died on September 7, 1959.

What Arthur Pap would have achieved if he had lived, no one can
say. But when one considers what he accomplished in the less than
twenty disturbed and anxious years between his arrival as a somewhat
forlorn immigrant boy in this country and his death at thirty-eight—five
technical books on philosophy, two more translated or edited, and
scores of able articles and reviews—one finds it hard to set limits to what
he might have done. Driving himself as he did unmercifully, he might,

of course, have burned himself out quickly. But he had a sturdy physique (I found that he had been an enthusiastic and vigorous soccer player in Switzerland), and while thinking with him was an arduous and exacting business, it was also a delight. If he had been able to continue the curve of work supplied by the short arc of his life, it would certainly have soared high; he would, I suspect, have come to be recognized as one of the outstanding thinkers of our time.

To those who knew him, the most striking thing about him was his total devotion to philosophy. This was not something reserved for class-room or office; it was an incessant gnawing torment and unending de-light. His gift of concentration was extraordinary. One would meet him walking the street with unseeing eyes, lost in his thoughts; he would calmly write on intricate points in epistemology in his living room with his children climbing happily over him. Indeed his absorption in analysis became almost too exclusive: he read little except professional literature, his idea of a cozy evening at home was a bout with Russell's last pronouncement on sense data and physics, he was frankly uninter-ested in any of the arts except music, and he was interested in religion only as a set of doctrines for which the evidence seemed tenuous. There was something astringent and almost withering in the singleness of his eye for fact and truth. To believe something because one wanted to believe it was for him (though he would never have used the word) a sin. To talk philosophy with such a man, if one was on one's toes, was a tonic. His gift for argument was formidable, but one did not feel that he argued for victory; he could and did change his opinions, though only in the light of evidence that seemed clear and cogent. Perhaps with a fuller presentiment than he admitted, he was reading on his hospital bed Ducasse's *Nature, Mind, and Death;* it was characteristic of him to conclude quietly that survival, while a logical possibility, was not empirically probable.

He was not as happy a man as one would wish. The lot of the scientist, it is often said, is happier than that of the artist; but Arthur Pap com-bined passionate theoretical curiosity with an artistic temperament, and that is not the best recipe for happiness. Moods of exhilaration when the current of thought ran clear were followed by moods of deep de-jection when a promising theory was deflated or when he could not intellectually see his way. One felt too that his pleasure in contacts with others reflected an unconscious estimate of their degree of devotedness to truth. For example, he had little use for students who took his courses merely for credit, and he at times made this sharply clear to them; on the other hand, students who were genuinely interested and ready for work he was willing to help untiringly. It was significant that his students' feeling for him as a teacher tended to vary directly with their own intellectual quality.

Of Pap's books it is no doubt his *Elements of Analytical Philosophy* that has had the widest reading. It was his first full-scale venture into print; it was written with the verve and iconoclasm of a man in his twenties who has seen through the metaphysicians and theologians and is determined to put them in their place. I hope many of them have read it, for even if they often disagree with it, they should be grateful, as I was, for the castigation. It has faults of brashness and overstatement, but it seems to me one of the most useful books produced by the analytic movement, notable for range as well as lucidity. *Semantics and Necessary Truth* is more mature and sophisticated, but is harder reading. With his eye always fixed on substance rather than form, and impatient to get on to something new rather than linger with a blue pencil over the old, Pap wrote with more firmness and clarity than grace. His writing was the thinking aloud of a disciplined mind, not the creation of a literary craftsman; its texture is close-knit and must be followed with an equally close attention if the path of the argument is not to be lost; but the path is firmly marked out and is made plainer by many examples, of which he had an inexhaustible supply.

Books on the philosophy of science often suffer from one or other of two faults: they are either so technical scientifically that the philosophers are lost among equations or so philosophical that the scientists are lost among the clouds. In this book the technicalities are not ignored, but the writer is never bogged down in them, and their bearing upon philosophical issues is unfailingly made clear. It is a great satisfaction to those who admired Arthur Pap to know that the last work of his amazingly fertile mind, so eager at once to make philosophy scientific and to make science philosophically responsible, is now available to us.

Index